Lecture Notes in Computer Science 14782

The series Lecture Notes in Computer Science (LNCS), including its subseries Lecture Notes in Artificial Intelligence (LNAI) and Lecture Notes in Bioinformatics (LNBI), has established itself as a medium for the publication of new developments in computer science and information technology research, teaching, and education.

LNCS enjoys close cooperation with the computer science R & D community, the series counts many renowned academics among its volume editors and paper authors, and collaborates with prestigious societies. Its mission is to serve this international community by providing an invaluable service, mainly focused on the publication of conference and workshop proceedings and postproceedings. LNCS commenced publication in 1973.

Maximilien Gadouleau · Alonso Castillo-Ramirez
Editors

Cellular Automata and Discrete Complex Systems

30th IFIP WG 1.5 International Workshop, AUTOMATA 2024
Durham, UK, July 22–24, 2024
Proceedings

Editors
Maximilien Gadouleau
Durham University
Durham, UK

Alonso Castillo-Ramirez
University of Guadalajara
Guadalajara, Mexico

ISSN 0302-9743 ISSN 1611-3349 (electronic)
Lecture Notes in Computer Science
ISBN 978-3-031-65886-0 ISBN 978-3-031-65887-7 (eBook)
https://doi.org/10.1007/978-3-031-65887-7

This Springer imprint is published by the registered company Springer Nature Switzerland AG
The registered company address is: Gewerbestrasse 11, 6330 Cham, Switzerland

Preface

This volume contains the full papers presented at the 30th International Workshop on Cellular Automata and Discrete Complex Systems, AUTOMATA 2024, which took place between 22 July, 2024 and 24 July, 2024, at Durham University, United Kingdom. These AUTOMATA workshops aim to establish and maintain a regular, international, multidisciplinary forum for the collaboration of researchers in the field of Cellular Automata (CA) and Discrete Complex Systems (DCS) while providing a platform for presenting and discussing new ideas and results.

These workshops support the development of theory and applications of CA and DCS (e.g. parallel computing, physics, biology, social sciences, and others) and identification and study within an interdisciplinary and multidisciplinary context of the important fundamental aspects, concepts, notions, and problems concerning CA and DCS. The AUTOMATA series is the official annual event of IFIP WG 1.5, Working Group 5 (on Cellular Automata and Discrete Complex Systems) of Technical Committee 1 (on Foundations of Computer Science) of the International Federation for Information Processing (IFIP).

At AUTOMATA 2024, we had four invited talks given by Alberto Dennunzio, Luca Mariot, Elisabeth Remy, and Agnieszka Rusinowska, and this volume contains an invited paper submitted by each of these speakers. Moreover, we received fourteen submissions as full papers for the conference. Each submission was reviewed by three members of the Program Committee. Based on these reviews and an open discussion, a total of ten papers were accepted to be presented at the conference and to be included in the proceedings. We thank all authors for their contributions and hard work that made this event possible.

The conference program also involved short presentations of exploratory papers that are not included in these proceedings, and we wish to extend our thanks to the authors of the exploratory submissions.

We are indebted to the Steering Committee and the Program Committee for their valuable help during the months before the conference.

We are very grateful for the support of the local Organizing Committee in ensuring all aspects of the event went smoothly.

Finally, we acknowledge the excellent cooperation from the Lecture Notes in Computer Science team of Springer for their help in producing this volume in time for the conference.

July 2024

Maximilien Gadouleau
Alonso Castillo-Ramirez

Organization

Steering Committee

Pedro Paulo Balbi	Universidade Presbiteriana Mackenzie, Brazil
Nazim Fatès	Inria & Université de Lorraine, France
Pierre Guillon	CNRS & Université d'Aix-Marseille, France
Luca Manzoni	University of Trieste, Italy
Dipanwita Roy Chowdhury	IIT Kharagpur, India

Program Committee

Jan Baetens	Ghent University, Belgium
Pedro Paulo Balbi	Universidade Presbiteriana Mackenzie, Brazil
Kamalika Bhattacharjee	National Institute of Technology, Tiruchirappalli, India
Alonso Castillo-Ramirez (Chair)	Universidad de Guadalajara, Mexico
Alberto Dennunzio	Università degli Studi di Milano-Bicocca, Italy
Nazim Fatès	Inria & Université de Lorraine, France
Enrico Formenti	Université de Nice, France
Maximilien Gadouleau (Chair)	Durham University, UK
Anahí Gajardo	Universidad de Concepción, Chile
Pierre Guillon	CNRS & Aix-Marseille Université, France
Katsunobu Imai	Fukuyama University, Japan
Jarkko Kari	University of Turku, Finland
Jia Lee	Chongqing University, China
Luca Manzoni	University of Trieste, Italy
Pedro Montealegre	Universidad Adolfo Ibáñez, Chile
Kévin Perrot	Aix-Marseille Université, France
Adrien Richard	CNRS & Université de Nice, France
Sara Riva	Université de Lille, France
Dipanwita Roy Chawdhury	IIT Kharagpur, India
Ville Salo	University of Turku, Finland
Ilkka Törmä	University of Turku, Finland
Guillaume Theyssier	CNRS & Aix-Marseille Université, France
Barbara Wolnik	University of Gdansk, Poland

Local Organizing Committee

Maximilien Gadouleau
Karl Southern

Contents

Invited Papers

Logical Modelling, Some Recent Methodological Advances Illustrated

Claudine Chaouiya[1], Pedro T. Monteiro[2,3], and Elisabeth Remy[1(✉)]

[1] Aix Marseille University, CNRS, I2M, Marseille, France
{claudine.chaouiya,elisabeth.remy}@univ-amu.fr
[2] INESC-ID, Lisbon, Portugal
[3] Instituto Superior Técnico (IST), Universidade de Lisboa, Lisbon, Portugal
pedro.tiago.monteiro@tecnico.ulisboa.pt

Abstract. Logical modelling is a popular mathematical framework for assessing the behaviour of regulatory and signalling networks. Despite its qualitative nature, it allows disclosing crucial dynamical properties.

Here we briefly present the modelling formalism and recent challenges arising when building models and analysing them. We then introduce a few methodological advances for model synthesis and analysis, and illustrate their effectiveness with two applications.

The first deals with a Boolean model explaining the early differentiation of Hematopoietic Stem Cells and biases that appear during ageing. This case study demonstrates a successful procedure for model synthesis from biological data as well as a method for model revision. The second application concerns the role of the micro-environment in the Epithelial to Mesenchymal Transition, a process by which epithelial cells lose their adhesive properties to gain migration ability. This case study illustrates the capacity of developed methods to handle networks with a few dozens components and to conclude on relevant dynamical properties. The paper ends with a discussion, pointing to open challenges that need to be tackled to further increase logical modelling applicability to disease networks.

Keywords: Regulatory disease networks · Logical models · Reachability properties · Model inference · Model revision

1 Introduction

Intricate molecular networks control cellular processes such as cell differentiation, proliferation, death, etc. Among the diversity of mathematical modelling approaches to tackle such complex behaviours, the logical formalism turned prominent for its capacity of disclosing relevant dynamical properties despite a high level of abstraction of the biological complexity (e.g., [2]). Thanks to methodological progresses over the last decades, logical models (Boolean or multi-valued) enable the consideration of regulatory and signalling networks of a few dozens components. They define discrete dynamical systems that lead to

Published by Springer Nature Switzerland AG 2024
M. Gadouleau and A. Castillo-Ramirez (Eds.): AUTOMATA 2024, LNCS 14782, pp. 3–22, 2024.
https://doi.org/10.1007/978-3-031-65887-7_1

classical challenges when it comes to analyse their properties. Indeed, the development of methods devoted to difficult problems has benefited the analysis of logical models. This is the case, for example, of model-checking, Satisfiability Testing (SAT), Answer set programming (ASP), etc. Furthermore, methodological developments specifically devoted to logical modelling have been also proposed.

This paper aims to illustrate a few challenging problems faced by the community working with logical models, and how these have been addressed relying on formal approaches developed in computer sciences, and by tweaking existing methods devoted to the analysis of discrete dynamical systems.

We first briefly present the formalism and challenges arising when building models and analysing them. Section 3 then introduces some methodological advances for model synthesis and analysis, illustrating their effectiveness with two applications in Sects. 4 and 5.

The first case study deals with early differentiation and aging of Hematopoietic Stem Cells (HSCs). These cells reside in the bone marrow, and give rise to all mature blood cells. This case study is used to demonstrate a successful procedure for model synthesis from biological data. Then, using a revision method, model modifications are identified to satisfy prescribed reachability properties. The second application deals with the role of the micro-environment in the Epithelial to Mesenchymal Transition (EMT), a process by which epithelial cells lose their adhesive properties to gain migration ability. This second case study shows that developed methods allow to handle networks with a few dozens components and to conclude on relevant dynamical properties.

The paper ends with a discussion, pointing to open challenges that need to be tackled to further increase logical modelling applicability to disease networks.

2 Basics on the Logical Modelling Approach

Here, we recall the basic definitions of logical models and their dynamical properties.

Definition 1. *A* logical model $\mathcal{M} = (G, R, F)$ *is defined by:*

- $G = \{g_1, \ldots, g_n\}$ *a set of* n *regulatory components, each component* g_i *being associated with a discrete variable* $x_i \in \{0, \ldots, m_i\}$ *that embodies the functional levels of* g_i *from* 0 *to a maximal value* m_i*;*
- $R \subset G \times G \times \{+, -, \pm\}$ *the set of signed regulatory interactions between components, which define an activation* $(g_i, g_j, +)$*, an inhibition* $(g_i, g_j, -)$*, or a dual regulation* $(g_i, g_j, \pm)$ *of* g_j *by* g_i*. The later indicates that* g_i *is both an activator and inhibitor of* g_j*, depending on the states of co-regulators;*
- *A* map $F : \Pi_{i=1}^{n}\{0, \ldots, m_i\} \to \Pi_{i=1}^{n}\{0, \ldots m_i\}$ *that specifies the evolution of the model* $\mathcal{M}$*, i.e., for each component* $g_i \in G$*,* $(F(x))_i$*, also denoted* $F_i(x)$*, defines the value of* x_i*, depending on the state* $x = (x_1, \ldots, x_n)$*.*

Note that when all the components have a maximal level equal to 1 ($m_i = 1, \forall i = 1, \ldots, n$), we have a Boolean model, and F is a Boolean map.

We refer to (G, R) as the *regulatory graph* or as the *regulatory network*. The set $\mathcal{S} = \Pi_{i=1}^{n}\{0, \ldots, m_i\}$ is the state space of the model. In the case of a Boolean model, elements of $\mathcal{S}$ are Boolean states, multi-valued states otherwise.

For a Boolean state x, $\overline{x}^i$ denotes the state differing from x on the sole ith element, with $(\overline{x}^i)_i = 1 - x_i$.

For a multi-valued state x and $i \in \{1, \ldots, n\}$:

- $x_i < m_i$, $\overline{x}^{i+}$ denotes the state differing from x on the sole ith position with $(\overline{x}^{i+})_i = x_i + 1$,
- $x_i > 0$, $\overline{x}^{i-}$ denotes the state differing from x on the sole ith position with $(\overline{x}^{i-})_i = x_i - 1$.

Definition 1 reflects the approach most often followed by modellers: first establish the regulatory graph, and only then define the behaviour of the components. However, the sole map is enough to define the regulatory interactions: $F_i(x) \neq F_j(\overline{x}^{i\sigma})$ (with $\sigma \in \{+, -\}$) indicates a regulatory effect of g_i onto g_j in state x.

Furthermore, a map F on $\Pi_{i=1}^{n}\{0, \ldots, m_i\}$ defines a dynamics that can be represented as a *State Transition Graph.*

Definition 2. *A map* $F : \mathcal{S} = \Pi_{i=1}^{n}\{0, \ldots, m_i\} \to \mathcal{S}$ *defines the asynchronous* State Transition Graph *(STG)* $E_F = (\mathcal{S}, T_F)$ *where:*

- $\mathcal{S}$ *is the set of nodes (the states);*
- $T_F \subseteq \mathcal{S}^2$ *is the set of transitions with* $(x, x') \in T_F$ *iff* $\exists i \in \{1, \ldots, n\}$ *s.t.* $F_i(x) \neq x_i$ *and* $x' = \overline{x}^{i+}$ *or* $x' = \overline{x}^{i-}$.

Transitions in E_F thus connect states (x, x') that differ on a unique component i, which image by F_i differs from its value in x with $x' = \overline{x}^{i+}$ if $F_i(x) > x_i$ and $x' = \overline{x}^{i-}$ if $F_i(x) < x_i$. Hence, in the asynchronous update scheme, a state x has as many successors as the number of components called to update, that is to say the number of indices i such that $F_i(x) \neq x_i$. In contrast, in the synchronous update scheme, transitions are defined as $(x, F(x))$, *i.e.*, all updates are performed simultaneously and any state has at most one successor (see [2] for further details). Other update schemes are used, each based on different possible combinations of the updating calls and supporting different scenarios of event sequences. Priority classes were also proposed as a way to resolve concurrency in asynchronous dynamics, accounting for biological knowledge about delays [10].

Recently, the *most permissive scheme* has been proposed in the context of Boolean models [32]. For each component, in addition to the two Boolean states 0 and 1, two intermediate states I (increasing) and D (decreasing) are added. Thus, $X_{m.p.} = \{0, 1, I, D\}^n$ is the state space. Any component must pass through intermediate levels to reach its target level, either 0 or 1. If a component is at an intermediate level, it may be considered by its targets to be at level 0 or level 1.

To each state x of $X_{m.p.}$ is associated a set of Boolean states:

$$\gamma(x) = \{y \in \{0,1\}^n; \forall j \in \{1,\ldots,n\}, (x_j = 0 \Rightarrow y_j = 0) \text{ and } (x_j = 1 \Rightarrow y_j = 1)\}.$$

Given a Boolean map F, there is a transition from a state $x \in X_{m.p.}$ to a state $x' \in X_{m.p.}$ if there exists $i \in \{1,...,n\}$ such that $x'_j = x_j$ for $j \neq i$, and one of the following statements occurs:

- $x_i \in \{0, D\}$ and $\exists y \in \gamma(x)$ such that $F_i(y) = 1$, and $x'_i = I$,
- $x_i \in \{1, I\}$ and $\exists y \in \gamma(x)$ such that $F_i(y) = 0$, and $x'_i = D$,
- $x_i = I$ and $x'_i = 1$,
- $x_i = D$ and $x'_i = 0$.

Given a Boolean model, the most permissive dynamics captures all the trajectories present in any of the other update schemes (synchronous, asynchronous, with priorities, etc.) [32]. Moreover, the most permissive dynamics does not miss any behaviour that can be obtained by a quantitative model following the same logic. These dynamics have structural properties that make a number of computational methods, such as model-checking, more efficient. However, the wealth of trajectories represented makes analysis and interpretation difficult.

Model trajectories and thus dynamical properties relate to paths and other properties of the STG. Let us introduce some further notation that will be needed to define these properties. For any two states x, x', $x \rightsquigarrow x'$ denotes the existence of a path from x to x' in the STG (*i.e.*, a sequence of transitions starting from x and leading to x'). In other words, $x \rightsquigarrow x'$ means that x' is reachable from x and, more generally, $x \rightsquigarrow X$ where X is a set of states, means that all the states in X are reachable from x. For convenience, we assume that $x \rightsquigarrow x$.

Definition 3. *Consider a logical model $\mathcal{M} = (G, R, F)$ and $E_F = (\mathcal{S}, T_F)$ its STG.*

- *$A \subseteq \mathcal{S}$ is a* Strongly Connected Component *(SCC) if it is a maximal set of mutually reachable states:* $\begin{cases} \forall x, x' \in A, x \rightsquigarrow x', \text{and } x' \rightsquigarrow x, \\ \forall x'' \notin A, \forall x \in A, x \not\rightsquigarrow x'' \text{ or } x'' \not\rightsquigarrow x. \end{cases}$
- *$A \subseteq \mathcal{S}$ is an* attractor *iff it is a* terminal SCC, i.e., *A is an SCC s.t.* $\forall x \in A, \exists x' \in \mathcal{S}$ s.t. $(x, x') \in T_F \implies x' \in A$.

From Definition 3, an attractor A is an invariant set of F: $F(A) = A$. When A is a singleton (a state from which no other state is reachable), it is a *stable state* (or *point attractor*), otherwise it is a *complex attractor* (or *cyclic attractor*).

With a simple Boolean model, Fig. 1 provides an illustration of different update schemes. In particular, one can observe that stable states are conserved by all updates, whereas their reachability properties may differ. The model includes an input component, which embodies an external signal, considered to be constant at its current value (the regulatory function of g_0 is defined as $F_0(x) = x_0$). STGs of models with inputs thus have as many disconnected graphs as the number of value combinations of input components. Finally, it is worth noting that priority classes lead to the loss of asynchronous transitions,

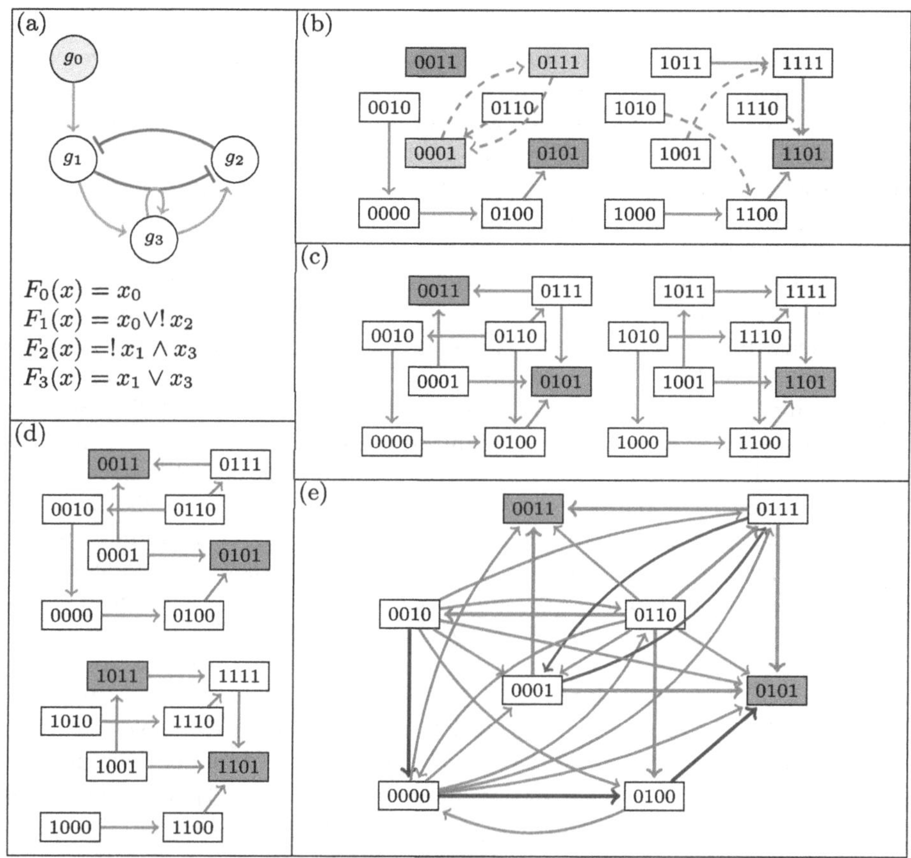

Fig. 1. Logical modelling illustrated: (a) Regulatory graph and regulatory functions ($\wedge$, $\vee$ and ! denote respectively the and, or and not logical connectors); (b) synchronous dynamics, red states are stable states, states in are part of a cyclic attractor, dashed transitions involve multiple variable updates; (c) asynchronous dynamics; (d) priority classes, where g_1 and g_3 are in a class faster than that of g_2; (e) most permissive dynamics (only for $x_0 = 0$ for the sake of space) where transitions in grey are common with the asynchronous update, in blue are common with the synchronous update, in violet are common with both, and remaining red transitions originate from the most permissive only. (Color figure online)

cancelling some paths, whereas the most permissive dynamics promotes reachability properties by defining additional transitions compared to the synchronous and asynchronous STGs.

3 A Few Methodological Advances

Attractors are salient properties to be checked when analysing a model. Indeed, they embody long term behaviours of the modelled network and, most often, correspond to cell fates such as differentiation, proliferation, death, etc. Beyond attractor identification, crucial properties relate to their reachability: given some initial conditions, which attractors are reachable? With what probabilities? Are there mandatory events along the trajectories leading to some attractor? etc. Furthermore, it is generally relevant to analyse the impact of model perturbations on these properties. Most often, a model perturbation consists in blocking the value of a variable which amounts to *e.g.*, an over-expression or a knock-out of the corresponding component.

The first challenge faced by any modeller is the proper model definition and its necessary revision when the model does not meet specific requirements. This issue is briefly discussed in Sect. 3.1. Then, given a model, checking its dynamical properties is a combinatorial problem due to the size of its state space (2^n for a Boolean model of n components). Concerning attractor reachability, Sect. 3.2 presents methods for attractor reachability quantification and reachability existence when switching input values. In this respect, formal methods have greatly enhanced modellers' apparatus to define and analyse logical models. In particular, model-checking has proved useful to verify if a model dynamics respects a set of reachability properties (see [26] and references therein). The computational tree logic (CTL) allows checking properties on asynchronous STGs, as it provides path quantifiers such as *Always* (A) and *Exists* (E) handling concurrent trajectories. SAT solvers also proved useful as various questions concerning logical models can be translated into Boolean satisfiability problems [9,38,39]. However, Answer Set Programming (ASP) provides higher expressive power and a clear declarative representation over SAT, being used for model inference [41], verification of model dynamics [32], or model revision [12]. Applications of formal methods are briefly described in Sect. 3.1 for model synthesis and revision, and in Sect. 3.2 for reachability analysis.

More classical approaches to analyse asynchronous (discrete) dynamics have also proved useful to check reachability properties in logical models. Section 3.2 presents two adaptations of Monte Carlo simulations.

3.1 Model Synthesis and Revision

Despite being facilitated by the abstraction level of the formalism, logical model definition is still a difficult task. Interactions between components can be recovered from literature data or from interaction databases, general such as Reactome [23] or SIGNOR [19], or more specific such as Atlas of Cancer Signalling Network[1]. However, having a regulatory graph, regulatory functions still need to be specified. There are 2^{2^k} potential regulatory functions for a Boolean component with k Boolean regulators. If fixed signs (positive or negative) of the interactions are given, one can consider only monotone Boolean functions whose number (Dedekind number[2]) grows exponentially with k. Model synthesis, or model inference, has been the subject of intensive research work in biological

[1] http://acsn.curie.fr/.
[2] https://oeis.org/A000372.

systems [33]. From biological (molecular) data, mathematical methods using expression correlation, information theory or regression approaches are used to infer influences between genes [14,40]. Integration more specific biological data allows the specification of the regulations. Recent emergence of data at the cellular level (in contrast to data collected from bulks of cells), is a great opportunity to infer contextualised GRN and has required the development of specific methods [16,25].

Most methods inferring Boolean models generate both regulatory graph and associated logical rules [13]. The approach proposed in [15] separates these tasks. It first builds the regulatory graph to only then infer the logical rules for each component using BoNesis tool [6]. Relying on an ASP solver, BoNesis solves a Boolean satisfiability problem and provides all the possible Boolean models that satisfy the constraints in the most permissive dynamics (see Sect. 4).

Methods for model synthesis typically enumerate all candidate models, which might be overwhelming to the user. A complementary approach is the use of model revision, where a (putative) model of reference and a set of observations are provided. Here, as new observations are considered, a model revision approach either indicates that the model is consistent with the current observations, or provides the set of minimal changes to the reference model, rendering it consistent. To avoid enumerating of all possible revisions and to limit the combinatorial explosion of the search space, a minimality criteria is considered, typically on the number of revision operations (*e.g.* changing a logical function, adding/removing a regulator, etc.). Due to the combinatorial nature of possible revisions, proposed methods rely heavily on Answer Set Programming (ASP) for their revision approaches. Recent examples are: unconstraining an inconsistent model [24] (potentially leading to under-constrained models), considering a set of rules of thumb over a subset of Boolean models [22] (potentially limiting the set of considered Boolean models), defining logical functions as logical gates in a circuit [17] (also potentially limiting the set of considered Boolean models). In contrast, ModRev[3] considers the rules proposed in [8] to navigate over the partially ordered set of all monotone non-degenerate Boolean functions, to produce repairs that are as close as possible to the original reference functions, including addition/removal of regulators [12]. ModRev is illustrated in Sect. 4 for the repair of the HSC model.

3.2 Assessing Reachability Properties

As it is essential to check the existence of trajectories from initial conditions to specific attractors, this section briefly discusses a few methods to assess reachability properties without pretending to exhaustivity.

Quantifying Reachability Under Different Updates. Under a deterministic, synchronous update, given an initial state x, an attractor A is either reachable or not. When considering all potential initial states $x \in \mathcal{S}$ (sampling the

[3] https://filipegouveia.github.io/ModRev/.

state space), the number of states from which A is reachable corresponds to the size of $B(A)$, the basin of attraction of A, or to its reachability probability (proportion of the states in the basin of A).

For an asynchronous update, it is similarly possible to assess the size of the basin of an attractor A (number of states from which A can be reached), as well as the probability to reach A from (a set of) initial state(s). In the lack of further knowledge, concurrent transitions in an asynchronous dynamics are considered as being equiprobable. However, it is possible to associate qualitative rates to the transitions that reflect known delays associated to biological processes (*e.g.*, protein degradation being slower than protein synthesis, or transcriptional activation being slower than post-transcriptional modification). These rates then translate into concurrent transition probabilities (such an asynchronous update scheme with the setting of different transition rates will be referred to as "rates" in what follows). Priority classes are a more extreme way of accounting for delays. They lead to the loss of some transitions (those involving updatable components that are in lower ranked classes than those of other updatable components).

Monte Carlo simulations are the simplest way to quantify attractor reachability, by simply running a large number of simulations (each following a single path in the STG) and getting relevant statistics (*e.g.*, how many trajectories led to a given attractor). MaBoSS (Markovian Boolean Stochastic Simulator) is a software tool for simulating continuous/discrete time Markov processes based on Boolean networks. Its foundations are continuous time Markov processes applied on Boolean state spaces. Performing adapted Monte Carlo simulations, temporal evolution of the model is specified through transition rates associated to each component. Given some initial conditions, MaBoSS produces the evolution of component activation probabilities over time [37].

In the context of the asynchronous update, Avatar, the algorithm introduced in [21], modifies Monte Carlo explorations to ensure that simulation runs are not trapped into transient SCCs (cyclical behaviours) while keeping correct measures of the calculated probabilities. It is thus also capable of dealing with complex attractors. Avatar is implemented in GINsim [27], and available in bioLQM [31]. The most recent version[4], to be integrated in the official release, allows for the consideration of priorities and transition rates settings [5]. Avatar capabilities are illustrated in Sect. 5.

Assessing the Behaviour upon Switching Inputs. A relevant question for models including input components relates to the behaviour of attractors when switching input values. Figure 1-c shows that the STG in made of disconnected sub-graphs, as many as input value combinations. One can compress this state-space by using transition labels indicating the input values that enable the transitions [29]. Model-checking proved useful to assess dynamical properties of logical models. In particular, the use of Action Restricted CTL (ARCTL [20]) handles labelled transition states as ARCTL includes the same temporal opera-

[4] https://github.com/chengyu163/bioLQM.

tors as CTL augmented with paths restrictions expressed with action formulae corresponding to input combinations [1,26].

4 The Case of Early Differentiation and Aging of Hematopoietic Stem Cells

The model presented in [15] focuses on the early differentiation of hematopoietic stem cells (HSCs). It explains the transcriptional mechanisms controlling this commitment and how they change with ageing. The authors proposed a workflow for building the Boolean Network Model. The first step is the construction of a regulatory graph by combining the GRN inference methods SCENIC [3], and prior knowledge of the biological process. Then, to infer the logical rules for each component, three sources of information have been combined:

1. The regulatory graph. Only Boolean models that use at most the listed regulations, with the right sign, are selected. Thus, some solutions may use only a subset of this regulatory graph.
2. The discrete configurations of nine cell states identified through the analysis of single-cell transcriptomic data: initial HSCs (iHSC); self-renewal (scHSC); quiescent (qHSC); interferon (ifnHSC); differentiation (preDiff). And the primed states: lymphoid (pLymph); neutrophils and mastocytes (pNeuMast); erythrocytes (pEr) and megakaryocytes (pMk).
3. Dynamical constraints imposed between these cell states, specifying stable states (the primed states) and reachability/unreachability between the states. That information was inferred from the analysis of transcriptomic data and pseudotime trajectories (issued from Monocle [34]).

By combining these three inputs, BoNesis tool [6] solves a Boolean satisfiability problem, relying on clingo [11] to solve an ASP encoding of the problem, and enumerates all the Boolean models satisfying the constraints under the most permissive dynamics. To reduce the large number of solutions (over 10^5), a combination of different strategies was used. A first selection allowed us to keep the solutions whose mutant simulations were in agreement with biological experiments and observations. Then, the number of edges in the regulatory graph was reduced by keeping those most supported by the databases (SCENIC [3], Cistrome [18]) and the literature. The 616 remaining solutions differed only in the logical rule of four nodes. For each of these nodes, the rule was chosen by manual curation and *ad hoc* criteria.

The resulting Boolean model, composed of 15 components and 36 regulatory interactions (see Fig. 2), exhibits five distinct stable states: pLymph, pNeuMast, pEr, pMk, and zeros (an inactive state). By simulating changes associated with ageing, the model identifies specific malfunctions that could explain the decline in HSC function and their reduced ability to differentiate into all mature blood cell types. It should be noted that, for computational efficiency reasons, the model has been inferred satisfying dynamical properties in the most permissive

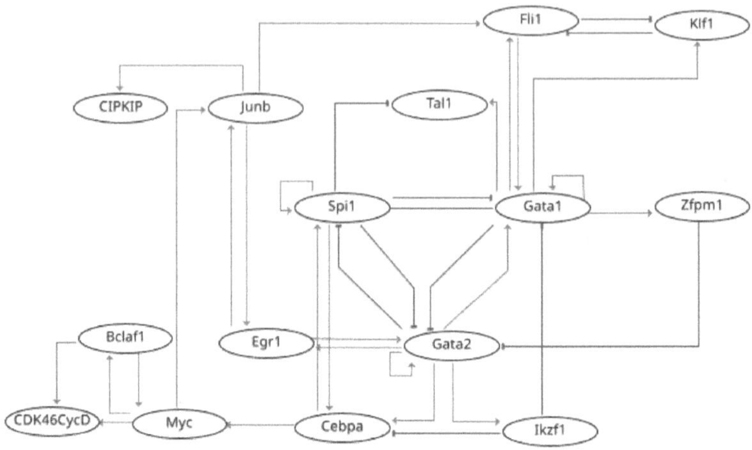

Fig. 2. Logical regulatory graph of the early differentiation of Hematopoietic Stem Cells (HCS) model.

dynamics. Many reachability properties are not satisfied in asynchronous dynamics. Thus, this resulting model (denoted M_0) presents reachabilities between some of the identified cell states (see Table 1) and the primed states (*e.g.*, iHSC towards pNeuMast), but cannot generate other reachabilities of interest (*e.g.*, iHSC towards pLymph), suggesting the need for the revision of the model.

To assist the model revision for the recovery of the missing reachabilities, we considered the use of ModRev [12]. Each revision requires that the resulting revised model is capable of an explicit additional reachability while maintaining the capability of generating 5 stable states as a constraint. We then relied on GINsim to confirm that each revised model conserved all previous reachabilities. Table 1 represents reachabilities observed with each model version, and Table 2 describes all logical functions from the HSC model in the corresponding model version changes.

The first revision considered model M_0 with the additional reachability from iHSC towards pLymph. ModRev suggests changing the logical function of Spi1

Table 1. Reachabilities observed with the corresponding HSC model version, from certain cell states in lines to primed cell states in columns. M_0 represents the original HSC model, R_1 the HSC model after the first revision, and R_2 the model after the second revision.

	zeros	pLymph	pNeuMast	pMk	pEr
iHSC	$M_0/R_1/R_2/R_3$	$R_1/R_2/R_3$	$M_0/R_1/R_2/R_3$	$M_0/R_1/R_2/R_3$	$M_0/R_1/R_2/R_3$
srHSC	$M_0/R_1/R_2/R_3$	$R_1/R_2/R_3$	$M_0/R_1/R_2/R_3$	$M_0/R_1/R_2/R_3$	$M_0/R_1/R_2/R_3$
qHSC	$M_0/R_1/R_2/R_3$	R_2/R_3	$M_0/R_1/R_2/R_3$	$M_0/R_1/R_2/R_3$	R_2/R_3
preDiff	R_3	R_3	$M_0/R_1/R_2/R_3$	$M_0/R_1/R_2/R_3$	R_3
pME	$M_0/R_1/R_2/R_3$	R_2/R_3	R_2/R_3	$M_0/R_1/R_2/R_3$	R_2/R_3

Table 2. Logical functions for all components in the: M_0 original HSC model, and the proposed revisions that originate model versions R_1, R_2, and R_3.

Component	Model version: Boolean function
Egr1	M_0: Gata2 ∧ Junb R_2: !Gata2 ∧ Junb
Junb	M_0: Egr1 ∨ Myc
Bclafl	M_0: Myc
Myc	M_0: Cebpa ∧ Bclafl
Fli1	M_0: Junb ∨ (Gata1 ∧ !Klf1)
Gata2	M_0: (Gata2 ∧ !Gata1 ∧ !Zfpm1) ∨ (Egr1 ∧ !Gata1 ∧ !Zfpm1 ∧ !Spi1)
Spi1	M_0: (Spi1 ∧ !Gata1) ∨ (Cebpa ∧ !Gata1 ∧ !Gata2)) R_1: (Spi1 ∧ !Gata1) ∨ (Cebpa ∧ !Gata1) ∨ (!Gata1 ∧ Gata2)) R_3: (Cebpa ∧ !Gata1 ∧ Spi1) ∨ (!Gata1 ∧ Gata2)
Cepba	M_0: (Gata2 ∧ !Ikzf1) ∨ (Spi1 ∧ !Ikzf1)
Gata1	M_0: Fli1 ∨ (Gata2 ∧ !Spi1) ∨ (Gata1 ∧ !Ikzf1 ∧ !Spi1)
Klf1	M_0: Gata1 ∧ !Fli1
Tal1	M_0: Gata1 ∧ !Spi1
Ikzf1	M_0: Gata2
Zfpm1	M_0: Gata1
CDK46CycD	M_0: Bclafl ∨ Myc
CIPKIP	M_0: Junb

from `(Spi1 ∧ !Gata1) ∨ (Cebpa ∧ !Gata1 ∧ !Gata2)` to `(Spi1 ∧ !Gata1) ∨ (Cebpa ∧ !Gata1) ∨ (!Gata1 ∧ Gata2)`, where Gata2 is now an activator, enabling Spi1 to become active at pLymph while inhibiting Tal1. Using GINsim to re-confirm all reachabilities we observe that this revision of Spi1 function additionally adds the reachability from srHSC towards pLymph. This revised model is denoted R_1.

We then used ModRev considering this revised R_1 model, to achieve the additional reachability from qHSC towards pLymph. ModRev suggests several revision possibilities, such as: changing the logical function of Junb from `(Egr1 ∨ Myc)` to `(Egr1 ∧ Myc)`; or changing the sign of regulator Gata2 on Egr1, from activator to inhibitor. These revisions proposals are related, since there is a cross-activation between Junb and Egr1, where both genes start active in qHSC and need to be inactive in pLymph. We considered the second suggestion (changing the sign of Gata2 on Egr1), and used GINsim to confirm that all previous reachabilities were still conserved. Interestingly, three additional reachabilities were also gained: qHSC towards pEr, pME towards pLymph, and pME towards pEr. Also, a new stable state is gained with an hybrid signature of pMk. This revised model is denoted R_2 in Table 1.

Starting from model R_2, we then used ModRev to recover the additional reachability from preDiff towards pLymph. ModRev took several days without finding a minimal revision, suggesting a search space too large. We then tried to limit the search space by preventing the revision on all components except one. This yielded a successful revision, changing once again the logical function of Spi1 from `(Spi1 ∧ !Gata1) ∨ (Cebpa ∧ !Gata1) ∨ (!Gata1 ∧ Gata2)` to `(Cebpa ∧ !Gata1 ∧ Spi1) ∨ (!Gata1 ∧ Gata2)`. GINsim was used to confirm all previous reachabilities with this new revised model, denoted R_3 in Table 1, were we observe that this revision also permitted to obtain the reachability from preDiff towards pEr.

5 The Case of the Role of Micro-Environmental Signals on the Epithelial to Mesenchymal Transition

The model developed in [35] aimed at exploring the role of environmental signals in controlling the Epithelial to Mesenchymal Transition (EMT) process, which has been associated with cancer metastasis. EMT leads to a shift from an epithelial phenotype in which cells are connected through adherens junctions (AJ) to a mesenchymal phenotype in which cells acquire migratory abilities through focal adhesions (FA). EMT thus involves the downregulation of epithelilal markers (*e.g.*, ECad and miR200) and the upregulation of mesenchymal markers (*e.g.*, SNAIL, ZEB). It also involves hybrid phenotypes with mixed epithelial and mesenchymal features. Figure 3 illustrates the regulatory network, which includes 10 input components embodying environmental signals, including paracrine and cell-cell adhesion depending signalling modelecules, growth factors, inflammatory signals, cell-cell and extra-cellular matrix state (ECM). The later represents the stiffening of the ECM, known to promote tumour invasion and metastasis. The 1283 stable states of the model are classified following the values of the two outputs that convey the states of the adherens junctions (AJ) and the focal adhesions (FA). The nomenclature for the most relevant phenotypes is recalled in the Fig. 4.

A model prediction is described together with its experimental validation in [35]. It relates to the inhibition of cell-cell contacts through the receptor-type tyrosine-protein phosphatases kappa (RPTP) by SRC. In the model, the later is represented by the multi-valued node FAK_SRC, the FAK SRC complex involved in the cytoskeleton organisation and migration. It is the reachability analysis of the overactivation of FAK_SCR that supports this prediction: starting from epithelial phenotypes with only ECM and cell-cell adhesion signals activated leads to a full mesenchymal phenotype (denoted M3), and the combined overactivation of FAK_SRC and RPTP leads to the appearance of a hybrid phenotype (denoted H3). Here, using Avatar (see Sect. 3.2), we revisit this analysis by enriching the definition of the updating schemes. Figure 4 displays the different reachability measures of the M3 and H3 phenotypes, depending on the choosen updates. This analysis shows that the reachability of the full mesenchymal phenotype (M3) strongly depends on the update scheme (in green in Fig. 4). M3

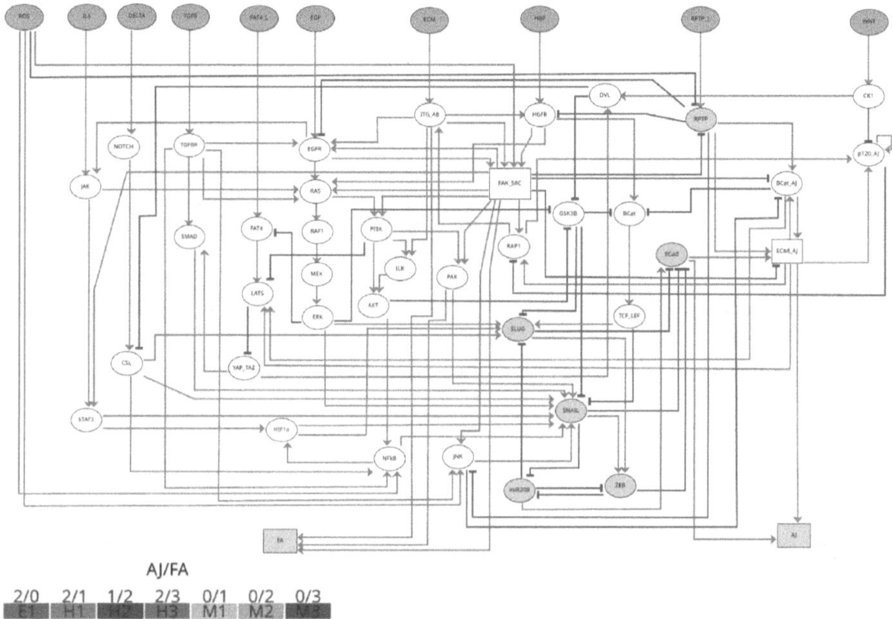

Fig. 3. Top: regulatory graph of the network controlling cell adhesion properties in response to environmental signals [35]. Red interactions denote inhibitions, green interactions denote activations. Ellipsoidal (resp. rectangular) nodes are Boolean (resp. multi-valued) components. Grey nodes are components transcriptionally regulated, violet nodes are inputs embodying external signals, and orange nodes are model outputs disclosing cell adhesion properties. **Bottom:** the seven phenotypes revealed by the model stable states, charaterised by the values of the output components (AJ and FA), according to the terminology adopted in [35], ranging from the epithelium (E1) to the mesenchymal (M1-3) going throught the hybrid (H1-3) phenotypes.

phenotype is lost when considering priority classes where transitions involving the transcription factors (TFs) SNAIL, SLUG, ZEB, miR200 and ECad (in grey in Fig. 3) are slower than those involving the other components. This suggests that all the transitions updating TFs values are in conflict with faster transitions. M3 reachability probability decreases when considering TF transition rates two or four times lower than that of other components.

Using the same EMT model, synergy between input components was studied in [36]. Figure 5 displays analyses revisiting the results presented in Fig. 3-D in [36] on the interplay between ECM (state of the extracellular matrix, stiff or not) and RPTP_L, the RPTP ligand of the R2B family, considering initial states in the epithelial phenotype (E1) and all remaining inputs absent. Considering an asynchronous update, in contrast to the case of a soft ECM (ECM component fixed to 0) whatever the state of RPTP_L, stiffening of the ECM (ECM to 1) with the presence of RPTP_L leads to the emergence of EMT phenotypes (full mesenchymal (M3) and hybrid (H3) phenotypes), and the maintenance of the epithelial

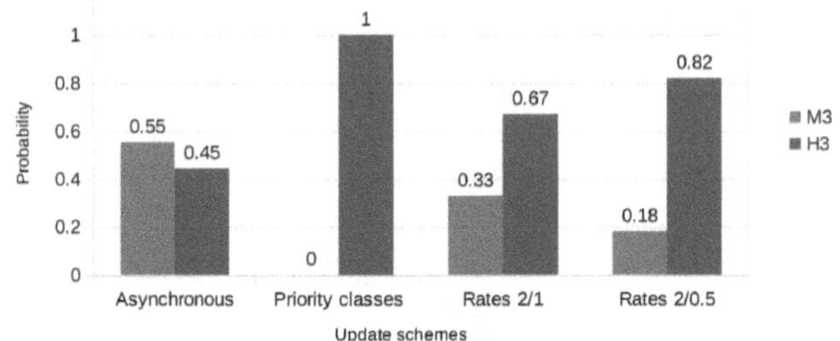

Fig. 4. Reachability analysis of the M3 and H3 phenotypes when FAK_SRC and RPTP are overactivated, starting from epithelial states. Avatar analyses considering different update schemes: asynchronous; two priority classes where the lower rank (slowest) is attributed to updates of the transcription factors SNAIL, SLUG, ZEB, miR200 and ECad; rates are associated to the transitions, faster (2) to all components but aforementioned transcription factors, which are associated to lower rates (1 and 0.5).

(E1) phenotype. However, the H3 phenotype is no longer reached when fixing RPTP_L to 0. This behaviour is maintained when associating TF transition rates two or four times lower than that of other components, whereas it is lost when associating TF transitions to a priority class with a lower rank than that of other components. Interestingly, for the combination (ECM=RPTL_L=1), M3 phenotype whose reachability probability is over 0.28 for an asynchronous update, is not reachable anymore for priority classes nor for transition rates.

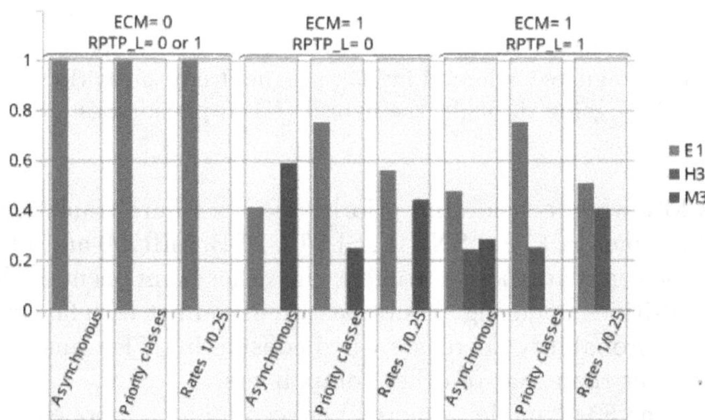

Fig. 5. Attractor reachability revealing ECM and RPTP_L cooperation when starting from E1 phenotype, with all remaining inputs to 0, varying updates as in Fig. 4.

Finally, beyond reachability quantification, it may be of interest to assess transient behaviours of specific components. MaBoSS ([37], briefly described in Sect. 3.2) provides this information. Figure 6 illustrates reachability properties of the mesenchymal (M3) and hybrid (H3) phenotypes under the asynchronous update *versus* rates, when starting from a naive state (in which all internal components are set to 0) with all inputs set to 0 but growth factors (EGF and HGF), ECM and RPTP_L. SLUG is a transcription factor known to be involved in cancer progression and in the regulation of EMT. In the EMT model, the corresponding component is fixed at 1 in all M3 states, and at 0 in all H3 states, In contrast, ECad, the model component representing the cell adhesion molecule E-Caderin, is at 1 in H3 states and at 0 in M3 states. While probabilities of the final SLUG and ECad values reflect the reachability probabilities of M3 and H3 phenotypes (compare Avatar and MaBoSS results in, respectively, the top and bottom parts of Fig. 6), MaBoSS analysis shows different transient behaviours for the asynchronous and rates updates.

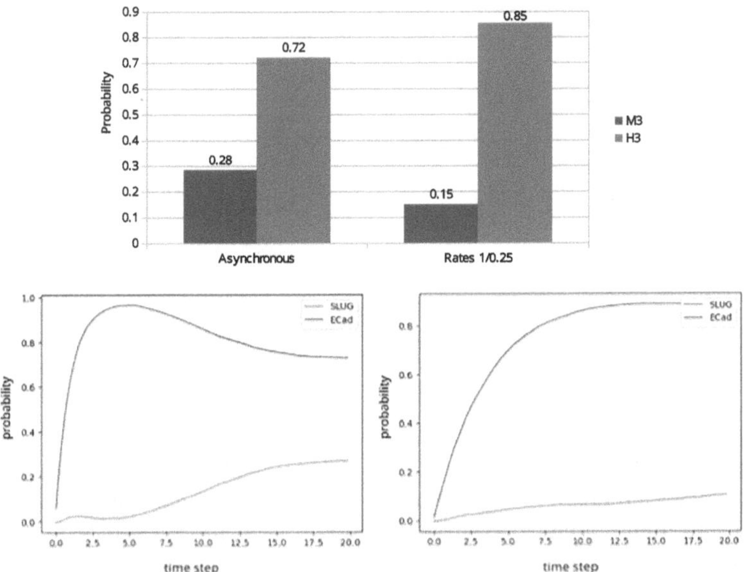

Fig. 6. Reachability analyses of the mesenchymal (M3) and hybrid (H3) phenotypes reachable from an initial naive state (all components to 0), and all inputs to 0 but the growth factors HGF, EGF, the extra-cellular matrix (ECM) and the RPTP ligand (RPTP_L). **Top:** probabilities returned by Avatar considering an asynchronous update *versus* transition rates with the rates four times slower for the TFs (SNAIL, SLUG, ZEB, miR200 and ECad). **Bottom:** probability of SLUG and ECad to be up over time by MaBoSS, considering the asynchronous update (left, all rates equal) and different rates (right) as specified above. In the M3 phenotype SLUG is expressed and ECad is not, whereas the reverse happens in the H3 phenotype.

Building a Reprogramming Graph. Reprogramming graphs provide global views of phenotype plasticity upon changes in environmental signals. Here, we

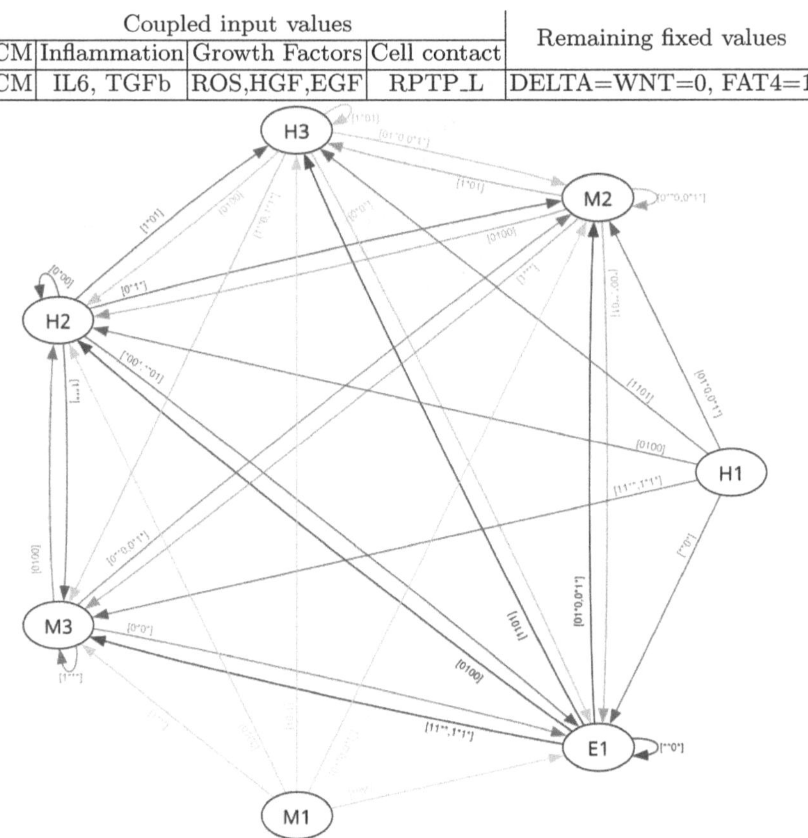

Coupled input values				Remaining fixed values
ECM	Inflammation	Growth Factors	Cell contact	
ECM	IL6, TGFb	ROS,HGF,EGF	RPTP_L	DELTA=WNT=0, FAT4=1

Fig. 7. Reprogramming graph for the EMT model displaying the existence of trajectories leaving phenotypes towards others under input combination constraints. Edge labels indicate input values following the simplification proposed in [36], with combinations of 4 values for the coupled inputs as indicated, the star symbol indicates that both values are possible.

performed this construction for the EMT model, using an ARCTL query expressing the constraint: given `input_comb`, there exists a state in `source_phenotype` for which there is a trajectory towards a state in `target_phenotype`, and all states in `target_phenotype` are stable for `input_comb`. Figure 7 displays the obtained reprogramming graph. The model includes ten inputs, but we considered `input_comb` with 4 values as follows: the first indicates the state of ECM, the second is 1 when all growth factors are present (0 otherwise), the third is 1 when all inflammatory signals are present (0 otherwise), and the last depends on the value of RPTP_L. Figure 7 shows that EMT phenotypes are highly plastic, suggesting a prominent role of micro-environmental signals. Absence of self-loops for the H1 and M1 phenotypes indicates that there are no `input_comb` for which those phenotypes are maintained. Indeed, states in H1 are stable in the presence of IL6 but in the absence of ROS, but here we considered combinations for identical, coupled values of IL6 and ROS. Similarly for M1, states in this phenotype are stable in the presence TGFb and/or IL6, but in the absence of ROS.

6 Discussion

With this paper, we aimed at illustrating the effectiveness of the logical modelling approach to handle complex regulatory networks that drive cellular behaviours. However, the current success of the logical modelling still calls for sophisticated methods to handle these models. Indeed, despite a high level of abstraction, logical models give rise to combinatorial issues mainly due to huge state spaces. Numerous challenges deal with model inference, revision, control, and analysis of dynamical properties. Here, we briefly discussed model inference, a critical topic if we are to have models matching observations coming out from huge volumes of data produced by biologists. Methods providing model alterations to solve unverified properties or to account to novel observations are also deeply needed. Section 4 illustrates the use of model inference and revision on a specific biological case study. This case study tends to show that inference process is not that simple, and that it requires a combination of methods and expertise. A connected topic relates to control strategy identification (see [7] and references therein). For example, for models dealing with disease networks, it is useful to identify potential therapeutic targets that would force the dynamics towards healthy attractors. In [7], the authors present a model-checking approach for optimal control strategies, illustrating it with the EMT model presented in Sect. 5.

Deserving a devoted review, which was not our intention here, the analysis of dynamical properties has recently led to a large variety of methods and computational tools developed for model simulation, attractor identification, reachability properties, etc. Here, we focused on attractor reachability for which, beyond a yes or no answer, a quantification can be evaluated. Section 5 underlines the impact of updating modes. Further progresses are needed to enable the definition of updates more biologically supported such as *e.g.*, context dependent transition rates. Specification of initial states also deserves a special attention. For example, in the case of the EMT model of Sect. 5, defining the 16 states of the epithelial states (E1) cannot be done with a single pattern. Finally, models with multiple inputs as the EMT model, require specific approaches to handle the high number of input combinations that reflect external signals.

It is worth mentioning that methods for model inference, revision as well as MaBoSS only deal with Boolean models. An appropriate "Booleanisation" of multi-valued models has been implemented GINsim [27] and bioLQM [31].

Methods for the analysis of logical models, with complementary capabilities, led to a proliferation of (formal and informal) workflows that are not always reproducible, due to lack of adequate documentation on parameters, tool versions, model formats, etc., or due to accessibility problems of older software/dataset versions. The Consortium for Logical Models and Tools (CoLoMoTo [30]) has developed SBML qual, an SBML package devoted to the storing and exchange of logical models [4]. Furthermore, the CoLoMoTo Interactive Notebook[5] aims at addressing reproducibility issues by providing a unified Python environment on top of a Docker framework [28]. Such a development involving the community facilitates the use of complementary methods that are needed to tackle comprehensive analyses of logical models.

References

1. Abou-Jaoudé, W., et al.: Model checking to assess t-helper cell plasticity. Front. Bioeng. Biotechnol. **2**, 86 (2015). https://doi.org/10.3389/fbioe.2014.00086
2. Abou-Jaoudé, W., et al.: Logical modeling and dynamical analysis of cellular networks. Front. Genetics **7**, 188073 (2016). https://doi.org/10.3389/fgene.2016.00094
3. Aibar, S., et al.: SCENIC: single-cell regulatory network inference and clustering. Nat. Methods **14**, 1083–1086 (2017). https://doi.org/10.1038/nmeth.4463
4. Chaouiya, C., et al.: SBML qualitative models: a model representation format and infrastructure to foster interactions between qualitative modelling formalisms and tools. BMC Syst. Biol. **7**, 135 (2013). https://doi.org/10.1186/1752-0509-7-135
5. Cheng, Y.: Attractor reachability estimation in logical models. Master's thesis, Instituto Superior Técnico - Universidade de Lisboa (2021)
6. Chevalier, S., Noël, V., Calzone, L., Zinovyev, A., Paulevé, L.: Synthesis and simulation of ensembles of boolean networks for cell fate decision. In: Lecture Notes in Computer Science, vol. 12314 LNBI (2020). https://doi.org/10.1007/978-3-030-60327-4_11
7. Cifuentes-Fontanals, L., Tonello, E., Siebert, H.: Control in boolean networks with model checking. Front. Appl. Math. Stat. **8**, 838546 (2022). https://doi.org/10.3389/fams.2022.838546
8. Cury, J.E.R., Monteiro, P.T., Chaouiya, C.: Partial order on the set of boolean regulatory functions (2019). https://doi.org/10.48550/arxiv.1901.07623
9. Dubrova, E., Teslenko, M.: A SAT-based algorithm for finding attractors in synchronous Boolean networks. IEEE/ACM Trans. Comput. Biol. Bioinf. **8**(5), 1393–1399 (2011). https://doi.org/10.1109/TCBB.2010.20
10. Fauré, A., Naldi, A., Chaouiya, C., Thieffry, D.: Dynamical analysis of a generic Boolean model for the control of the mammalian cell cycle. Bioinformatics **22**(14), e124–e131 (2006). https://doi.org/10.1093/bioinformatics/btl210
11. Gebser, M., Kaminski, R., Kaufmann, B., Schaub, T.: Multi-shot ASP solving with clingo. CoRR **abs/1705.09811** (2017). https://doi.org/10.48550/arXiv.1705.09811
12. Gouveia, F., Lynce, I., Monteiro, P.T.: ModRev - model revision tool for Boolean logical models of biological regulatory networks. In: Abate, A., Petrov, T., Wolf, V. (eds.) CMSB 2020. LNCS, vol. 12314, pp. 339–348. Springer, Cham (2020). https://doi.org/10.1007/978-3-030-60327-4_18
13. Hamey, F., Nestorowa, S., Kinston, S., Kent, D., Wilson, N., Göttgens, B.: Reconstructing blood stem cell regulatory network models from single-cell molecular profiles. PNAS **114**, 5822–5829 (2017). https://doi.org/10.1073/pnas.1610609114
14. Huynh-Thu, V., Irrthum, A., Wehenkel, L., Geurts, P.: Inferring regulatory networks from expression data using tree-based methods. PLoS ONE **5** (2010). https://doi.org/10.1371/journal.pone.0012776

[5] https://colomoto.github.io/colomoto-docker/.

15. Hérault, L., Poplineau, M., Duprez, E., Remy, E.: A novel Boolean network inference strategy to model early hematopoiesis aging. Comput. Struct. Biotechnol. J. **21**, 21–33 (2023). https://doi.org/10.1016/j.csbj.2022.10.040
16. Hérault, L., Poplineau, M., Remy, E., Duprez, E.: Single cell transcriptomics to understand HSC heterogeneity and its evolution upon aging. Cells **11** (2022). https://doi.org/10.3390/cells11193125
17. Lemos, A., Lynce, I., Monteiro, P.T.: Repairing Boolean logical models from time-series data using answer set programming. Algorithms Molecular Biol. **14**(1), 16 (Mar 2019). https://doi.org/10.1186/s13015-019-0145-8
18. Liu, T., et al.: Cistrome: an integrative platform for transcriptional regulation studies. Genome Biol. **12**, 1–10 (2011). https://doi.org/10.1186/gb-2011-12-8-r83
19. Lo Surd, P., et al.: SIGNOR 3.0, the signaling network open resource 3.0: 2022 update. Nucleic Acids Res. 1083–1086 (2022). https://doi.org/10.1093/nar/gkac883
20. Lomuscio, A., Pecheur, C., Raimondi, F.: Automatic verification of knowledge and time with NuSMV. In: Proceedings of the Twentieth International Joint Conference on Artificial Intelligence, pp. 1384–1389. IJCAI/AAAI Press (2007). https://www.ijcai.org/Proceedings/07/Papers/223.pdf
21. Mendes, N., Henriques, R., Remy, E., Carneiro, J., Monteiro, P., Chaouiya, C.: Estimating attractor reachability in asynchronous logical models. Front. Psychol. **9**, 1161 (2018). https://doi.org/10.3389/fpsyg.2018.01681
22. Merhej, E., Schockaert, S., De Cock, M.: Repairing inconsistent answer set programs using rules of thumb: a gene regulatory networks case study. Int. J. Approx. Reason. **83**, 243–264 (2017). https://doi.org/10.1016/j.ijar.2017.01.012
23. Milacic, M., et al.: The Reactome pathway knowledgebase 2024. Nucleic Acids Res. **52**(D1), D672–D678 (Nov2023). https://doi.org/10.1093/nar/gkad1025, http://dx.doi.org/10.1093/nar/gkad1025
24. Mobilia, N., Rocca, A., Chorlton, S., Fanchon, E., Trilling, L.: Logical modeling and analysis of regulatory genetic networks in a non monotonic framework. In: Ortuño, F., Rojas, I. (eds.) IWBBIO 2015. LNCS, vol. 9043, pp. 599–612. Springer, Cham (2015). https://doi.org/10.1007/978-3-319-16483-0_58
25. Badia-Mompel, P., et al.: Gene regulatory network inference in the era of single-cell multi-omics. Nat. Rev. Genet. **24**(11), 739–754 (2023). https://doi.org/10.1038/s41576-023-00618-5
26. Monteiro, P., Abou-Jaoudé, W., Thieffry, D., Chaouiya, C.: Model checking logical regulatory networks. In: IFAC Proceedings Volumes (IFAC-PapersOnline), vol. 9 (2014). https://doi.org/10.3182/20140514-3-FR-4046.00135
27. Naldi, A., Hernandez, C., Abou-Jaoudé, W., Monteiro, P., Chaouiya, C., Thieffry, D.: Logical modeling and analysis of cellular regulatory networks with GINsim 3.0. Front. Physiol. **9** (2018). https://doi.org/10.3389/fphys.2018.00646
28. Naldi, A., et al.: The CoLoMoTo interactive notebook: accessible and reproducible computational analyses for qualitative biological networks. Front. Physiol. **9** (2018). https://doi.org/10.3389/fphys.2018.00680
29. Naldi, A., Monteiro, P.T., Chaouiya, C.: Efficient handling of large signalling-regulatory networks by focusing on their core control. In: Gilbert, D., Heiner, M. (eds.) Computational Methods in Systems Biology, pp. 288–306. Springer, Berlin Heidelberg (2012). https://doi.org/10.1007/978-3-642-33636-2_17
30. Naldi, A., et al.: Cooperative development of logical modelling standards and tools with CoLoMoTo. Bioinformatics **31**(7), 1154–1159 (2015). https://doi.org/10.1093/bioinformatics/btv013

31. Naldi, A.: BioLQM: A java toolkit for the manipulation and conversion of logical qualitative models of biological networks. Front. Physiol. **9**, 382371 (11 2018). https://doi.org/10.3389/fphys.2018.01605
32. Paulevé, L., Kolčák, J., Chatain, T., Haar, S.: Reconciling qualitative, abstract, and scalable modeling of biological networks. Nature Commun. **11**(1), 4526 (2020). https://doi.org/10.1038/s41467-020-18112-5
33. Pratapa, A., Jalihal, A.P., Law, J.N., Bharadwaj, A., Murali, T.: Benchmarking algorithms for gene regulatory network inference from single-cell transcriptomic data. Nat. Methods **17**, 147–154 (2020). https://doi.org/10.1038/s41592-019-0690-6
34. Qiu, X., et al.: Reversed graph embedding resolves complex single-cell trajectories. Nat. Methods **10**, 979–82 (2017). https://doi.org/10.1038/nmeth.4402
35. Selvaggio, G., et al.: Hybrid epithelial-mesenchymal phenotypes are controlled by microenvironmental factors. Cancer Res. **80**(11), 2407–2420 (2020). https://doi.org/10.1158/0008-5472.CAN-19-3147
36. Selvaggio, G., Chaouiya, C., Janody, F.: In silico logical modelling to uncover cooperative interactions in cancer. Int. J. Molecular Sci. **22**(9), 4897 (2021). https://doi.org/10.3390/ijms22094897
37. Stoll, G., et al.: MaBoSS 2.0: an environment for stochastic Boolean modeling. Bioinformatics **33**(14), 2226–2228 (2017). https://doi.org/10.1093/bioinformatics/btx123
38. Tonello, E., Farcot, E., Chaouiya, C.: Local negative circuits and cyclic attractors in Boolean networks with at most five components. SIAM J. Appl. Dyn. Syst. **18**(1), 68–79 (2019). https://doi.org/10.1137/18M1173988
39. Varela, P.L., Lynce, I., Manquinho, V., Chaouiya, C., Monteiro, P.T.: Stable states of Boolean regulatory networks composed over hexagonal grids. Electron. Notes Theor. Comput. Sci. **335**, 113–130 (2018). 7th International Workshop on Static Analysis and Systems Biology (SASB 2016). https://doi.org/10.1016/j.entcs.2018.03.011, https://www.sciencedirect.com/science/article/pii/S1571066118300148
40. Verny, L., Sella, N., Affeldt, S., Singh, P., Isambert, H.: Learning causal networks with latent variables from multivariate information in genomic data. PLoS Comput. Biol. **13**(10), e1005662 (2017). https://doi.org/10.1371/journal.pcbi.1005662
41. Videla, S., et al.: Learning boolean logic models of signaling networks with ASP. Theoret. Comput. Sci. **599**, 79–101 (2015). https://doi.org/10.1016/j.tcs.2014.06.022

Easy to Check Algebraic Characterizations of Dynamical Properties for Linear CA and Additive CA over a Finite Abelian Group

Alberto Dennunzio(✉)

Dipartimento di Informatica, Sistemistica e Comunicazione, Università Degli Studi di Milano-Bicocca, Viale Sarca 336, 20126 Milano, (MI), Italy
alberto.dennunzio@unimib.it

Abstract. We focus on how the dynamical properties of any Linear CA over $(\mathbb{Z}/m\mathbb{Z})^n$ are hidden inside the characteristic polynomial of its defining matrix, namely, a polynomial of degree n in the indeterminate t and with Laurent polynomials over $\mathbb{Z}/m\mathbb{Z}$ as coefficients. In particular, as far as Linear CA over $(\mathbb{Z}/m\mathbb{Z})^n$ are concerned, we review the mostly recent algebraic decidable characterizations of the following properties: injectivity, surjectivity, sensitivity to the initial conditions, equicontinuity, topological transitivity, and positive expansivity. These characterizations are easy to check, i.e., related decision algorithms can be designed is such a way that exponential terms in their computational complexity are avoided as much as possible. In particular, gcd operations are involved, while the prime factor decomposition of m is bypassed. Finally, we recall how such characterizations regarding Linear CA over $(\mathbb{Z}/m\mathbb{Z})^n$ can be exploited to decide the above mentioned dynamical properties for the whole class of Additive CA over a finite abelian group.

Keywords: Cellular Automata · Linear Cellular Automata · Additive Cellular Automata · Discrete Dynamical Systems · Decidability

1 Introduction

Cellular automata (CA) are well-known formal models that find application in several disciplines and their different subdomains. In practical applications one needs to know if the CA used for modelling a certain system exhibits some specific property regarding the dynamics of the system and that knowledge is also interesting in its own from a theoretical point of view. However, this can be a severe issue. Indeed, a strong result by Jarkko Kari [12] states that all non-trivial dynamical behaviors are undecidable. From this seminal result, a long sequence followed.

Luckily, the undecidability issue can be tackled by imposing some constraints on the model. As it often happens - and this is the environment we deal with - the alphabet and the global updating map are constrained to be a finite abelian group and an additive function, respectively, giving rise to *Additive CA over a*

Published by Springer Nature Switzerland AG 2024
M. Gadouleau and A. Castillo-Ramirez (Eds.): AUTOMATA 2024, LNCS 14782, pp. 23–34, 2024.
https://doi.org/10.1007/978-3-031-65887-7_2

finite abelian group or, briefly, *Additive CA* or the subclass of *Linear CA* over $(\mathbb{Z}/m\mathbb{Z})^n$, i.e., those Additive CA having $(\mathbb{Z}/m\mathbb{Z})^n$ as alphabet and a local rule defined by $n \times n$ matrices over $\mathbb{Z}/m\mathbb{Z}$. We stress that such requirements do not prevent Additive CA at all from being successfully used for practical purposes. On the contrary, since Additive CA are able to exhibit most of the complex behaviors of general CA, they are often exploited for designing many applications (see, for instance, [15,16]). Moreover, general Additive CA are more expressive and they give rise to much more complex dynamics than the already investigated subclass of Linear CA over the alphabet $(\mathbb{Z}/m\mathbb{Z})^n$ with $n = 1$ (see [5]). As a matter of fact, the study of Linear CA over $\mathbb{Z}/m\mathbb{Z}$ received a great attention and characterizations of the main theoretic set and dynamical properties were provided [3,11,14].

In this paper, we review the mostly recent algebraic and decidable characterizations of the main theoretic set and dynamical properties for Linear CA over the alphabet $(\mathbb{Z}/m\mathbb{Z})^n$ with $n > 1$, namely, injectivity, surjectivity, sensitivity to the initial conditions, equicontinuity, topological transitivity, and positive expansivity. These characterizations turn out to be *easy to check* (or, *efficiently computable*), i.e., related decision algorithms can be designed is such a way that exponential terms in their computational complexity are avoided as much as possible. In particular, gcd operation are involved inside the efficient algorithms, while the prime factor decomposition of m is bypassed. We stress that sometimes efficient decision algorithms are not immediately derived from the algebraic characterizations and, hence, the latter can be named easy to check only once such algorithms have been exhibited. Finally, we recall how such characterizations regarding Linear CA over $(\mathbb{Z}/m\mathbb{Z})^n$ can be exploited to decide the above mentioned dynamical properties for the whole class of Additive CA over a finite abelian group.

2 Basic Notions and Background

Let $\mathbb{K}$ be any commutative ring and let $A \in \mathbb{K}^{n\times n}$ be an $n \times n$-matrix over $\mathbb{K}$. We denote by χ_A the characteristic polynomial $\det(tI_n - A) \in \mathbb{K}[t]$ of A, where I_n always stands for the $n \times n$ identity matrix (over whatever ring we are considering). Furthermore, $\mathbb{K}[X, X^{-1}]$ denotes the set of Laurent polynomials with coefficients in $\mathbb{K}$. In particular, whenever $\mathbb{K} = \mathbb{Z}/m\mathbb{Z}$ for some natural $m > 1$, we will write $\mathbb{L}_m$ instead of $\mathbb{Z}/m\mathbb{Z}[X, X^{-1}]$.

Let $\mathbb{K} = \mathbb{Z}/m\mathbb{Z}$ for some natural $m > 1$ and let $q > 1$ be a natural dividing m. If P is any polynomial from $\mathbb{K}[t]$ (resp., a Laurent polynomial from $\mathbb{L}_m$) (resp., a matrix from $(\mathbb{L}_m)^{n\times n}$), $P \bmod q$ denotes the polynomial (resp., the Laurent polynomial) (resp., the matrix) obtained by P by taking all its coefficients modulo q.

Let Σ be a finite set (also called *alphabet*). A *CA configuration* (or, briefly, a *configuration*) is any function from $\mathbb{Z}$ to Σ. Given a configuration $c \in \Sigma^{\mathbb{Z}}$ and any integer $i \in \mathbb{Z}$, the value of c in position i is denoted by c_i. The set $\Sigma^{\mathbb{Z}}$, called *configuration space*, is as usual equipped with the standard Tychonoff distance d defined as

$$\forall c, c' \in \Sigma^{\mathbb{Z}},\ d(c, c') = \begin{cases} 0, & \text{if} \quad c = c', \\ 2^{-\min\{|j|\,:\,j\in\mathbb{Z},\, c_j \neq c'_j\}}, & \text{otherwise} \end{cases} .$$

Whenever the term *linear* is involved the alphabet Σ is $\mathbb{K}^n$, where $\mathbb{K} = \mathbb{Z}/m\mathbb{Z}$ for some natural $m > 1$. Clearly, in that case both $\mathbb{K}^n$ and $(\mathbb{K}^n)^{\mathbb{Z}}$ become $\mathbb{K}$-modules in the obvious (i.e., entrywise) way. On the other hand, whenever the term *additive* is involved the alphabet Σ is a finite abelian group G and the configuration space turns $G^{\mathbb{Z}}$ turns out to be an abelian group, too, where the group operation of $G^{\mathbb{Z}}$ is the componentwise extension of the group operation of G, both of them will be denoted by $+$.

A *one-dimensional CA* (or, briefly, a *CA*) over Σ is a pair $(\Sigma^{\mathbb{Z}}, \mathcal{F})$, where $\mathcal{F}\colon \Sigma^{\mathbb{Z}} \to \Sigma^{\mathbb{Z}}$ is the uniformly continuous transformation (called *global rule*) defined as $\forall c \in \Sigma^{\mathbb{Z}}, \forall i \in \mathbb{Z}, \mathcal{F}(c)_i = f(c_{i-r}, \ldots, c_{i+r})$, for some fixed natural number $r \in \mathbb{N}$ (called *radius*) and some fixed function $f\colon \Sigma^{2r+1} \to \Sigma$ (called *local rule* of radius r). In the sequel, when no misunderstanding is possible, we will sometimes identify any CA with its global rule.

A CA $(\Sigma^{\mathbb{Z}}, \mathcal{F})$ is *topologically transitive*, or, simply *transitive*, if for any pair of nonempty open subsets $U, V \subseteq \Sigma^{\mathbb{Z}}$ there exists a natural $h > 0$ such that $\mathcal{F}^h(U) \cap V \neq \emptyset$, while it is said to be *topologically mixing*, or, simply *mixing*, if the latter intersection condition holds ultimately. A CA $(\Sigma^{\mathbb{Z}}, \mathcal{F})$ has *dense periodic orbits* if the set of its periodic points is dense in $\Sigma^{\mathbb{Z}}$, where a periodic point for is any configuration $c \in \Sigma^{\mathbb{Z}}$ such that $F^h(c) = c$ for some natural $h > 0$.

A CA $(\Sigma^{\mathbb{Z}}, \mathcal{F})$ is *sensitive to the initial conditions* or, simply *sensitive*, if there exists $\epsilon > 0$ such that for any $\delta > 0$ and $c \in \Sigma^{\mathbb{Z}}$ there is a configuration $c' \in \Sigma^{\mathbb{Z}}$ with $0 < d(c', c) < \delta$ such that $d(\mathcal{F}^h(c'), \mathcal{F}^h(c')) \geq \epsilon$ for some natural h. A CA $(\Sigma^{\mathbb{Z}}, \mathcal{F})$ is said to be *equicontinuous* if for any $\epsilon > 0$ there exists $\delta > 0$ such that for all $c, c' \in \Sigma^{\mathbb{Z}}$, $d(c', c) < \delta$ implies that $\forall k \in \mathbb{N}$, $d(\mathcal{F}^k(c'), \mathcal{F}^k(c')) < \epsilon$. As dynamical properties, sensitivity and equicontinuity represent the main features of unstable and stable dynamical systems, respectively. While the latter is a strong form of stability, the former is the well-known basic component and essence of the chaotic behaviour of discrete time dynamical systems. Indeed, sensitivity, topological transitivity and dense periodic orbits are the features that together define the popular notion of *chaos* according to the Devaney definition (see [10]).

We recall that a CA $(\Sigma^{\mathbb{Z}}, \mathcal{F})$ is *positively expansive* if for some constant $\varepsilon > 0$ it holds that for any pair of distinct configurations $c, c' \in \Sigma^{\mathbb{Z}}$ there exists a natural number ℓ such that $d(\mathcal{F}^\ell(c), \mathcal{F}^\ell(c')) \geq \varepsilon$. We stress that CA positive expansivity is a condition of strong chaos. Indeed, on one hand, positive expansivity is a stronger condition than sensitivity. On the other hand, any positively expansive CA is also topologically transitive (even topologically mixing) and, at the same time, it has dense periodic orbits. Therefore, any positively expansive

CA is chaotic according to the Devaney definition of chaos. Finally, we recall that if a CA $\mathcal{F}$ is positively expansive then $\mathcal{F}$ is surjective.

2.1 Linear and Additive CA

Let $\mathbb{K} = \mathbb{Z}/m\mathbb{Z}$ for some natural $m > 1$ and let $n \in \mathbb{N}$ with $n \geq 1$. Let G be a finite abelian group.

A local rule $f\colon (\mathbb{K}^n)^{2r+1} \to \mathbb{K}^n$ of radius r is said to be *linear* if it is defined by $2r+1$ matrices $A_{-r}, \ldots, A_r \in \mathbb{K}^{n\times n}$ as follows: $\forall (x_{-r}, \ldots, x_r) \in (\mathbb{K}^n)^{2r+1}, f(x_{-r}, \ldots, x_r) = \sum_{i=-r}^{r} A_i \cdot x_i$. A one-dimensional *linear CA (LCA)* over $\mathbb{K}^n$ is a CA $\mathcal{F}$ based on a linear local rule. The Laurent polynomial (or matrix)

$$A = \sum_{i=-r}^{r} A_i X^{-i} \in \mathbb{K}^{n\times n}[X, X^{-1}] \cong (\mathbb{L}_m)^{n\times n}$$

is said to be the *the matrix associated with $\mathcal{F}$*.

We recall the characterizations of the above mentioned properties for LCA over $\mathbb{Z}/m\mathbb{Z}$.

Theorem 1 ([3,11,14]). *Let $\mathcal{F}$ be any LCA over $\mathbb{Z}/m\mathbb{Z}$ and let $A_{-r}, \ldots, A_r \in \mathbb{Z}/m\mathbb{Z}$ define the 1×1 matrix $A \in \mathbb{L}_m$ associated with $\mathcal{F}$, where m is any natural with $m > 1$. Let $\mathcal{P}$ be the set of all prime factors of m. The following characterizations hold:*

$$\begin{aligned}
\mathcal{F} \textit{ is injective iff } & \forall p \in \mathcal{P}\ \exists! A_i : p \nmid A_i \\
\mathcal{F} \textit{ is surjective iff } & \gcd(m, A_{-r}, \ldots, A_r) = 1 \\
\mathcal{F} \textit{ is sensitive iff } & \exists p \in \mathcal{P} : p \nmid \gcd(m, A_{-r}, \ldots, A_{-1}, A_1, \ldots, A_r) \\
\mathcal{F} \textit{ is equicontinuous iff } & \forall p \in \mathcal{P} : p \mid \gcd(m, A_{-r}, \ldots, A_{-1}, A_1, \ldots, A_r) \\
\mathcal{F} \textit{ is transitive iff } & \gcd(m, A_{-r}, \ldots, A_{-1}, A_1, \ldots, A_r) = 1 \\
\mathcal{F} \textit{ is positively expansive iff } & \gcd(m, A_{-r}, \ldots, A_{-1}, A_1, \ldots, A_r) = 1
\end{aligned}$$

We stress that the criteria proposed for deciding whether a LCA over $\mathbb{Z}/m\mathbb{Z}$ satisfies those properties require only gcd computations and their computational complexity is polynomial in $\log m$ and in the number of coefficients of the local rule [14].

We now recall the notion of Additive CA, a wider class than LCA. An *Additive CA* over a finite abelian group G is a CA $(G^{\mathbb{Z}}, \mathcal{F})$ where the global rule $\mathcal{F} : G^{\mathbb{Z}} \to G^{\mathbb{Z}}$ is an endomorphism of $G^{\mathbb{Z}}$. We stress that the local rule $f : G^{2r+1} \to G$ of an Additive CA of radius r over a finite abelian group G can be written as $\forall (x_{-r}, \ldots, x_r) \in G^{2r+1}, f(x_{-r}, \ldots, x_r) = \sum_{i=-r}^{r} f_i(x_i)$, where the functions f_i are endomorphisms of G. Moreover, as a consequence of the application of the fundamental theorem of finite abelian groups to Additive CA (see [6], for details), as far as Additive CA are concerned, we assume that $G = \mathbb{Z}/p^{k_1}\mathbb{Z} \times \ldots \times \mathbb{Z}/p^{k_n}\mathbb{Z}$ for some naturals $k_1, \ldots, k_n$ with $k_1 \geq k_2 \geq \ldots \geq k_n$. Indeed, any finite abelian group is isomorphic to a direct sum of a certain number of its subgroups (with pairwise coprime cardinality), each of them being as such a G, and an Additive CA over a finite abelian group splits into the direct sum of Additive CA over those subgroups. Hence, the former CA turns out to satisfy P if and only if all the CA components of that sum satisfy P, where P is any of the above mentioned properties except sensitivity (in the case of such a property, it holds that the former CA is sensitive if and only if at least one CA component is sensitive).

Let $\hat{G} = (\mathbb{Z}/p^{k_1}\mathbb{Z})^n$ and let $\psi : G \to \hat{G}$ be the map defined as $\forall h \in G, \forall i = 1, \ldots, n, \psi(h)^i = h^i\, p^{k_1-k_i}$, where, for a sake of clarity, we stress that h^i denotes the i-th component of h, while $p^{k_1-k_i}$ is just the $(k_1 - k_i)$-th power of p. Let $\Psi : G^{\mathbb{Z}} \to \hat{G}^{\mathbb{Z}}$ be the componentwise extension of ψ, i.e., the function defined as $\forall c \in G^{\mathbb{Z}}, \forall j \in \mathbb{Z}, \Psi(c)_j = \psi(c_j)$. The function Ψ turns out to be continuous and injective.

We recall that for any Additive CA over G an LCA over $(\mathbb{Z}/p^{k_1}\mathbb{Z})^n$ associated with it can be defined as follows. With a further abuse of notation, in the sequel we will write p^{-m} with $m \in \mathbb{N}$ even if this quantity might not exist in $\mathbb{Z}/p^k\mathbb{Z}$. However, we will use it only when it multiplies $p^{m'}$ for some integer $m' > m$. In such a way $p^{m'-m}$ is well-defined in $\mathbb{Z}/p^k\mathbb{Z}$ and we will note it as product $p^{-m} \cdot p^{m'}$.

Let $(G^{\mathbb{Z}}, F)$ be any Additive CA and let $f : G^{2r+1} \to G$ be its local rule defined, by $2r + 1$ endomorphisms $f_{-r}, \ldots, f_r$ of G. For each $z \in \{-r, \ldots, r\}$, let $A_z = (a^{(z)}_{i,j})_{1\le i\le n,\, 1\le j\le n} \in (\mathbb{Z}/p^{k_1}\mathbb{Z})^{n\times n}$ be the matrix such that $\forall i, j \in \{1, \ldots, n\}, a^{(z)}_{i,j} = p^{k_j-k_i} \cdot (f_z(e_j))^i$. The *LCA associated with the Additive CA* $(G^{\mathbb{Z}}, F)$ is $(\hat{G}^{\mathbb{Z}}, L)$, where L is defined by $A_{-r}, \ldots, A_r$ or, equivalently, by $A = \sum_{z=-r}^{r} A_z X^{-z} \in \mathbb{Z}/p^{k_1}\mathbb{Z}\left[X, X^{-1}\right]^{n\times n}$. We stress that the following diagram commutes

$$\begin{array}{ccc} G^{\mathbb{Z}} & \xrightarrow{F} & G^{\mathbb{Z}} \\ \Psi \big\downarrow & & \big\downarrow \Psi \\ \hat{G}^{\mathbb{Z}} & \xrightarrow[L]{} & \hat{G}^{\mathbb{Z}} \end{array},$$

i.e., $L \circ \Psi = \Psi \circ F$. Therefore, $(\hat{G}^{\mathbb{Z}}, L)$ is said to be the LCA associated with $(G^{\mathbb{Z}}, F)$ *via the embedding* Ψ. In general, $(G^{\mathbb{Z}}, F)$ is not topologically conjugated (i.e., homeomorphic) to $(\hat{G}^{\mathbb{Z}}, L)$ but $(G^{\mathbb{Z}}, F)$ is a subsystem of $(\hat{G}^{\mathbb{Z}}, L)$ and the latter condition alone is not enough in general to immediately lift dynamical properties from a one system to the other one.

We recall that for Additive CA, transitivity and mixing are equivalent properties. The same also holds for surjectivity and dense periodic orbits. Since all transitive CA are both surjective and sensitive, as a consequence, chaos turns out to be equivalent to transitivity for Additive CA [5]. We stress that whether transitivity and mixing, as well as surjectivity and dense periodic points, are equivalent property are open questions for general CA.

3 Dynamical Behavior of LCA

We now review the results about the set theoretic and dynamical properties of LCA over $(\mathbb{Z}/m\mathbb{Z})^n$ in terms of easy to check characterizations for them.

3.1 Injectivity and Surjectivity

Theorem 2 ([2,13]). *Let $\mathcal{F}$ be any LCA over $(\mathbb{Z}/m\mathbb{Z})^n$ and let $A \in \mathbb{L}_m^{n\times n}$ be the matrix associated with $\mathcal{F}$, where m and n are any two naturals with $m > 1$ and $n > 1$. Let $\alpha_0 = \det(A)$ be the constant term of the characteristic polynomial $\chi_A(t)$ of A ($\alpha_0 \in \mathbb{L}_m$ is the 1×1 matrix associated with a LCA over $\mathbb{Z}/m\mathbb{Z}$). The following characterizations hold:*

$\mathcal{F}$ is injective iff α_0 is the matrix associated with an injective LCA over $\mathbb{Z}/m\mathbb{Z}$
$\mathcal{F}$ is surjective iff α_0 is the matrix associated with a surjective LCA over $\mathbb{Z}/m\mathbb{Z}$

3.2 Sensitivity and Equicontinuity

Theorem 3 ([7]). *Let $\mathcal{F}$ be any LCA over $(\mathbb{Z}/m\mathbb{Z})^n$ and let $A \in \mathbb{L}_m^{n\times n}$ be the matrix associated with $\mathcal{F}$, where m and n are any two naturals with $m > 1$ and $n > 1$. Let $\chi_A(t) = \alpha_0 + \alpha_1 t + \cdots + \alpha_{t-1}t^{t-1} + t^n$ be the characteristic polynomial of A, where each $\alpha_i \in \mathbb{L}_m$ and as such is the 1×1 matrix associated with a LCA over $\mathbb{Z}/m\mathbb{Z}$. The following characterization holds:*

$\mathcal{F}$ is sensitive (resp., equicontinuous) iff at least one (resp., each) α_i is the matrix associated with a sensitive (resp., equicontinuous) LCA over $\mathbb{Z}/m\mathbb{Z}$.

3.3 Topological Transitivity

Theorem 4 ([4]). *Let $\mathcal{F}$ be any LCA over $(\mathbb{Z}/m\mathbb{Z})^n$ and let $A \in \mathbb{L}_m^{n\times n}$ be the matrix associated with $\mathcal{F}$, where m and n are any two naturals with $m > 1$ and $n > 1$. Let $p_1, \dots, p_l$ be all the primes appearing inside the prime factor decomposition of m (i.e., $m = p_1^{k_1} \cdots p_l^{k_l}$). The following characterization holds:*

$\mathcal{F}$ is topologically transitive iff for every $j \in \{1, \dots, l\}$ both the following conditions hold

$$\det(A \bmod p_j) \neq 0$$
$$\gcd(\chi_{A \bmod p_j}(t), t^{p^h-1} - 1) = 1 \quad \text{for all } h \in \{1, \dots, n\}$$

Although the previous characterization is decidable, the algorithm that directly tests it is far from being efficient from the computational point of view, first of all because the prime decomposition of m is required. Moreover, since computing the gcd of two polynomials of degree at most d costs $O(d^2)$ operations using classical methods, or $O(d \cdot \log^2(d) \cdot \log(\log d))$ operations using fast methods, the algorithm directly derived from the previous characterization on its own has an exponential computational complexity in the worst case since its run may compute the gcd of two polynomials one of them having degree $p^n - 1$.

In [9], an efficient algorithm for deciding topological transitivity for LCA over $(\mathbb{Z}/p^k\mathbb{Z})^n$ was provided. It comes from a new characterization of transitivity based on an idea which is completely different from that in [4]. Indeed, unlike [4], the characteristic polynomial $\det(tI_n - A)$ of the matrix A associated with a LCA over $(\mathbb{Z}/p^k\mathbb{Z})^n$ is now considered as Laurent polynomial with coefficients from $(\mathbb{Z}/p^k\mathbb{Z})[t]$ (instead of a classic polynomial in the indeterminate t and, since LCA over $(\mathbb{Z}/p^k\mathbb{Z})^n$ are involved, with Laurent polynomials over $(\mathbb{Z}/p^k\mathbb{Z})$ as coefficients). As a matter of fact, transitivity is characterized by a decidable condition on the degree of the gcd of those polynomial coefficients (elements from $(\mathbb{Z}/p^k\mathbb{Z})[t]$) when their coefficients (elements from $\mathbb{Z}/p^k\mathbb{Z}$) are taken modulo p. In this way, the exponential factor in the complexity of the decision procedure directly derived from Theorem 4 no longer appears.

Theorem 5. *Let $\mathcal{F}$ be any LCA over $(\mathbb{Z}/p^k\mathbb{Z})^n$ and let A be the matrix associated with $\mathcal{F}$, where p, k, and n are any three naturals with p prime, $k > 0$, and $n > 1$. Let $\xi_p(X, X^{-1})$ be the polynomial characteristic $\chi_{A \bmod p}(t)$ of $A \bmod p$ expressed as polynomial in the variables X and X^{-1}. Let $\gamma_p(t) \in (\mathbb{Z}/p\mathbb{Z})[t]$ be the* gcd *of the coefficients of $\xi_p(X, X^{-1})$. The following characterization holds:*

$$\mathcal{F} \text{ is topologically transitive iff } \deg(\gamma_p(t)) < 1 \tag{1}$$

Corollary 1. *Let $\mathcal{F}$ be any LCA over $(\mathbb{Z}/m\mathbb{Z})^n$ and let $A \in \mathbb{L}_m^{n\times n}$ be the matrix associated with $\mathcal{F}$, where m and n are any two naturals with $m > 1$ and $n > 1$. Let $p_1, \ldots, p_l$ be all the primes appearing inside the prime factor decomposition of m (i.e., $m = p_1^{k_1} \cdots p_l^{k_l}$). The following characterization holds:*

$$\mathcal{F} \text{ is topologically transitive iff } \deg(\gamma_{p_j}(t)) < 1 \text{ for every } j \in \{1, \ldots, l\},$$

where $\gamma_{p_j}(t)$ is as in Theorem 5.

In [9], authors also exhibit an efficient algorithm for deciding transitivity for LCA over $(\mathbb{Z}/m\mathbb{Z})^n$ where m is any natural with $m > 1$. Indeed, in that algorithm the prime factor decomposition of m is bypassed, while the latter is still required if the condition from Corollary 1 is directly tested. Let us summarize the efficient algorithm provided in [9]. The polynomial characteristic of the matrix associated with a LCA over $(\mathbb{Z}/m\mathbb{Z})^n$ is again expressed as polynomial in the variables X and X^{-1} i.e., a Laurent polynomial with coefficients from $(\mathbb{Z}/m\mathbb{Z})[t]$. The procedure has as input such coefficients (elements from $(\mathbb{Z}/m\mathbb{Z})[t]$) and it aims at testing a condition equivalent to transitivity which is essentially the same expressed in (1), i.e., the one for LCA over $(\mathbb{Z}/p^k\mathbb{Z})^n$, but now, since $(\mathbb{Z}/m\mathbb{Z})$ is not in general a field, an "unconventional gcd" is involved and hence the situation is more complicated. As a matter of fact, the procedure exploits an unconventional use of the Euclidean algorithm for the computation of the gcd of two polynomials from $(\mathbb{Z}/m\mathbb{Z})[t]$, where, by unconventional use, we means that the Euclidean algorithm is used although $(\mathbb{Z}/m\mathbb{Z})$ is not a field. Namely, its run proceeds until it encounters a division of two polynomials that can not be performed because the leading coefficient of the divisor is not coprime with m. If such a situation happens, we say that a "crash" occurs and, as a consequence, m is decomposed (by means of gcd operation) as a product $m_1 \cdot m_2$ (or as power $m_1^{s_1}$) where m_1 and m_2 are coprime. In this way, a given LCA $\mathcal{F}$ over $(\mathbb{Z}/m\mathbb{Z})^n$ is decomposed into the product of two LCA $\mathcal{F}_1$ and $\mathcal{F}_2$ too, one over $(\mathbb{Z}/m_1\mathbb{Z})^n$ and the other over $(\mathbb{Z}/m_2\mathbb{Z})^n$ (or, a single LCA $\mathcal{F}_1$ over $(\mathbb{Z}/m_1\mathbb{Z})^n$ is determined), and, once the procedure recursively decides transitivity for each of the two components (or, for the single LCA over $(\mathbb{Z}/m_1\mathbb{Z})^n$), it is able to decide transitivity for the given LCA over $(\mathbb{Z}/m\mathbb{Z})^n$. This is possible since $\mathcal{F}$ is transitive iff both $\mathcal{F}_1$ and $\mathcal{F}_2$ are transitive (or, $\mathcal{F}_1$ is transitive). Otherwise, i.e., if no crash occurs - and this situation defines the basis case of the recursion - the procedure computes an "unconventional gcd" of polynomials from $(\mathbb{Z}/m\mathbb{Z})[t]$ and it decides transitivity on the basis of its degree according to (1), as m was a prime number (even though is not). For the details regarding the decompositon of m and $\mathcal{F}$ together with the correctness of the algorithm we address the reader to [9].

3.4 Positive Expansivity

In order to deal with the characterization of positive expansivity, we need to introduce the following notions.

Definition 1 (Positive and Negative Degree). *The* positive *(resp.,* negative*) degree of any given polynomial $\alpha \in \mathbb{L}_m$ with $\alpha \neq 0$, denoted by $\deg^+(\alpha)$ (resp., $\deg^-(\alpha)$), is the maximum (resp, minimum) value among the degrees of the monomials of α. Furthermore, the previous notions are extended to $\alpha = 0$ as follows: $\deg^+(0) = -\infty$ and $\deg^-(0) = +\infty$.*

Example 1. The following are the values of the positive and negative degree of some polynomials:
$\deg^+(X^{-3}+X^{-2}) = -2$, $\deg^+(X^{-3}+X^{-2}+1) = 0$, $\deg^+(X^{-3}+X^{-2}+1+X^4) = 4$, $\deg^+(1) = 0$
$\deg^-(X^3+X^2) = 2$, $\deg^-(X^3+X^2+1) = 0$, $\deg^-(X^{-3}+1+X^4) = -3$, $\deg^-(1) = 0$

Definition 2 (Expansive Polynomial and Expansive Matrix). *Let $\pi(t) = \alpha_0 + \alpha_1 t + \cdots + \alpha_{n-1}t^{n-1} + t^n$ be any polynomial from $\mathbb{L}_m[t]$. We say that $\pi(t)$ is* expansive *if both the following two conditions are satisfied:*

(i) $\deg^+(\alpha_0) > 0$ and $\deg^+(\alpha_0) > \deg^+(\alpha_i)$ for every $i \in \{1, \ldots, n-1\}$;
(ii) $\deg^-(\alpha_0) < 0$ and $\deg^-(\alpha_0) < \deg^-(\alpha_i)$ for every $i \in \{1, \ldots, n-1\}$;

A matrix $A \in \mathbb{L}_m^{n\times n}$ is said to be expansive *if its characteristic polynomial is expansive.*

Theorem 6 ([8]). *Let $\mathcal{F}$ be any LCA over $(\mathbb{Z}/m\mathbb{Z})^n$ and let $A \in \mathbb{L}_m^{n\times n}$ be the matrix associated with $\mathcal{F}$, where m and n are any two naturals with $m > 1$. Let $p_1, \ldots, p_l$ be all the primes appearing inside the prime factor decomposition of m (i.e., $m = p_1^{k_1} \cdots p_l^{k_l}$). The following characterization holds:*

(C) *$\mathcal{F}$ is positively expansive iff $A \bmod p_j$ is expansive for every $j \in \{1, \ldots, l\}$*

Equivalently, $\mathcal{F}$ is positively expansive iff both the following conditions are satisfied:

(C1) *α_0 is the matrix associated with a positively expansive LCA over $\mathbb{Z}/m\mathbb{Z}$;*
(C2) *for every $i \in \{1, \ldots, n-1\}$ it holds that*
  (C2a) *for every $j \in \{1, \ldots, l\}$,*
    $\deg^+(\alpha_0 \bmod p_j) > \deg^+(\alpha_i \bmod p_j)$
  and
  (C2b) *for every $j \in \{1, \ldots, l\}$,*
    $\deg^-(\alpha_0 \bmod p_j) < \deg^-(\alpha_i \bmod p_j)$,

It is clear that characterization **(C)** requires that the prime factor decomposition of m is known. We now recall how positive expansivity can be decided without decomposing m into prime factors and by only making use of gcd operations, i.e., how condition **(C2)** can be efficiently checked since **(C1)** is clearly an efficiently testable condition. The method has been designed under the assumption that condition **(C1)** is satisfied. To proceed, for any $a \in \mathbb{Z}/m\mathbb{Z}$ define

$$y_a = \begin{cases} \prod_{j \in \mathcal{P}_a} p_j^{k_j}, & \text{if } \mathcal{P}_a \neq \emptyset \\ 1, & \text{otherwise} \end{cases},$$

where $\mathcal{P}_a = \{j \in \{1, \ldots, l\} : \gcd(a, p_j) = 1\}$. We emphasize that y_a is the greatest divisor of m having as prime factors all (and only) those prime factors of m that are not prime factors of a. Moreover, y_a can be computed without knowing $p_1, \ldots, p_l$ and $k_1, \ldots, k_l$, i.e., without the need of decomposing m into its prime factors. Indeed, consider the elements of the sequence m_ℓ recursively defined by $m_{\ell+1} = m_\ell / \gcd(m_\ell, a)$, where $m_0 = m$. Clearly, there exists ℓ^* such that $m_{\ell^*+1} = m_{\ell^*}$ and it holds that $y_a = m_{\ell^*+1} = m_{\ell^*}$.

In the sequel, we will deal with how to test condition **(C2a)** for every $i \in \{1, \ldots, n-1\}$ (the argument regarding condition **(C2b)** is symmetric). For any $i \in \{0, 1, \ldots, n-1\}$ and any monomial $a_d^{(i)} X^d$ of degree d inside α_i, with a little abuse of notation, let us denote by $y_{i,d}$ the quantity $y_{a_d^{(i)}}$. Clearly, for every $j \in \mathcal{P}_{a_d^{(i)}}$ it holds that $a_d^{(i)} \bmod p_j \neq 0$.

Fix now $i \in \{1, \ldots, n-1\}$. The following procedure to be repeated for every $i \in \{1, \ldots, n-1\}$ tests condition **(C2a)**, i.e., as far as α_i is concerned, it checks whether $\deg^+(\alpha_0 \bmod p_j) > \deg^+(\alpha_i \bmod p_j)$ for every $j \in \{1, \ldots, l\}$. The procedure consists of the following steps:

(S1) Let $a_{d_0}^{(0)} X^{d_0}$ be the monomial of maximum degree inside α_0 with $y_{0,d_0} \neq 1$. If condition **(C1)** is satisfied then $d_0 > 0$. We stress that $a_{d_0}^{(0)} \bmod p_j \neq 0$ for every $j \in \mathcal{P}_{a_{d_0}^{(0)}}$.

(S2) Consider the monomials $a_d^{(i)} X^d$ of degree $d \geq d_0$ inside α_i (while jump to step (S3.2) if $\deg^+(\alpha_i) < d_0$). For each of such monomials compute $y_{i,d}$ and $g_d = \gcd(y_{0,d_0}, y_{i,d})$.

(S3.1) If $g_d > 1$ for some $d \geq d_0$, it means that there exists $j \in \mathcal{P}_{a_{d_0}^{(0)}} \cap \mathcal{P}_{a_d^{(i)}} \neq \emptyset$ such that $\deg^+(\alpha_0 \bmod p_j) \leq \deg^+(\alpha_i \bmod p_j)$ and, hence, **(C2a)** is not satisfied.

(S3.2) Otherwise, since $a_{d_0}^{(0)} \bmod p_j \neq 0$ and $a_d^{(i)} \bmod p_j = 0$ for every $j \in \mathcal{P}_{a_{d_0}^{(0)}}$ and every $d \geq d_0$, the inequality inside condition **(C2a)** holds for every $j \in \mathcal{P}_{a_{d_0}^{(0)}}$. To check if it also holds for every $j \notin \mathcal{P}_{a_{d_0}^{(0)}}$, replace m by $m/y_{0,d_0}$, and, referring to this new value of m, if $m \neq 1$, restart from step (S1) with $(\alpha_0 - a_{d_0}^{(0)} X^{d_0}) \bmod m$ and $\alpha_1 \bmod m$ in place of α_0 and α_1, respectively, inside the new background $\mathbb{Z}/m\mathbb{Z}$. If, on the contrary, $m = 1$, it means that condition **(C2a)** is satisfied.

4 Dynamical Behavior of Additive CA on a Finite Abelian Group

Finally, we recall how to lift the characterization results regarding all the mentioned properties for LCA over $(\mathbb{Z}/m\mathbb{Z})^n$ to the whole class Additive CA over any finite abelian group. We stress that the characterization results are stated for Additive CA over $G = \mathbb{Z}/p^{k_1}\mathbb{Z} \times \ldots \times \mathbb{Z}/p^{k_n}\mathbb{Z}$, but this is not a restriction, as explained in Sect. 2. The following result illustrates how to lift the characterizations of the set theoretic and dynamical properties from LCA over $(\mathbb{Z}/m\mathbb{Z})^n$ to the whole class Additive CA over any finite abelian group.

Theorem 7 ([6,8]). *Let $\mathcal{F} : G^{\mathbb{Z}} \to G^{\mathbb{Z}}$ be any Additive CA over a finite abelian group G, where $G = \mathbb{Z}/p^{k_1}\mathbb{Z} \times \ldots \times \mathbb{Z}/p^{k_n}\mathbb{Z}$ for some prime p and some non zero naturals $k_1, \ldots, k_n$ with $k_1 \geq k_2 \geq \ldots \geq k_n$. Let $\mathcal{L}$ be the LCA over $\hat{G}$ associated with $\mathcal{F}$ via the embedding Ψ, where $\hat{G} = (\mathbb{Z}/p^{k_1}\mathbb{Z})^n$. It holds that*

(i) $\mathcal{F}$ is injective (resp., surjective) if and only if $\mathcal{L}$ is injective (resp., surjective);
(ii) $\mathcal{F}$ is sensitive to the initial conditions (resp., equicontinuous) if and only if $\mathcal{L}$ is sensitive to the initial conditions (resp., equicontinuous);
(iii) $\mathcal{F}$ is topologically transitive if and only if $\mathcal{L}$ is topologically transitive;
(iv) $\mathcal{F}$ is positively expansive if and only if $\mathcal{L}$ is positively expansive.

5 Conclusions

We reviewed the mostly recent easy to check characterizations of the following properties for Linear CA over $(\mathbb{Z}/m\mathbb{Z})^n$: injectivity, surjectivity, sensitivity to the initial conditions, equicontinuity, topological transitivity, and positive expansivity. Moreover, we also recall how such characterizations regarding Linear CA over $(\mathbb{Z}/m\mathbb{Z})^n$ can be exploited to decide the above mentioned dynamical properties for the whole class of Additive CA over a finite abelian group. Providing (efficient) algorithms that, as far as such CA are concerned, decide other meaningful dynamical properties such as strong transitivity or compute some useful quantities as topological entropy is an important step for further research in this domain. In [1], authors proved that, among other properties, sensitivity and equicontinuity are decidable for the wider class of *Group CA* (i.e., CA having *any* group as alphabet and a group endomorphism as global rule), but, as noted by themselves, "the existing characterizations in the literature typically provide easy to check conditions on the local rule of the cellular automaton for the considered properties, while algorithms extracted from our proofs are impractical and only serve the purpose of proving decidability". So, further investigations could focus on finding out easy to check characterizations of the above mentioned properties for Group CA.

References

1. Béaur, P., Kari, J.: Effective projections on group shifts to decide properties of group cellular automata. Int. J. Found. Comput. Sci. **35**(1&2), 77–100 (2024)
2. Bruyn, L.L., den Bergh, M.V.: Algebraic properties of linear cellular automata. Linear Algebra Appl. **157**, 217–234 (1991)
3. Cattaneo, G., Formenti, E., Manzini, G., Margara, L.: Ergodicity, transitivity, and regularity for linear cellular automata over $\mathbb{Z}_m$. Theoret. Comput. Sci. **233**(1–2), 147–164 (2000)
4. Dennunzio, A., Formenti, E., Grinberg, D., Margara, L.: Chaos and ergodicity are decidable for linear cellular automata over $(\mathbb{Z}/m\mathbb{Z})^n$. Inf. Sci. **539**, 136–144 (2020)
5. Dennunzio, A., Formenti, E., Grinberg, D., Margara, L.: Dynamical behavior of additive cellular automata over finite abelian groups. Theoret. Comput. Sci. **843**, 45–56 (2020)
6. Dennunzio, A., Formenti, E., Grinberg, D., Margara, L.: Decidable characterizations of dynamical properties for additive cellular automata over a finite abelian group with applications to data encryption. Inf. Sci. **563**, 183–195 (2021)
7. Dennunzio, A., Formenti, E., Grinberg, D., Margara, L.: An efficiently computable characterization of stability and instability for linear cellular automata. J. Comput. Syst. Sci. **122**, 63–71 (2021)
8. Dennunzio, A., Formenti, E., Margara, L.: An easy to check characterization of positive expansivity for additive cellular automata over a finite abelian group. IEEE Access **11**, 121246–121255 (2023)
9. Dennunzio, A., Formenti, E., Margara, L.: An efficient algorithm deciding chaos for linear cellular automata over $(\mathbb{Z}/m\mathbb{Z})^n$ with applications to data encryption. Inf. Sci. **657**, 119942 (2024)
10. Devaney, R.L.: An Introduction to Chaotic Dynamical Systems. Addison-Wesley, Addison-Wesley advanced book program (1989)
11. Ito, M., Osato, N., Nasu, M.: Linear cellular automata over $\mathbb{Z}_m$. J. Comput. Syst. Sci. **27**, 125–140 (1983)
12. Kari, J.: Rice's theorem for the limit sets of cellular automata. Theor. Comput. Sci. **127**(2), 229–254 (1994). https://doi.org/10.1016/0304-3975(94)90041-8
13. Kari, J.: Linear cellular automata with multiple state variables. In: Reichel, H., Tison, S. (eds.) STACS 2000: 17th Annual Symposium on Theoretical Aspects of Computer Science Lille, France, February 17–19, 2000 Proceedings, pp. 110–121. Springer Berlin Heidelberg, Berlin, Heidelberg (2000). https://doi.org/10.1007/3-540-46541-3_9

14. Manzini, G., Margara, L.: A complete and efficiently computable topological classification of d-dimensional linear cellular automata over $\mathbb{Z}_m$. Theoret. Comput. Sci. **221**(1–2), 157–177 (1999)
15. Nandi, S., Kar, B.K., Chaudhuri, P.P.: Theory and applications of cellular automata in cryptography. IEEE Trans. Comput. **43**(12), 1346–1357 (1994)
16. Rubio, C.F., Encinas, L.H., White, S.H., del Rey, Á.M., Sánchez, G.R.: The use of linear hybrid cellular automata as pseudo random bit generators in cryptography. Neural Parall. Sci. Comput. **12**(2), 175–192 (2004)

Insights Gained After a Decade of Cellular Automata-Based Cryptography

Luca Mariot(✉)

Semantics, Cybersecurity and Services Group, University of Twente, Drienerlolaan 5, 7522NB Enschede, The Netherlands
l.mariot@utwente.nl

Abstract. Cellular Automata (CA) have been extensively used to implement symmetric cryptographic primitives, such as pseudorandom number generators and S-boxes. However, most of the research in this field, except the very early works, seems to be published in non-cryptographic venues. This phenomenon poses a problem of relevance: are CA of any use to cryptographers nowadays? This paper provides insights into this question by briefly outlining the history of CA-based cryptography. In doing so, the paper identifies some shortcomings in the research addressing the design of symmetric primitives exclusively from a CA standpoint, alongside some recommendations for future research. Notably, the paper remarks that researchers working in CA and cryptography often tackle similar problems, albeit under different perspectives and terminologies. This observation indicates that there is still ample room for fruitful collaborations between the CA and cryptography communities in the future.

Keywords: cellular automata · cryptography · stream ciphers · block ciphers · Boolean functions · pseudorandom number generators

1 Introduction

Following the generic definition given by Goldreich [21], the research field of *cryptography* addresses the design of systems that should be resistant to any abuse. Historically, cryptography has been concerned mainly with secure communication: enabling two or more parties to communicate reliably in the presence of adversaries. In this sense, cryptography usually focuses on three aspects of secure communication: *confidentiality*, meaning that only the intended recipient of a message can read it; *integrity*, where the goal is to avoid any tampering of a message by an adversary; and *authenticity*, ensuring that the legit sender has indeed transmitted the message.

Nowadays, the confidentiality requirement of secure communication is still one of the primary use cases considered in cryptographic research, and it is mainly addressed through the design of appropriate *encryption schemes*, usually classified as *symmetric* or *asymmetric* schemes. In what follows, we consider only the former breed of symmetric encryption scheme, where encryption and decryption use the same key.

Published by Springer Nature Switzerland AG 2024
M. Gadouleau and A. Castillo-Ramirez (Eds.): AUTOMATA 2024, LNCS 14782, pp. 35–54, 2024.
https://doi.org/10.1007/978-3-031-65887-7_3

Cellular Automata (CA) provide an interesting framework for symmetric encryption schemes. The motivation is twofold. First, by leveraging their massive parallelism, CA can realize cryptographic transformations very efficiently, especially when targeting hardware implementations. Second, the dynamic evolution of CA can become quite complex and unpredictable, depending on the underlying local rule used by the cells to update their states. In principle, cryptographic mappings can exploit this complexity so that they are not easily invertible without knowing the corresponding encryption key.

CA started to raise some interest among cryptographers in the 1980s when Wolfram proposed a pseudorandom generator (PRG) based on the chaotic dynamics of a one-dimensional CA defined by rule 30 [62]. However, a few years later, Wolfram's generator was shown to be vulnerable against some attacks [31,45], and this research trend apparently faded away in the cryptography community. Indeed, many subsequent works appeared in conferences and journals with a non-cryptographic focus [17,33,35,43,53,57]. This fact gives the impression that the CA and cryptography research communities diverged from each other, prompting a legitimate question: *Are CA relevant for designing practical cryptographic primitives?*

Actually, upon closer inspection of the literature, it turns out that CA *are still* heavily used by cryptographers, with a large body of works published in cryptography-related venues [10,12,20,23,34,51]. The difference lies in the different terminology (e.g., shift-invariant mappings, rotation symmetric S-boxes, and liftings instead of CA) and the different approaches used to analyze the security and efficiency of the resulting primitives.

This paper aims to investigate the above question through the following three-fold contribution:

- Give a brief outline of the history of CA-based cryptography and how it evolved separately in the CA and cryptography research communities, highlighting commonalities and differences.
- List some shortcomings of the works on CA-based cryptography published in non-cryptographic venues, explaining why they are of limited utility.
- Provide some recommendations to mitigate the above shortcomings and align the research effort between the two communities of CA and cryptography.

A critical remark is that the goal is not to give a comprehensive overview of CA-based cryptography. Instead, this paper revolves around two reference use cases: CA for the design of stream ciphers and block ciphers. These two research strands represent a reasonable subset of the literature, large enough to draw insights into CA's utility in cryptography. Consequently, the paper intentionally leaves out other cryptographic applications of CA such as hash functions [11,15,46], public-key encryption schemes [1,8,27] and secret sharing schemes [37,38,50]. A second caveat is that, despite considering only CA for stream and block ciphers, the exposition of the paper is not entirely objective; rather, it builds upon the author's experience in this field accumulated in the past decade. Comments and suggestions on the perspectives proposed in this paper are encouraged and welcome.

2 Background

This section briefly recalls the background concepts used throughout the paper, starting with the CA models most often used for cryptographic applications. Then, a recap of the basic notions and results related to symmetric cryptography is given, explicitly focusing on stream and block ciphers.

2.1 Cellular Automata

Cellular Automata (CA) are a computational model defined over regular lattices of *cells*. Each cell updates its state at each discrete time step by evaluating a *local rule* on itself and its neighboring cells. The states of the cells range over a finite *alphabet* A, and the lattice size can be either finite or infinite.

Several variations of this model are possible depending on the size and dimension of the lattice, the topology of the neighborhood, the uniformity of the local rule, the alphabet, and so on. The simplest case corresponds to *binary one-dimensional CA*: the cells are arranged over a one-dimensional array (finite or infinite), and each cell applies the same local rule to update its state in parallel. The alphabet is the binary set $A = \{0, 1\}$, which, depending on the application, may be endowed with an appropriate algebraic structure such as a finite field (i.e., $A = \mathbb{F}_2$). Thus, the local rule is a *Boolean function* $f : \{0, 1\}^d \to \{0, 1\}$, where d is the *diameter* of the CA that specifies the size of the neighborhood, that is, the number of cells that each cell needs to look at (including itself) to compute its next state.

A further parameter is the *offset* $\omega \in \{0, \cdots, d-1\}$, which defines the neighborhood's shift with respect to the cell under update. For example, a classic case is the *symmetric neighborhood* where $d = 2r + 1$ (with $r \in \mathbb{N}$ being called the *radius* of the CA), and $\omega = r$. This means that the neighborhood of each cell is composed of itself, the r cells to its left, and the r cells to its right. Another typical setting is the *one-sided neighborhood* with $\omega = 0$. In this case, each cell looks at itself and the $d - 1$ cells to its right.

When the cellular lattice is a bi-infinite string, the *global rule* of a CA resulting from the parallel application of the local rule over all cells is a map F from the *full-shift space* $A^{\mathbb{Z}}$ to itself. The Curtis-Hedlund-Lyndon theorem [25] characterizes CA as those maps $F : A^{\mathbb{Z}} \to A^{\mathbb{Z}}$ that are both *shift-invariant* and uniformly continuous under the Cantor distance. Research on infinite CA usually considers the long-term dynamic behavior of the dynamical system obtained by iterating the global map $F : A^{\mathbb{Z}} \to A^{\mathbb{Z}}$.

Clearly, for practical applications (such as those concerning cryptography) CA are necessarily defined over finite lattices of $n \in N$ cells. This usually leads to the problem of updating the cells at the boundaries since they do not have a complete neighborhood. One common approach is to consider *periodic boundary conditions*, where the one-dimensional lattice corresponds to a ring, with the first cell following the last one. This induces a global map $F : \{0, 1\}^n \to \{0, 1\}^n$ defined for all $x = (x_0, \cdots, x_{n-1}) \in \{0, 1\}^n$ as:

$$F(x_0, \cdots, x_{n-1}) = (f(x_{0-\omega}, \cdots, x_{0-\omega+d-1}), \cdots f(x_{n-1-\omega}, \cdots, x_{n-\omega+d-2})) \ ,$$

where all indices are taken modulo n. Therefore, a finite binary *Periodic Boundary CA* (PBCA) corresponds to a vectorial Boolean function defined by *shift-invariant coordinate functions*, with periodic boundary conditions. It is possible to iterate the global rule of a PBCA for an indefinite number of steps as in the infinite case. However, the dynamics are ultimately periodic, as after at most 2^n steps, the orbit of the CA will repeat itself.

Periodic CA are probably the most used type of CA for cryptographic applications, ranging from the design of pseudorandom number generators [17,33,62] to S-boxes [4,49,56]. Another model considered to some extent in cryptography is the *No-Boundary* CA (NBCA) [41]. An NBCA only updates the cells with a complete neighborhood, meaning that the cells at the boundaries do not carry over to the next iteration, with the lattice shrinking after applying the global rule. Consequently, an NBCA can only be iterated for a finite number of time steps as long as there are enough cells to form at least one complete neighborhood. This is usually not a concern since certain applications (such as the design of S-boxes) only require a single evaluation of the global rule. Usually, the offset ω of NBCA is always 0, leading to the following global rule $F : \{0,1\}^n \to \{0,1\}^{n-d+1}$:

$$F(x_0, \ldots, x_{n-1}) = (f(x_0, \ldots, x_{d-1}), f(x_1, \ldots, x_d), \ldots, f(x_{n-d}, \ldots, x_{n-1})) \ ,$$

for all $x \in \{0,1\}^n$. As we mentioned earlier, in the binary case, the local rule of a CA is a Boolean function $f : \{0,1\}^d \to \{0,1\}$ of d variables. The most natural way to represent f is its truth table, which lists for each possible input vector $x \in \{0,1\}^d$ the corresponding output value $f(x)$. Assuming that the vectors of $\{0,1\}^d$ are totally ordered (e.g., through the lexicographic ordering), the 2^d-bit vector Ω_f that represents the output column of the truth table uniquely identifies the rule f. The decimal encoding of this vector is also called the *Wolfram code* of the rule, customary of the CA literature [60]. As an example, Fig. 1 depicts respectively an NBCA and a PBCA with $n = 6$ cells defined by the elementary local rule 150 of diameter $d = 3$, defined as $f(x_1, x_2, x_3) = x_1 \oplus x_2 \oplus x_3$.

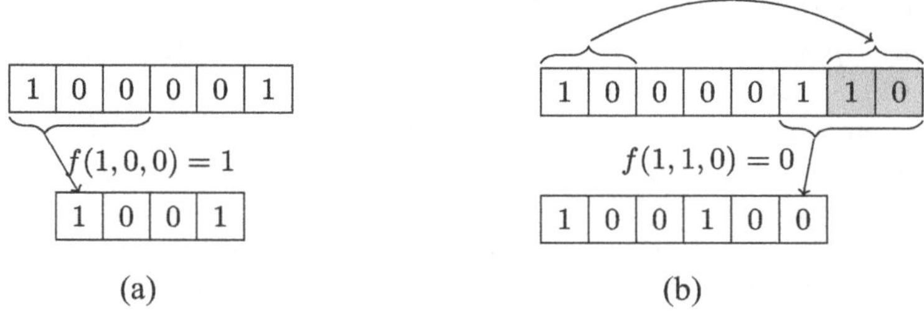

Fig. 1. Examples of NBCA and PBCA with local rule 150.

For a more comprehensive introduction to the basic notions and results related to CA, see the chapter by Kari [28].

2.2 Cryptography

This section focuses only on the *confidentiality* of secure communication mentioned in the Introduction, which guarantees that only the intended recipient of a message can read it. Symmetric encryption schemes are one of the main approaches studied in cryptography to enforce this property. In an abstract setting, the sender, Alice, wants to transmit a plaintext message $P \in \{0,1\}^l$ to the receiver, Bob, over a channel wiretapped by an opponent, Oscar. The opponent can observe everything that passes over the channel. Therefore, Alice and Bob use an encryption scheme composed of the following steps. First, Alice gives the plaintext message P in input to an encryption function E, parameterized over a secret key K. This key is known only to Alice and Bob, who agreed on it before the communication takes place[1]. The output of the encryption function is a ciphertext $C \in \{0,1\}^l$, which Alice transmits to Bob over the channel (and thus, eventually observed by Oscar). On the other end of the channel, Bob gives the ciphertext C in input to a decryption function D, parameterized on the same secret key K. The output of D is the original plaintext message P that Alice meant to send to Bob. The functions E and D must be the inverses of one another once they use the same secret key; otherwise, Bob cannot retrieve the correct message from the ciphertext.

The confidentiality of this scheme relies on the assumption that Oscar cannot recover the plaintext message P by observing the ciphertext C when sent through the channel. Any sound encryption scheme should follow *Kerchoff's principle*, according to which the security of the overall scheme should rely only on the secrecy of the key and not on the secrecy of the encryption and decryption functions, which are assumed to be public. Therefore, since E and D are known to Oscar, they must be designed not to leak any useful information on the plaintext if K is not known.

A standard classification of symmetric encryption schemes divides them into *stream ciphers* and *block ciphers*. The difference is that a stream cipher combines each plaintext symbol with a corresponding symbol of a *keystream*, computed from the initial secret key through a *keystream generator algorithm*. On the other hand, a block cipher encrypts the plaintext in *blocks* of a fixed size, combining them iteratively with several *round keys* generated from the secret key through a scheduling algorithm.

One of the most well-known models of stream ciphers is the *Vernam-like cipher*, in which the messages are binary strings of arbitrary length. The encryption amounts to the bitwise XOR between the plaintext and the keystream. Decryption is symmetric since by computing again the bitwise XOR between the ciphertext and the keystream, one obtains the original plaintext. The keystream generator algorithm is a *Pseudorandom Generator* (PRG), which stretches the initial secret key into a pseudorandom sequence that matches the length of the plaintext.

[1] For instance, the key agreement can be achieved with public-key cryptography, which is, however, not the focus of this paper. Here, the assumption is that Alice and Bob already shared the encryption key securely.

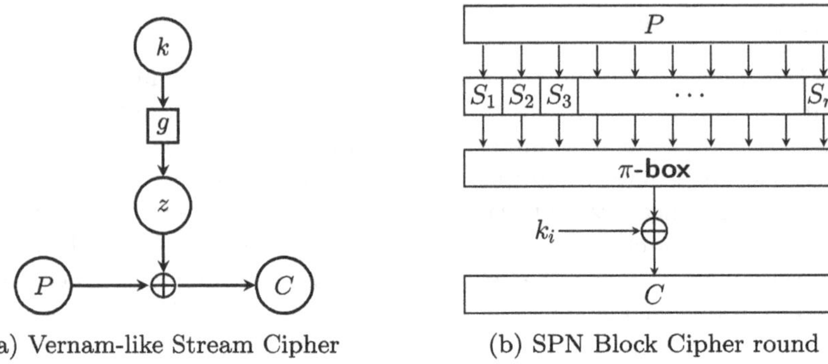

(a) Vernam-like Stream Cipher (b) SPN Block Cipher round

Fig. 2. Diagrams for Vernam-like stream ciphers and SPN block ciphers.

The *Substitution-Permutation Network* (SPN) is a typical design paradigm for block ciphers. Assuming that the plaintext is divided into equal-sized blocks, each block is encrypted by first applying a *confusion phase*, followed by a *diffusion phase*, and finally by the *key combination phase* with the current round key. This procedure is then iterated for a certain number of *rounds*. Decryption performs the same operations but in reverse order. Figure 2 displays the block diagrams for the Vernam-like stream cipher and the SPN block cipher.

Shannon [54] set forth the properties of *confusion* and *diffusion* as guiding principles for the design of secure symmetric encryption schemes to withstand statistical attacks. Confusion aims to make the relationship between the plaintext message and the secret key as complex as possible. On the other hand, diffusion aims to spread the statistical structure of the plaintext over the ciphertext, the idea being that the ciphertext should look indistinguishable from random noise.

Per se, the notions of confusion and diffusion are abstract and need to be specified concretely with respect to the underlying cipher model. For example, the security of a Vernam-like stream cipher can be reduced to the properties of the underlying PRG, which are, in turn, designed by following different approaches. In the *combiner model*, the PRG comprises n Linear Feedback Shift Registers (LFSRs) initialized with the secret key. At each clock cycle, a Boolean function $f : \mathbb{F}_2^n \to \mathbb{F}_2$ of n variables combines the outputs of the leftmost LFSRs bits. The output of f constitutes the next bit in the pseudorandom keystream. The security of this PRG is then analyzed in terms of the properties of the combiner function f. The rationale is that some cryptanalytic attacks can be carried out more efficiently by an adversary if f does not meet specific criteria. The goal of these attacks could include, for instance, the recovery of the LFSR initial states (and thus, the secret key).

The study of the cryptographic criteria of Boolean functions is a whole research field in itself, and a proper overview is out of scope for the present paper. Carlet's book [6] is the standard reference for this topic. Essential properties recalled in the remainder of this paper include *balancedness* (the truth table vector of f is composed of an equal number of zeros and ones), *nonlinear-*

ity (which is the Hamming distance of f from the set of linear functions, defined using only XOR operations), *correlation immunity* (which is the statistical correlation between subsets of input variables and the output of f) and *algebraic degree* (which is the degree of the polynomial that defines the *Algebraic Normal Form* of f).

A similar discussion applies to block ciphers designed around the SPN paradigm, whose security primarily resides in the properties of the confusion and diffusion layers. The diffusion layer is usually implemented as a transformation (a P-box) that acts globally on the whole cipher state to shuffle the message bits. The confusion layer, on the other hand, is usually realized through a set of smaller *Substitution boxes* (S-Boxes), which act on smaller chunks of the block. From a mathematical standpoint, S-boxes are basically *vectorial* Boolean functions $S : \mathbb{F}_2^n \to \mathbb{F}_2^n$ with n inputs and n outputs. Analogously to the combiner model for stream ciphers, the security of the confusion layer can be reduced to the study of the security properties of the S-boxes. Similarly to the one-bit output case, criteria of interest include *balancedness* (which here corresponds to bijectivity, necessary to allow for decryption), nonlinearity, and *differential uniformity* (which is related to differential cryptanalysis attacks). Further information on the properties of S-boxes can be found in [6]. An excellent reference for a general introduction to cryptographic schemes and models is [29].

3 Stream Ciphers Based on CA

This section reviews the history of CA-based cryptography regarding the design of pseudorandom number generators and stream ciphers. Next, it gives an overview of the primary attacks on this approach and outlines some improvements in subsequent research. Finally, the section concludes with a discussion of the pitfalls in the CA literature on the design of stream ciphers and gives some insights on how to overcome them.

3.1 Early Works

The first attempt to define a stream cipher based on CA can be traced back to Wolfram [62]. The author proposed using an *elementary* CA (i.e., a one-dimensional CA with diameter $d = 3$ and symmetric neighborhood) defined by the local rule 30. The underlying idea is to represent the stream cipher's secret key as the CA lattice's initial configuration, with periodic boundary conditions. Then, the CA evolves for multiple time steps, and the sequence of states taken by the central cell is the pseudorandom sequence of a Vernam-like stream cipher.

The rationale for choosing rule 30 was that Wolfram classified it among the so-called *class 3* rules [61], which induce CA with chaotic dynamics over the full-shift. Hence, it is reasonable to expect that CA based on such rules exhibit good confusion and diffusion properties. Wolfram thoroughly investigated the dynamics of his system based on rule 30 using statistical and empirical tests, such as the computation of Lyapunov's exponent. The results of these tests indicated that a CA defined by this local rule could produce pseudorandom sequences of good quality that are difficult to predict for an adversary when used in a Vernam-like stream cipher. Wolfram proposed using a CA with a lattice size of at least $n = 127$ cells, adopting different sampling strategies to destroy correlations among the sequence of bits. One of these strategies was to sample the central cell in alternating time steps. This strategy requires iterating the CA for twice the number of steps to construct a sufficiently long pseudorandom sequence.

3.2 Attacks on Wolfram's PRNG and Improvements

It did not take long until a few attacks were demonstrated against Wolfram's PRG, proving that it was very weak from a cryptographic point of view. Meier and Staffelbach proposed the first attack in [45], where the authors showed that a CA induced by rule 30 is vulnerable to a known-plaintext attack based on the algebraic structure of rule 30. More precisely, the algebraic normal form of rule 30 is $f(x_1, x_2, x_3) = x_1 \oplus x_2 \oplus x_1 x_2 \oplus x_3$; thus, it depends linearly on the rightmost variable x_3. This property is also called *permutivity* or *quasi-linearity* [47] and allows one to rewrite the rule in an equivalent expression where the initial seeds are not equiprobable. Later, Koc and Apohan [31] proposed a second attack on Wolfram's PRG, exploiting the best affine approximation of rule 30.

The two attacks described above are a direct consequence of the poor cryptographic properties of rule 30 when interpreted as a Boolean function. More specifically, Meier and Staffelbach's attack can be carried out efficiently because rule 30 does not satisfy first-order correlation immunity. In contrast, Koc and Apohan's attack depends on the fact that the nonlinearity of rule 30 is very low. Therefore, a possible solution would be to select a different local rule to mitigate these issues. Martin [43] showed by an exhaustive search that no elementary local rules are simultaneously nonlinear and first-order correlation immune.

Thus, the only way to salvage Wolfram's PRG is to look for local rules of a larger diameter with a better trade-off of cryptographic properties, which posits a combinatorial optimization problem. The space of d-variable Boolean functions $f : \mathbb{F}_2^d \rightarrow \mathbb{F}_2$ contains 2^{2^d} elements; hence it grows super-exponentially in d. Exhaustive enumeration is possible only up to $d = 5$ variables. For larger diameters, one must resort to algebraic constructions [6], metaheuristic optimization algorithms [16], or combinatorial techniques to reduce the search space. Formenti et al. undertook the latter path in [17]. There, the authors used the classification of Boolean functions of $d = 5$ variables conducted by Braeken et al. [5], which partitions the space into 48 equivalence classes. Formenti et al. then performed an exhaustive search among representatives of these classes, finding those susceptible to preserve first-order correlation immunity after two iterations of a CA. Finally, the authors performed statistical tests from the DIEHARD suite [42] on the pseudorandom sequences produced by Wolfram's PRG with these new rules plugged in, sifting those that passed all the tests.

Leporati and Mariot [32] also focused on the space of rules of diameter $d = 5$. In this case, the authors considered *bipermutive local rules* (i.e., rules that depend linearly on both the left and rightmost variables). The rationale was that such rules induce CA that satisfy strong definitions of topological chaos [7]. Therefore, they seem good candidates for generating pseudorandom sequences with good statistical properties. Moreover, Leporati and Mariot proved that bipermutive rules are 1-resilient, i.e., balanced and first-order correlation immune[2]. Since the space of bipermutive local rules of diameter 5 is composed of 256 rules, the authors performed an exhaustive search to find those rules that are both 2-resilient and have maximum nonlinearity. Subsequently, the authors used statistical tests from the ENT [58] and NIST [2] test suites to filter only those rules that produced good pseudorandom sequences when plugged into Wolfram's PRG. The same authors later expanded this research in [33] by considering further properties besides nonlinearity and resiliency and extended the exhaustive search experiments for bipermutive local rules of diameter $d = 7$.

More recently, Manzoni et al. [35] considered Wolfram's PRG from a different angle, namely by extending the model to *asynchronous CA*, where the cells do not update necessarily in parallel at each time step. An interesting finding from the statistical tests of the NIST suite reported in [35] is that certain local rules produce better pseudorandom sequences under a small amount of asynchrony.

3.3 Shortcomings and Insights

The story of Wolfram's PRG shows quite clearly the first shortcoming shared by many works in the literature of CA-based cryptography:

Shortcoming 1. *Grounding security claims of CA-based cryptographic primitives on statistical or empirical tests or criteria unrelated to cryptography (e.g., chaos-based properties) can be misleading.*

Rule 30 is a paradigmatic example of this pitfall: despite faring well under statistical tests, and even if it induces a CA that is chaotic in Devaney's sense [7], it is entirely useless to generate pseudorandom sequences for cryptographic purposes, as demonstrated by the Meier-Staffelbach and Koc-Apohan attacks. The underlying problem here is that passing a battery of statistical tests is only a *necessary condition* for a good pseudorandom generator. As such, these tests help discard bad generators, but it is not possible to claim security just by observing that a rule is passing all tests in a suite. The reason is that there is an infinity of statistical tests, and passing a finite subset of them does not guarantee that the PRG will not fail on others. Similarly, system-theoretic and chaos-related properties are not necessarily related to actual cryptanalytic attacks. Although they might tell us that a CA is difficult to predict or invert by just observing its current state, cryptanalysis usually considers more powerful attack models, where the adversary can also have access to some pairs of plaintexts and ciphertexts (as in a known-plaintext attack). For this reason, the cryptographic properties studied for Boolean functions target specific attacks; this leads to the following first insight to deal with this problem of CA-based cryptography:

[2] This is actually a particular case of a result proved much earlier by Siegenthaler [55].

Insight 1. *Statistical tests are fine only to filter out bad CA-based cryptographic primitives. For a proper security analysis, at a minimum, the cryptographic properties of the underlying local rules should be carefully investigated.*

Under this light, even recent works such as [35] should be revisited to check whether the selected rules have good cryptographic properties.

Is Insight 1 enough? If so, the design of good CA-based pseudorandom generators for stream ciphers could be reduced just to the search of local rules with a good trade-off of cryptographic properties along the lines of works such as [17,33]. However, as we mentioned in Sect. 2.2, the criteria for Boolean functions refer to specific models of keystream generators, e.g., the combiner model. This is quite different from Wolfram's PRG model, where we are iterating the CA for multiple time steps and sampling the trace of the central cell. The *filter model* [6] looks more similar to Wolfram's PRG but still has notable differences. Consequently, this leads to the following shortcoming:

Shortcoming 2. *Claiming that a Wolfram-like PRG is secure due to the cryptographic properties of the underlying local rule is not enough, because some attacks on the combiner or filter model might not be relevant in the CA setting. On the other hand, it could be that the current known cryptographic criteria of Boolean functions do not capture other types of attacks unique to the CA model.*

The remark above is also probably connected to why research on CA-based stream ciphers is seldom published in cryptographic venues. After the initial attempt by Wolfram (whose rule 30-based PRG was published in CRYPTO), cryptographers preferred to shift to other designs where attacks can be modeled and investigated more easily. Wolfram's PRG model still needs to be better understood regarding cryptanalytic attacks. The Meier-Staffelbach and Koc-Apohan attacks concern the correlation immunity and the nonlinearity of the CA local rule, respectively. However, there are many other criteria of Boolean functions tailored for other attacks on the combiner and the filter model. This remark brings up the following:

Insight 2. *Consistently link the proposed CA model with the security properties and the related attacks. Each cryptographic property considered in the security analysis should be thoroughly motivated in terms of attacks specifically tailored for the CA model, not the combiner or the filter model.*

To provide a concrete research direction for the future, the *algebraic degree* is among those properties of Boolean functions that should be considered in the works on CA-based PRG. This property is, in fact, quite crucial since it is related to the Berlekamp-Massey attack in the combiner model [44] and the Rønjom-Helleseth algebraic attack in the filter model [52].

The upshot of these attacks is that the algebraic degree of the underlying Boolean function should be as high as possible (ideally $n-1$, which is the maximum possible for balanced functions). A related cryptographic criterion, the *algebraic immunity* of f, should also be the highest possible to thwart the Rønjom-Helleseth algebraic attack. Moreover, especially in the combiner model, one should use combiner functions of at least $n = 13$ variables.

It would be interesting to investigate the algebraic degree and the algebraic immunity of the local rules used in CA-based PRG. This direction would entail, in particular, adapting the Berlekamp-Massey and the Rønjom-Helleseth attack to the CA model, provided they are relevant. If that is the case, it would also be interesting to consider the minimum diameter a local rule should possess to make these attacks inefficient. CA are usually attractive because even small local rules can generate CA with complex behaviors. Efficiency issues would likely arise in a CA-based PRG model when considering large diameters such as $d = 13$.

As remarked by Carlet [6], the combiner and the filter models are only models and are mainly helpful in studying attacks. However, the designs of stream ciphers are more complicated in practice. Hence, a practical stream cipher based on CA would likely require a design that is more sophisticated than Wolfram's PRG. As a concrete research direction, Mariot et al. [39] observed that the GRAIN stream cipher [26], selected as a finalist for the eSTREAM competition, has a structure that closely resembles the computation of a CA preimage. In particular, the state of GRAIN is determined by concatenating a Nonlinear Feedback Shift Register (NFSR) with a LFSR. An interesting open problem is determining whether the tools developed in [39] could be exploited to cryptanalyze the GRAIN stream cipher or develop analogous models for concrete stream ciphers.

4 Block Ciphers Based on CA

This section surveys the main results related to the design of CA-based symmetric primitives for block ciphers. Researchers in the CA and cryptography communities have extensively considered this use case, although it does not seem to be the case from a superficial view. The reason is that researchers in symmetric cryptography adopt a different terminology to refer to cellular automata, calling them instead shift-invariant mappings, rotation symmetric S-boxes, or liftings. The following discussion attempts to identify commonalities between the two research tracks, drawing related shortcomings and insights at the end.

4.1 Encryption by Iterating CA

Historically, the research concerning block ciphers based on CA followed an approach similar to the stream cipher/PRG strand initiated by Wolfram in [62]: the basic idea is to exploit the complexity of the patterns emerging from the iterated evolution of the CA for multiple time steps, considered as a dynamical system. With block ciphers, new issues arise that are not relevant for CA-based PRGs: the most evident one is that *reversibility* of the underlying CA is often sought since it is necessary for decryption. On the other hand, reversibility is already guaranteed by the symmetry of the XOR operation in Vernam-like stream cipher, so it is not a primary concern in CA-based PRGs[3].

[3] Actually, (partial) reversibility could even represent a security problem, as demonstrated by the Meier-Staffelbach attack on Wolfram's PRG.

Gutowitz [24] was the first to propose a block cipher wholly based on the dynamics of CA. The cipher design employed both irreversible and reversible CA, respectively, for diffusion and confusion. The irreversible part consisted of permutive CA, for which a simple algorithm exists to compute a random preimage of a configuration. On the other hand, the author proposed to employ *block CA* for the reversible part, where a fixed mapping is applied on sub-blocks of the configuration, shifted one cell to the right with periodic boundary conditions to emulate the shift-invariance property of CA. The reversibility of this system is trivially guaranteed by the fact that the mapping is a permutation.

Seredynsky et al. [53] investigated *second-order* CA for the design of S-boxes, where reversibility is enforced by computing the XOR between the output of the local rule with the state of the cell at the *previous* time step. The authors investigated the S-boxes defined by iterating second-order CA for multiple time steps with respect to their *avalanche effect*, a property related to the resistance of block ciphers against differential cryptanalysis [59].

Marconi et al. investigated a third approach by proposing `Crystal` [36], a block cipher based on the dynamics of *Lattice Gases Automata* (LGA). LGA are a CA variant usually employed as a discrete fluid model, based on the *collision-propagation* paradigm. In particular, if the local rule implements a reversible physical process, the overall system is reversible and equal to its inverse. This observation is especially interesting for constrained hardware implementations since the same circuitry can be used both for encryption and decryption. The authors claimed that `Crystal` can provide scalable and efficient encryption (up to 10Gbps on dedicated hardware). However, the security of the block cipher was analyzed only through a few empirical tests.

Yet another direction was explored by Szaban et al., who designed S-boxes based on the iteration of CA [56]. Instead of starting from known reversible CA, the authors considered all elementary local rules, retaining only those that resulted in invertible S-boxes of size 8×8 with the best nonlinearity and autocorrelation properties after evolving the CA for a certain number of steps. More recently, Ghoshal et al. [19] investigated S-boxes of size 4×4 with optimal nonlinearity and differential uniformity defined by multiple iterations of CA rules and showed efficient *threshold implementations* for them.

4.2 The Single-Step CA Approach

All works surveyed in the previous section exploit the iterated behavior of CA to implement a block cipher or a lower-level primitive thereof. A different perspective is considering a CA evolved only for a single time step instead. This approach was pioneered by Daemen et al. in [12], where the authors investigated CA with local rules defined by *complementing landscapes*. A complementing landscape is a simple regular expression representing a set of patterns occurring in the neighborhood of a cell. When any of these patterns appear, the cell flips its state; otherwise, it remains in the same state. Daemen et al. considered a simple local rule, which they named χ, that flips the bit of the cell if the pattern

10 occurs in the two neighboring cells to its right[4]. Interestingly, the authors showed that the resulting PBCA is invertible only if the lattice size is odd due to an inversion algorithm based on the idea of *seeds* and *leaps*. However, this inversion algorithm is inherently sequential, which means that the inverse is not described by a cellular automaton.

Additionally, the authors of [12] remarked that χ has good correlation and propagation characteristics, making it a good candidate to construct S-boxes and confusion layers resistant to linear and differential cryptanalysis. This rule (and its one's complement, called γ) appeared in the design of several primitives, such as the hash functions PANAMA [10] and RADIOGATÚN [3]. Interestingly, the permutation in the KECCAK sponge construction [3], an instantiation of which has been adopted by the NIST as the SHA-3 standard for cryptographic hash functions, uses a PBCA of size $n = 5$ defined by rule χ as its sole nonlinear component. This is perhaps the best-known example of a CA-based cryptographic primitive that partakes in the design of a major cryptographic standard, although it is pretty well hidden. Indeed, the authors of KECCAK do not call this mapping a CA but rather a shift-invariant function.

Daemen further investigated the idea of applying complementing landscapes CA to design symmetric ciphers in his PhD thesis [9]. There, the author also considered the so-called *locally invertible* transformations: CA whose local rules are still described by a set of complementing landscapes, where, however, the inverse is itself a CA. In this case, the CA is actually an involution, i.e., the local rule equals its inverse. As noted in the previous section with the LGA paradigm, having an involution is interesting for implementation reasons since the same operation can be used both for encryption and decryption. However, very recently, Mariot et al. [40] showed through evolutionary algorithms that locally invertible CA usually have bad cryptographic properties. The reason is that the complementing landscapes must not overlap in this case; otherwise, reversibility is destroyed. This constraint forces the cell to flip its state only rarely. Consequently, globally invertible rules such as χ seem a better option, although a CA cannot implement their inverse.

More recently, Grassi et al. [23] generalized the study of χ-like mappings to non-binary alphabets, with the motivation of developing symmetric primitives for secure multiparty computation (SMPC), zero-knowledge proofs (ZKP) and fully homomorphic encryption schemes (FHE). The main result proved by the authors is that PBCA (there called *liftings*) defined by quadratic rules of diameter $d = 2$ and $d = 3$ over the finite field $\mathbb{F}_p$ (for a prime $p \geq 3$) are never invertible. In follow-up work, Giordani et al. [20] overcame this problem by considering *non-uniform* CA, i.e., CA, where each cell can use a different local rule to update its state. Again, the terminology of this paper is not aligned with the CA literature, as this type of mapping is called a shift-invariant lifting with multiple local maps instead. From a different angle, Grassi [22] considered instead non-invertible mappings with bounded surjectivity since invertibility is not strictly

[4] χ is actually the elementary rule 210 under Wolfram's code convention, taken however with offset $\omega = 0$.

required in SMPC, ZKP, or FHE applications. In particular, the author proved that the simple local rule $F : \mathbb{F}_p^2 \rightarrow \mathbb{F}_p$ of the form $F(x_0, x_1) = x_0^2 + x_1$ gives rise to a PBCA $F : \mathbb{F}_p^n \rightarrow \mathbb{F}_p^n$ that minimizes the probability of collisions, and it is 2^n-bounded surjective. Daemen et al. [13] analyzed the differential and linear propagation properties of this mapping, discovering the fascinating fact that they follow the same rules up to a relabeling of the digits.

A related research trend concerns *rotation symmetric S-boxes*, which are, in essence, PBCA where the diameter of the local rule equals the size of the CA lattice. Hence, the neighborhood of each cell corresponds to the entire CA input up to cyclic shifts. Rijmen et al. [51] proved that bijective S-boxes defined as *power maps* are linearly equivalent to rotation-symmetric S-boxes. This result is particularly interesting since S-boxes based many practical symmetric primitives employ power maps. Kavut [30] classified all 6×6 bijective rotation-symmetric S-boxes up to affine equivalence, remarking that there exist only 4 functions with the best possible trade-off of nonlinearity, differential uniformity, and algebraic degree. Later, Liu et al. [34] provided a construction for rotation-symmetric S-boxes satisfying *perfect diffusion*.

When the size increases beyond 6×6, exhaustive enumeration of rotation-symmetric S-boxes becomes unfeasible, even by resorting to equivalence classes techniques as done by Kavut. Similarly to the metaheuristics-based search for local rules with good cryptographic properties, a research trend took hold for the search of rotation-symmetric S-boxes. Picek et al. [48] explored the use of Genetic Programming (GP) to optimize rotation-symmetric S-boxes with sizes between 5×5 to 8×8, achieving optimal values of nonlinearity and differential uniformity up to 7×7. Then, in follow-up research, Picek et al. [49] further investigated this GP optimization strategy by considering implementation criteria besides the cryptographic properties. The authors obtained rotation-symmetric S-boxes with optimal nonlinearity, differential uniformity, and low implementation costs comparable to those of other S-boxes in the state of the art. Finally, Mariot et al. [41] proved that the best bounds on nonlinearity and differential uniformity for CA-based S-boxes correspond to the rotation-symmetric case (i.e., diameter equal to the CA size). Moreover, the authors used GP to reverse-engineer an S-box by finding the shortest CA rule that synthesizes it.

4.3 Shortcomings and Insights

The survey in the previous section shows that the CA approach is extensively used also by cryptographers to design block ciphers, although the terminology may vary. Nonetheless, one can still see a sharp methodological difference between the papers published in CA/natural computing venues and those published in cryptography conferences and journals. In particular, it is possible to identify a third shortcoming:

Shortcoming 3. *Using non-standard paradigms to design block ciphers, such as iterating CA as dynamical systems, hinders the security analysis. A general appeal to the confusion and diffusion principles, either by similarity or metaphor, is not a sound approach.*

The issue here is quite similar to Shortcoming 2 for the design of CA-based PRG with non-relevant models of pseudorandom generators. Most of the properties of S-boxes, such as nonlinearity and differential uniformity, are linked to attacks against specific paradigms of block ciphers, such as the Substitution-Permutation Network or components thereof. However, as remarked in Sect. 4.1, several works in the iterating CA design paradigm make security claims either based on empirical tests or by considering properties that have not been proven relevant for this model of block cipher. Thus, the following insight is relatively straightforward:

Insight 3. *Confusion and diffusion, as formulated by Shannon, are abstract properties. As such, they need to be translated into practical design principles. It is preferable to work with well-established design paradigms for block ciphers (e.g., SPN ciphers and sponges) and insert CA as building blocks inside those paradigms (e.g., as S-boxes).*

It is always possible to propose a CA-based design paradigm for block ciphers, but a lot more effort is required to vet its security: in practice, this would entail performing rigorous linear and differential cryptanalysis and providing bounds for the best attacks. Hence, the recommendation to work with well-known paradigms is merely a matter of convenience since their security is better understood. Moreover, as illustrated in Sect. 4.2, there are plenty of directions for future research on low-level primitives based on CA to be plugged into known symmetric designs. An interesting open problem here is to verify or refute Grassi et al.'s conjecture in [23], which states that there exists a finite integer $n_{max}(m)$ such that a PBCA $F : \mathbb{F}_p^n \to \mathbb{F}_p^n$ based on a quadratic rule of diameter m is never invertible for all $n \geq n_{max}(m)$.

Upon closer inspection, there is even a more basic reason why it is not a good idea to base the design of a block cipher entirely on CA, which explains why cryptographers only use them as sub-components for the confusion layer. The following last shortcoming summarizes this aspect:

Shortcoming 4. *CA are simply bad for diffusion.*

Indeed, ciphertext differences cannot spread arbitrarily fast in a CA since the local rule's diameter binds their propagation speed. Hence, using only CA for the diffusion layer of a cipher usually entails the iteration of the CA for multiple time steps, as done in Gutowitz's proposal [24]. However, this approach is not ideal for efficiency reasons: why should a cryptographer prefer a CA-based diffusion layer, which requires several time steps (and thus, clock cycles) when there are non-local methods that allow to achieve the same effect in a *single step*? This leads the discussion to a concluding insight:

Insight 4. *For certain components of a block cipher, it is better to abandon the CA approach. Non-local transformations are usually better, especially for the diffusion phase.*

Alternatively, a possible direction for future research would be to investigate how to implement CA-based diffusion layers with the minimal number of steps possible and compare it to the best non-local transformations in the state of the art. An interesting idea here is to leverage the combinatorial designs perspective on CA adopted in some works such as [18, 37]. Specifically, a CA-based construction for generic orthogonal arrays could be employed to obtain MDS matrices, which are widely used in designing optimal diffusion layers (the best-known example being the diffusion layer of AES [14]).

5 An Outlook on Future Research

This paper gave a partial overview of the vast field of CA-based cryptography, narrowing the attention to the use cases of stream and block ciphers. As a result, this short survey identified four shortcomings in the literature that addresses the design of CA-based symmetric primitives mainly from the CA standpoint: over-reliance on empirical and statistical tests to make security claims, misalignment between the PRG models studied in cryptography and Wolfram's PRG model, adoption of non-standard paradigms for block ciphers, and poor diffusion inherent to the CA model. Accordingly, the paper also formulated four corresponding insights to mitigate such shortcomings, looking at how the cryptography literature analyzes the security properties of stream and block ciphers.

The discussion also emphasized that cryptographers extensively use CA in their works. However, the difference in the terminology could explain the little permeability between the CA and cryptography research communities. The hope is that this paper will help to bridge these two communities, as they often work on closely related problems, and there are broad avenues for future collaborations.

Acknowledgements. This research is partially supported by the PRIN 2022 PNRR project "Cellular Automata Synthesis for Cryptography Applications (CASCA)" (P2022MPFRT) financed by the European Union–Next Generation EU.

References

1. Applebaum, B., Ishai, Y., Kushilevitz, E.: Cryptography by cellular automata or how fast can complexity emerge in nature? In: Yao, A.C. (ed.) Proceedings of the Innovations in Computer Science - ICS 2010, Tsinghua University, Beijing, 5–7 January 2010, pp. 1–19. Tsinghua University Press (2010)
2. Bassham III, L.E., et al.: Sp 800-22 rev. 1a. A Statistical Test Suite for Random and Pseudorandom Number Generators for Cryptographic Applications (2010)
3. Bertoni, G., Daemen, J., Peeters, M., Assche, G.V.: Radiogatún, a belt-and-mill hash function. IACR Cryptol. ePrint Archiv. **2006**, 369 (2006)
4. Bertoni, G., Daemen, J., Peeters, M., Assche, G.V.: The Keccak Reference (2011). http://keccak.noekeon.org/
5. Braeken, A., Borissov, Y., Nikova, S., Preneel, B.: Classification of boolean functions of 6 variables or less with respect to some cryptographic properties. In: Caires, L., Italiano, G.F., Monteiro, L., Palamidessi, C., Yung, M. (eds.) ICALP 2005.

LNCS, vol. 3580, pp. 324–334. Springer, Heidelberg (2005). https://doi.org/10.1007/11523468_27

6. Carlet, C.: Boolean Functions for Cryptography and Coding Theory. Cambridge University Press (2021)
7. Cattaneo, G., Finelli, M., Margara, L.: Investigating topological chaos by elementary cellular automata dynamics. Theor. Comput. Sci. **244**(1–2), 219–241 (2000)
8. Clarridge, A., Salomaa, K.: A cryptosystem based on the composition of reversible cellular automata. In: Dediu, A.H., Ionescu, A.M., Martín-Vide, C. (eds.) LATA 2009. LNCS, vol. 5457, pp. 314–325. Springer, Heidelberg (2009). https://doi.org/10.1007/978-3-642-00982-2_27
9. Daemen, J.: Cipher and hash function design strategies based on linear and differential cryptanalysis. Ph.D. thesis, Doctoral Dissertation, March 1995, KU Leuven (1995)
10. Daemen, J., Clapp, C.S.K.: Fast Hashing and Stream Encryption with PANAMA. In: Fast Software Encryption, 5th International Workshop (FSE 1998), Paris, 23–25 March 1998, pp. 60–74 (1998)
11. Daemen, J., Govaerts, R., Vandewalle, J.: A framework for the design of one-way hash functions including cryptanalysis of Damgård's one-way function based on a cellular automaton. In: Imai, H., Rivest, R.L., Matsumoto, T. (eds.) ASIACRYPT 1991. LNCS, vol. 739, pp. 82–96. Springer, Heidelberg (1993). https://doi.org/10.1007/3-540-57332-1_7
12. Daemen, J., Govaerts, R., Vandewalle, J.: Invertible shift-invariant transformations on binary arrays. Appl. Math. Comput. **62**(2), 259–277 (1994)
13. Daemen, J., Kuijsters, D., Mella, S., Verbakel, D.: Propagation properties of a non-linear mapping based on squaring in odd characteristic. Cryptogr. Commun. (2024). https://doi.org/10.1007/s12095-024-00711-4
14. Daemen, J., Rijmen, V.: The Design of Rijndael: The Advanced Encryption Standard (AES). Springer, Heidelberg (2020)
15. Damgård, I.: A design principle for hash functions. In: Brassard, G. (ed.) CRYPTO 1989, LNCS, vol. 435, pp. 416–427. Springer, New York (1989). https://doi.org/10.1007/0-387-34805-0_39
16. Djurasevic, M., Jakobovic, D., Mariot, L., Picek, S.: A survey of metaheuristic algorithms for the design of cryptographic boolean functions. Cryptogr. Commun. **15**(6), 1171–1197 (2023)
17. Formenti, E., Imai, K., Martin, B., Yunès, J.: Advances on random sequence generation by uniform cellular automata. In: Calude, C.S., Freivalds, R., Iwama, K. (eds.) Computing with New Resources - Essays Dedicated to Jozef Gruska on the Occasion of His 80th Birthday. LNCS, vol. 8808, pp. 56–70. Springer, Cham (2014). https://doi.org/10.1007/978-3-319-13350-8_5
18. Gadouleau, M., Mariot, L., Picek, S.: Bent functions in the partial spread class generated by linear recurring sequences. Des. Codes Cryptogr. **91**(1), 63–82 (2023)
19. Ghoshal, A., Sadhukhan, R., Patranabis, S., Datta, N., Picek, S., Mukhopadhyay, D.: Lightweight and side-channel secure 4×4 s-boxes from cellular automata rules. IACR Trans. Symmetric Cryptol. **2018**(3), 311–334 (2018)
20. Giordani, G., Grassi, L., Onofri, S., Pedicini, M.: Invertible quadratic non-linear functions over F_p^n via multiple local maps. In: Mrabet, N.E., Feo, L.D., Duquesne, S. (eds.) AFRICACRYPT 2023. LNCS, vol. 14064, pp. 151–176. Springer, Cham (2023). https://doi.org/10.1007/978-3-031-37679-5_7
21. Goldreich, O.: The Foundations of Cryptography - Volume 1: Basic Techniques. Cambridge University Press (2001)

22. Grassi, L.: Bounded surjective quadratic functions over fnp for mpc-/zk-/fhe-friendly symmetric primitives. IACR Trans. Symmetric Cryptol. **2023**(2), 94–131 (2023)
23. Grassi, L., Onofri, S., Pedicini, M., Sozzi, L.: Invertible quadratic non-linear layers for mpc-/fhe-/zk-friendly schemes over fnp application to poseidon. IACR Trans. Symmetric Cryptol. **2022**(3), 20–72 (2022)
24. Gutowitz, H.: Cryptography with dynamical systems. In: Cellular Automata and Cooperative Systems, pp. 237–274. Springer, Dordrecht (1993). https://doi.org/10.1007/978-94-011-1691-6_21
25. Hedlund, G.A.: Endomorphisms and automorphisms of the shift dynamical systems. Math. Syst. Theory **3**(4), 320–375 (1969)
26. Hell, M., Johansson, T., Maximov, A., Meier, W.: The grain family of stream ciphers. In: Robshaw, M.J.B., Billet, O. (eds.) New Stream Cipher Designs - The eSTREAM Finalists. LNCS, vol. 4986, pp. 179–190. Springer, Heidelberg (2008). https://doi.org/10.1007/978-3-540-68351-3_14
27. Kari, J.: Cryptosystems Based on Reversible Cellular Automata. Manuscript (1992)
28. Kari, J.: Basic concepts of cellular automata. In: Rozenberg, G., Bäck, T., Kok, J.N. (eds.) Handbook of Natural Computing, pp. 3–24. Springer, Heidelberg (2012). https://doi.org/10.1007/978-3-540-92910-9_1
29. Katz, J., Lindell, Y.: Introduction to Modern Cryptography, 3rd edn. CRC Press (2021)
30. Kavut, S.: Results on rotation-symmetric S-boxes. Inf. Sci. **201**, 93–113 (2012)
31. Koc, C., Apohan, A.: Inversion of cellular automata iterations. IEE Proc. Comput. Digit. Techniq. **144**(5), 279–284 (1997)
32. Leporati, A., Mariot, L.: 1-Resiliency of bipermutive cellular automata rules. In: Proceedings of the Cellular Automata and Discrete Complex Systems - 19th International Workshop (AUTOMATA 2013), Gießen, 17–19 September 2013, pp. 110–123 (2013)
33. Leporati, A., Mariot, L.: Cryptographic properties of bipermutive cellular automata rules. J. Cell. Autom. **9**(5–6), 437–475 (2014)
34. Liu, J., Mesnager, S., Chen, L.: On the diffusion property of iterated functions. In: Proceedings of the Cryptography and Coding - 15th IMA International Conference (IMACC 2015), Oxford, 15–17 December 2015, pp. 239–253 (2015)
35. Manzoni, L., Mariot, L.: Cellular automata pseudo-random number generators and their resistance to asynchrony. In: Mauri, G., Yacoubi, S.E., Dennunzio, A., Nishinari, K., Manzoni, L. (eds.) ACRI 2018. LNCS, vol. 11115, pp. 428–437. Springer, Cham (2018). https://doi.org/10.1007/978-3-319-99813-8_39
36. Marconi, S., Chopard, B.: Discrete physics, cellular automata and cryptography. In: Yacoubi, S.E., Chopard, B., Bandini, S. (eds.) ACRI 2006. LNCS, vol. 4173, pp. 617–626. Springer, Heidelberg (2006). https://doi.org/10.1007/11861201_72
37. Mariot, L., Gadouleau, M., Formenti, E., Leporati, A.: Mutually orthogonal latin squares based on cellular automata. Des. Codes Cryptogr. **88**(2), 391–411 (2020)
38. Mariot, L., Leporati, A.: Sharing secrets by computing preimages of bipermutive cellular automata. In: Was, J., Sirakoulis, G.C., Bandini, S. (eds.) ACRI 2014. LNCS, vol. 8751, pp. 417–426. Springer, Cham (2014). https://doi.org/10.1007/978-3-319-11520-7_43
39. Mariot, L., Leporati, A., Dennunzio, A., Formenti, E.: Computing the periods of preimages in surjective cellular automata. Nat. Comput. **16**(3), 367–381 (2017)

40. Mariot, L., Picek, S., Jakobovic, D., Leporati, A.: Evolutionary algorithms for designing reversible cellular automata. Genet. Prog. Evolvable Mach. **22**(4), 429–461 (2021)
41. Mariot, L., Picek, S., Leporati, A., Jakobovic, D.: Cellular automata based s-boxes. Cryptogr. Commun. **11**(1), 41–62 (2019)
42. Marsaglia, G.: The Marsaglia random number CDROM including the diehard battery of tests of randomness (2008). http://www.stat.fsu.edu/pub/diehard/
43. Martin, B.: A walsh exploration of elementary CA rules. J. Cell. Autom. **3**(2), 145–156 (2008)
44. Massey, J.L.: Shift-register synthesis and BCH decoding. IEEE Trans. Inf. Theory **15**(1), 122–127 (1969)
45. Meier, W., Staffelbach, O.: Analysis of pseudo random sequence generated by cellular automata. In: Proceedings of the Advances in Cryptology - EUROCRYPT 1991, Workshop on the Theory and Application of Cryptographic Techniques, Brighton, 8–11 April 1991, pp. 186–199 (1991)
46. Mihaljevic, M.J., Zheng, Y., Imai, H.: A cellular automaton based fast one-way hash function suitable for hardware implementation. In: Imai, H., Zheng, Y. (eds.) PKC 1998. LNCS, vol. 1431, pp. 217–233. Springer, Heidelberg (1998). https://doi.org/10.1007/BFb0054027
47. Moore, C.: Quasilinear cellular automata. Physica D **103**(1–4), 100–132 (1997)
48. Picek, S., Mariot, L., Leporati, A., Jakobovic, D.: Evolving s-boxes based on cellular automata with genetic programming. In: Bosman, P.A.N. (ed.) Companion Proceedings of GECCO 2017, pp. 251–252. ACM (2017)
49. Picek, S., Mariot, L., Yang, B., Jakobovic, D., Mentens, N.: Design of s-boxes defined with cellular automata rules. In: Proceedings of CF 2017, pp. 409–414. ACM (2017)
50. del Rey, Á.M., Mateus, J.P., Sánchez, G.R.: A secret sharing scheme based on cellular automata. Appl. Math. Comput. **170**(2), 1356–1364 (2005)
51. Rijmen, V., Barreto, P.S.L.M., Filho, D.L.G.: Rotation symmetry in algebraically generated cryptographic substitution tables. Inf. Process. Lett. **106**(6), 246–250 (2008)
52. Rønjom, S., Helleseth, T.: A new attack on the filter generator. IEEE Trans. Inf. Theory **53**(5), 1752–1758 (2007)
53. Seredynski, F., Bouvry, P., Zomaya, A.Y.: Cellular automata computations and secret key cryptography. Parallel Comput. **30**(5–6), 753–766 (2004)
54. Shannon, C.E.: Communication theory of secrecy systems. Bell Labs Tech. J. **28**(4), 656–715 (1949)
55. Siegenthaler, T.: Correlation-immunity of nonlinear combining functions for cryptographic applications. IEEE Trans. Inf. Theory **30**(5), 776–780 (1984)
56. Szaban, M., Seredynski, F.: Cryptographically strong s-boxes based on cellular automata. In: Proceedings of the Cellular Automata, 8th International Conference on Cellular Automata for Research and Industry, ACRI 2008, Yokohama, 23–26 September 2008, pp. 478–485 (2008)
57. Tomassini, M., Perrenoud, M.: Cryptography with cellular automata. Appl. Soft Comput. **1**(2), 151–160 (2001)
58. Walker, J.: MS Windows NT kernel description. https://www.fourmilab.ch/random/. Accessed 05 May 2024
59. Webster, A.F., Tavares, S.E.: On the design of s-boxes. In: Williams, H.C. (ed.) CRYPTO 1985. LNCS, vol. 218, pp. 523–534. Springer, Heidelberg (1985). https://doi.org/10.1007/3-540-39799-X_41

60. Wolfram, S.: Statistical mechanics of cellular automata. Rev. Mod. Phys. **55**(3), 601 (1983)
61. Wolfram, S.: Universality and complexity in cellular automata. Physica D **10**(1–2), 1–35 (1984)
62. Wolfram, S.: Cryptography with cellular automata. In: Williams, H.C. (ed.) CRYPTO 1985. LNCS, vol. 218, pp. 429–432. Springer, Heidelberg (1986). https://doi.org/10.1007/3-540-39799-X_32

Binary Opinion Models of Influence and Opinion Dynamics in Social Networks

Agnieszka Rusinowska[1,2,3](✉) and Michel Grabisch[1,3]

[1] Centre d'Economie de la Sorbonne, 106-112 Bd de l'Hôpital, 75647 Paris, France
{agnieszka.rusinowska,michel.grabisch}@univ-paris1.fr
[2] CNRS, Paris, France
[3] Paris School of Economics, Université Paris 1 Panthéon-Sorbonne, Paris, France
https://sites.google.com/site/rusinowskagrabisch/,
https://sites.google.com/site/michelgrabisch/

Abstract. The process of influence and opinion dynamics is predominant in many kinds of real-life situations involving agents' interactions. This phenomenon is extensively analyzed in different fields and with the help of various methods and tools. Network analysis is particularly suitable for the study of influence and opinion formation. The aim of this paper is to provide an overview of selected results on models of influence and opinion dynamics in social networks with non-strategic updating of binary opinions. We start with presenting some results on the relation between a static binary opinion model of influence with influence indices, follower and influence functions, and a framework of simple games called command games. Then, we focus on binary opinion dynamics with non-strategic agents embedded in a social network. In this overview, a special attention is paid to models based on aggregation functions which can be seen as a generalization of the threshold model. In particular, we present some of the main results of the convergence analysis concerning anonymous social influence, conformism and anti-conformism in social networks. Also the phenomenon of diffusion in large networks with the diffusion mechanism represented by an aggregation function is briefly presented. Finally, we conclude this overview paper by indicating some possible directions for future research on the discrete opinion dynamics in social networks.

Keywords: Social Network · Influence · Opinion Dynamics · Binary Opinion · Aggregation Function

1 Introduction

Modeling influence and opinion dynamics in social networks has received a lot of attention for over sixty years in different scientific fields, like complex systems, computer science, control theory, economics, mathematics, physics, psychology, sociology, statistics, among others. Influence and opinion formation appear to be very central in interdisciplinary studies using various methodological approaches; see [25] for a survey. In computer science, mathematics and statistics, many works focus on (probabilistic) automata models and processes

Published by Springer Nature Switzerland AG 2024
M. Gadouleau and A. Castillo-Ramirez (Eds.): AUTOMATA 2024, LNCS 14782, pp. 55–73, 2024.
https://doi.org/10.1007/978-3-031-65887-7_4

that can model opinion dynamics on (infinite) lattices [28,29,37]. In physics and statistical physics, where agents are considered as particles, different techniques from statistical physics are used [9,34]. In the economics literature, many models incorporate strategic aspects and utility considerations; see [1,4,33] for collections of theoretical and empirical works on opinion formation, learning and information diffusion in networks.

In the vast literature on opinion dynamics, a special attention is paid to binary opinion models, where opinions take values 0 and 1, or -1 and $+1$. Complementary to frameworks with continuous opinions, models with binary opinions, where 'yes' and 'no' can be naturally represented, or more general settings with discrete opinions taking only finitely many values find easily their applications in modeling various real-life situations. The threshold model [12,27, 42], the voter model [6,29] and its generalizations like the q-voter model [5,34] are among the most natural binary opinion models.

Opinions can be updated via different mechanisms like Bayesian or non-Bayesian updating, or a combination of both. In contrast to Bayesian models, where agents use the Bayesian rule when updating their opinions, in non-Bayesian models, agents update their opinions on the basis of opinions held by other agents; see [1] for a survey. When taking into account opinions of others, agents frequently exhibit conformity behavior (e.g., when following the trend) whose study has been particularly undertaken by psychologists, sociologists and economists for a long time. In contrast to conformity, agents can exhibit non-conformity behavior and be anticonformists or simply independent (or stubborn) when updating their opinions. While the classical threshold model is conformist, there exist more and more studies focusing on nonconformist behavior [10,13,38,39].

In this survey, we focus on binary opinions, non-Bayesian updating, and both conformity and anticonformity behavior in social networks. We aim at providing an overview of selected results proven in a series of our works on models of influence and binary opinion dynamics with non-strategic updating of opinions. In Sect. 2 we recall some basic standard definitions that will be used in the paper. Since our study on opinion formation has been initiated by several works on a static model of influence, in Sect. 3 we first briefly present the one-step model of influence in social networks [17] and its relation with a special class of cooperative (simple) games [16,21] called command games. Then, in Sect. 4 we focus on the models of opinion dynamics with aggregation functions and recall some results shown in [8,15,23,26]. Our studies present insights and considerations from economics and social sciences which are complementary to related works from different fields, in particular, from computer science and discrete mathematics [2,40]. Finally, we conclude in Sect. 5 by mentioning some possible lines for future research.

2 Basic Definitions

2.1 Lattices and Posets

We start by recalling some basic definitions on finite posets and lattices [7].

- A function $F : 2^N \to 2^N$ is *isotone* or *monotone nondecreasing* if $S \subseteq T \subseteq N$ implies $F(S) \subseteq F(T)$. If the first inclusion is reversed, then F is said to be *antitone* or *monotone nonincreasing.* A function is *monotone* if it is either isotone or antitone.
- A *partially ordered set* $(P, \leq)$ or *poset* for short, is a set P endowed with a partial order $\leq$, that is, a binary relation being reflexive, antisymmetric and transitive.
- A *lattice* L is a poset such that for any $x, y \in L$ their least upper bound $x \vee y$ and greatest lower bound $x \wedge y$ always exist.
- A lattice is said to be *distributive* if $\vee, \wedge$ obey distributivity.
- A lattice is *autodual* if reversing the order relation, the same lattice is obtained (up to an isomorphism).
- A lattice is *Boolean* if it is isomorphic to some lattice of subsets $(2^N, \subseteq)$. Every Boolean lattice is distributive and autodual.
- For any $x, y \in L$, x *is covered by* y or y *covers* x if $x < y$ and there is no $z \in L$ such that $x < z < y$. An element $j \in L$ is *join-irreducible* if it covers only one element.
- The height of a lattice is the length of a longest path from the least to the greatest element. The height of a distributive lattice is the number of join-irreducible elements.

2.2 Markov Chains and Directed Graphs

We recall some concepts of Markov chain theory [35,43] applied to opinion dynamics.

We define the *state* at a given discrete time as the set $S \subseteq N$ of agents whose opinion is 'yes'. Given S, there is a certain probability $b_{S,T}$ that the next state is T knowing that the current state is S. We consider a homogeneous Markovian chain, i.e., we assume that $b_{S,T}$ is constant over time and depends only on S and T and not on the whole history.

Let $\mathbf{B} := [b_{S,T}]_{S,T \subseteq N}$ denote the *transition matrix* which is a $2^n \times 2^n$ row-stochastic matrix. The transition matrix can be equivalently represented by the *transition graph* $\Gamma = (2^N, E)$, which is a directed graph (digraph), where the vertices are all possible states, E is the set of arcs, and an arc (S, T) from S to T exists if and only if $b_{S,T} > 0$.

- A *path* in Γ from S to T is a sequence of states $S = S_0, S_1, S_2, \ldots, S_{k-1}, S_k = T$ such that $(S_i, S_{i+1}) \in E$ for $i = 0, \ldots, k-1$.
- A nonempty collection of states $\mathcal{C}$ is *strongly connected* if either $\mathcal{C} = \{S\}$, or for every distinct $S, T \in \mathcal{C}$, there is a path in $\mathcal{C}$ from S to T (and from T to S).

- A *class*, also called a *strongly connected component*, is a collection $\mathcal{C}$ of states which is strongly connected and maximal w.r.t. inclusion for this property.
- A class is *absorbing* if for every $S \in \mathcal{C}$ there is no arc in Γ from S to a state outside $\mathcal{C}$. It is *transient* if there are states $S \in \mathcal{C}$ and $T \notin \mathcal{C}$ such that $(S, T) \in E$ (i.e., there is an *outgoing arc*).
- An absorbing class $\mathcal{C}$ is *periodic of period* k if it can be partitioned in blocks $\mathcal{C}_1, \ldots, \mathcal{C}_k$ such that for $i = 1, \ldots, k$, every outgoing arc of every state $S \in \mathcal{C}_i$ goes to some state in $\mathcal{C}_{i+1}$, with the convention $k + 1 = 1$. Otherwise, $\mathcal{C}$ is said to be *aperiodic*.
- An absorbing class reduced to a single state is called an *absorbing state*. We call $\emptyset$ and N *trivial absorbing states*.

2.3 Hypergraphs

Next, we summarize some basic concepts on hypergraphs [3].

- A *hypergraph* H is a pair $(N, \mathcal{E})$ where N is the set of nodes and $\mathcal{E}$ the set of *hyperedges*, where a hyperedge $S \in \mathcal{E}$ is a nonempty subset of N. If $|S| = 2$ for all $S \in \mathcal{E}$, then we have a classical graph.
- A *directed hypergraph* on N is a hypergraph on N where each hyperedge S is an ordered pair (S', S'') (called an *hyperarc* from S' to S''), with S', S'' being nonempty and $S' \cup S'' = S$. If in addition $S' \cap S'' = \emptyset$, the hyperarc is *normal*.
- We say that S has an ingoing (normal) hyperarc $T = (T', T'')$ in some hypergraph if $T' \subseteq N \setminus S$ and $T'' \subseteq S$ (and *vice versa* for outgoing).
- For any hypergraph H we define its restricted version $\hat{H}$ by removing all hyperarcs that are not normal.

3 The One-Step Model of Influence in Social Networks

In this section, we recall some selected studies on a one-step model of influence in a social network, where agents have binary opinions that can be updated due to influence between agents. The basic framework has been originally introduced in [30] and then further developed and analyzed in [16–18,21]; see also [19,41] for some surveys of various studies of the model.

3.1 The Static Model and Influence Indices

We consider a social network with a set $N := \{1, 2, ..., n\}$ of agents (players) who make a decision to accept or reject a specific proposal [16,17,21]. Each agent $k \in N$ has an initial opinion also called an *inclination* $x_k \in \{0, 1\}$ to say either 'no' ($x_k = 0$) or 'yes' ($x_k = 1$). Let $x = (x_1, x_2, ..., x_n)$ denote the *inclination vector* and $X := \{0, 1\}^n$ the set of all inclination vectors. For any coalition $S \subseteq N$, $|S| \geq 1$, we define

$$X_S := \{x \in X \mid \forall k, j \in S,\ x_k = x_j\}$$

the set of all inclination vectors under which all members of S have the same inclination, with $X_k := X$ for any $k \in N$. Let x_S denote the value x_k for some $k \in S$, $x \in X_S$.

Agents may influence each other and due to the influence, the decision of an agent may be different from his inclination. Formally, each inclination vector $x \in X$ is transformed into a *decision vector* $Bx = ((Bx)_1, ..., (Bx)_n)$, where $B : X \to X$, $x \to Bx$ is the *influence function*. Let $\mathcal{B}$ denote the set of all influence functions.

For each $S \subseteq N$ and $j \in N$, we define the set of all inclination vectors of:

- potential direct influence of S on j

$$X_{S \to j} := \{x \in X_S \mid x_j = 1 - x_S\}$$

- observed direct influence of S on j under given $B \in \mathcal{B}$

$$X^*_{S \to j}(B) := \{x \in X_{S \to j} \mid (Bx)_j = x_S\}$$

- potential opposite influence of S on j

$$X^{op}_{S \to j} := \{x \in X_S \mid x_j = x_S\}$$

- observed opposite influence of S on j under given $B \in \mathcal{B}$

$$X^{*op}_{S \to j}(B) := \{x \in X^{op}_{S \to j} \mid (Bx)_j = 1 - x_S\}.$$

For each $S \subseteq N$ and $j \in N \setminus S$, we introduce a set of weights $\alpha_x^{S \to j} \in [0, 1]$, for all inclination vectors $x \in X_{S \to j}$ and $x \in X^{op}_{S \to j}$, where $\alpha_x^{S \to j}$ represents how much x is important when computing the influence of S over j. We assume that for each $S \subseteq N$ and $j \in N \setminus S$, there exists $x \in X_{S \to j}$ such that $\alpha_x^{S \to j} > 0$, and there exists $x \in X^{op}_{S \to j}$ such that $\alpha_x^{S \to j} > 0$. Moreover, for simplicity we impose the symmetry assumption that $\alpha_x^{S \to j}$ depends solely on $|\{i \in N \setminus j \mid x_i = x_S\}|$, i.e., on the number of agents with the same inclination as agents of S under $x \in X_S$ (including the agents from S, but excluding agent j).

Given $B \in \mathcal{B}$, for each $S \subseteq N$, $j \in N \setminus S$, we define:

- the *weighted direct influence index* of S on j under B

$$d_\alpha(B, S \to j) := \frac{\sum_{x \in X^*_{S \to j}(B)} \alpha_x^{S \to j}}{\sum_{x \in X_{S \to j}} \alpha_x^{S \to j}} \in [0, 1]$$

- the *weighted opposite influence index* of S on j under B

$$d_\alpha^{op}(B, S \to j) := \frac{\sum_{x \in X^{*op}_{S \to j}(B)} \alpha_x^{S \to j}}{\sum_{x \in X^{op}_{S \to j}} \alpha_x^{S \to j}} \in [0, 1].$$

3.2 Influence Functions and Follower Functions

Let $x = (1_S, 0_{N\setminus S})$ be the inclination vector, where all members of S are 'yes'-voters, all members of $N \setminus S$ are 'no'-voters, and 1_S is the characteristic vector of S, i.e., $(1_S)_j = 1$ if $j \in S$ and $(1_S)_j = 0$ otherwise. We use set notation and denote $(1_S, 0_{N\setminus S})$ by the set S of 'yes'-voters. Similarly, if x corresponds to S, we denote Bx by $B(S)$, where $B(S) \subseteq N$ is the set of voters whose decision is 'yes'. An influence function $B : X \to X$ can therefore be seen as a mapping from 2^N to 2^N. We denote set complementation by $\overline{S} := N \setminus S$.

A *follower* of a given coalition is a voter who follows the inclination of that coalition whenever all its members have the same inclination. The *follower function* of $B \in \mathcal{B}$ is a mapping $F_B : 2^N \to 2^N$ defined as

$$F_B(S) := \{k \in N \mid \forall x \in X_S,\ (Bx)_k = x_S\}, \quad \forall S \subseteq N, S \neq \emptyset$$

or equivalently in set notation as

$$F_B(S) = \bigcap_{S' \supseteq S} B(S') \cap \bigcap_{S' \subseteq N\setminus S} \overline{B(S')}, \quad \forall S \subseteq N, S \neq \emptyset$$

and $F_B(\emptyset) := \emptyset$. $F_B(S)$ is the *set of followers of S under B*. [17] shows that F_B is isotone and $F_B(S) \cap F_B(T) = \emptyset$ whenever $S \cap T = \emptyset$. Let $\mathcal{F}$ denote the set of all follower functions.

Assume that F_B is not identically the empty set. The *kernel* of B is defined as

$$\mathcal{K}(B) := \{S \in 2^N \mid F_B(S) \neq \emptyset, \text{ and } S' \subset S \Rightarrow F_B(S') = \emptyset\}$$

and corresponds to the set of minimal coalitions having followers, or the set of 'truly' influential coalitions. The kernel is well defined due to isotonicity of F_B.

[21] establishes the exact relation between influence functions and follower functions. We define the mapping $\Phi : \mathcal{B} \to (2^N)^{(2^N)}$ by

$$B \mapsto \Phi(B) := F_B$$

which is neither a surjection nor an injection. We have $\Phi(\mathcal{B}) =: \mathcal{F}$. We recall some results of [21]; see also [22] for a short survey of using lattice theory to the study of influence.

Result 1 ([21], Proposition 1). *A function $F : 2^N \to 2^N$ is a follower function of some $B \in \mathcal{B}$ (i.e., $F_B = F$, or $\Phi(B) = F$) if and only if it satisfies the following three conditions:*

(i) $F(\emptyset) = \emptyset$;
(ii) F *is isotone;*
(iii) If $S \cap T = \emptyset$, *then* $F(S) \cap F(T) = \emptyset$.

Moreover, the smallest and greatest influence functions belonging to $\Phi^{-1}(F)$ are respectively the influence functions $\underline{B}_F$ and $\overline{B}_F$, defined by, in set notation:

$$\underline{B}_F(S) = F(S), \quad \overline{B}_F(S) = \overline{F(\overline{S})}, \quad \forall S \subseteq N.$$

We call these influence functions the *lower and upper inverses* of F. All elements of the inverse of F are between $\underline{B}_F$ and $\overline{B}_F$, with the usual order $\leq$ on functions, which means that $(\Phi^{-1}(F), \leq)$ is a poset, being a subset of $([\underline{B}_F, \overline{B}_F], \leq)$. Let us define

$$D_S := \overline{B}_F(S) \setminus \underline{B}_F(S), \quad S \subseteq N.$$

We denote an element of $[\underline{B}_F, \overline{B}_F]$ by the 2^n-dim vector $(T_\emptyset, \ldots, T_N)$ with $T_S \subseteq D_S$ for each $S \subseteq N$, $\underline{B}_F$ by $(\emptyset, \ldots, \emptyset)$ and $\overline{B}_F$ by $(D_\emptyset, \ldots, D_N)$.

Result 2 ([21], Proposition 2). *Let $B := (T_\emptyset, \ldots, T_N) \neq \overline{B}_F$ be an element of $\Phi^{-1}(F)$. Then for any $S \subseteq N$ such that $D_S \setminus T_S \neq \emptyset$, and any $k \in D_S \setminus T_S$, $B' := (T_\emptyset, \ldots, T_S \cup \{k\}, \ldots, T_N)$ is an element of $\Phi^{-1}(F)$ if and only if one of the following conditions is NOT satisfied:*

(i) For any $S' \supset S$, $k \in B(S')$;
(ii) For any $S' \subseteq N \setminus S$, $k \notin B(S')$.

Result 3 ([21], Theorem 1). *For any $F \in \mathcal{F}$, the set $\Phi^{-1}(F)$, endowed with the usual ordering of functions, has the following properties:*

(i) The greatest and least elements are $\overline{B}_F$ and $\underline{B}_F = F$.
(ii) It is a lattice, with supremum and infimum given by, for any $S \in 2^N$:

$$(B \vee B')(S) := B(S) \cup B'(S)$$
$$(B \wedge B')(S) := B(S) \cap B'(S)$$

(iii) $\Phi^{-1}(F)$ is autodual, i.e., $(\Phi^{-1}(F), \leq)$ and $(\Phi^{-1}(F), \geq)$ are isomorphic. The duality is expressed as follows: to each element $B := (T_\emptyset, \ldots, T_S, \ldots, T_N)$ of $\Phi^{-1}(F)$ corresponds the element $B' := (D_N \setminus T_N, \ldots, D_{\overline{S}} \setminus T_{\overline{S}}, \ldots, D_\emptyset \setminus T_\emptyset)$.
(iv) There are $\sum_{S \subseteq N} |D_S|$ join-irreducible elements, one for each $k \in D_S$, $S \subseteq N$, either of the form $(k_S \emptyset)$ if this element belongs to $\Phi^{-1}(F)$, otherwise of the form $(k_S k_{\overline{S}} \emptyset)$, where the notation $(k_S \emptyset)$ is a shorthand for $(\emptyset, \ldots, \emptyset, k, \emptyset, \ldots, \emptyset)$, where k is at position S, and similarly for $(k_S k_{\overline{S}} \emptyset)$.
(v) The lattice is distributive and its height is $h = \sum_{S \subseteq N} |D_S|$.

3.3 Command Games and Command Functions

We recall the concept of command games [31, 32] studied in [16, 21]; see also [19] for a survey. [31, 32] consider the set of agents $N = \{1, ..., n\}$, where for any $k \in N$ and $S \subseteq N \setminus k$:

- S is a *boss set* for k if S determines the choice of k;
- S is an *approval set* for k if k can act with an approval of S.

Let Boss_k and App_k be the collections of boss sets for k and approval sets for k, respectively. For each $k \in N$, the associated *command game for k* is a simple game $(N, \mathcal{W}_k)$ with the set of winning coalitions given by

$$\mathcal{W}_k := \{S \mid S \in \mathsf{Boss}_k\} \cup \{S \cup k \mid S \in \mathsf{Boss}_k \cup \mathsf{App}_k\}.$$

Given $\mathcal{W}_k$, we can recover the boss and approval sets for k by

$$\mathsf{Boss}_k = \{S \subseteq N \setminus k \mid S \in \mathcal{W}_k\} = \mathcal{W}_k \cap 2^{N\setminus k}$$

$$\mathsf{App}_k = \{S \subseteq N \setminus k \mid S \cup k \in \mathcal{W}_k \text{ but } S \notin \mathcal{W}_k\}$$

and consider the *minimal boss sets* and the *minimal approval sets* for k

$$\mathsf{Boss}^*_k := \{S \in \mathsf{Boss}_k \mid S' \subset S \Rightarrow S' \notin \mathsf{Boss}_k\}$$

$$\mathsf{App}^*_k := \{S \in \mathsf{App}_k \mid S' \subset S \Rightarrow S' \notin \mathsf{App}_k\}.$$

Given a set $\{(N, \mathcal{W}_k), k \in N\}$, the *command function* $\omega : 2^N \to 2^N$ is defined by

$$\omega(S) := \{k \in N \mid S \in \mathcal{W}_k\}, \ \forall S \subseteq N$$

where $\omega(S)$ is the *set of all members that are 'commandable' by* S.

3.4 Relation Between Command Games and Influence Functions

[21] notices that $\{(N, \mathcal{W}_k), k \in N\}$ can be expressed by $\Omega : N \times 2^N \to \{0, 1\}$, with

$$(k, S) \mapsto \Omega(k, S) = \begin{cases} 1, & \text{if } S \in \mathcal{W}_k \\ 0, & \text{otherwise} \end{cases}.$$

There exists a bijection $\Psi : 2^{N\times 2^N} \to (2^N)^{(2^N)}$ defined by

$$\Psi(\Omega) = \omega, \qquad \text{with } \omega(S) := \{k \in N \mid \Omega(k, S) = 1\}, \quad \forall S \subseteq N$$
$$\Psi^{-1}(\omega) = \Omega, \qquad \text{with } \Omega(k, S) = 1 \text{ iff } k \in \omega(S).$$

Hence, ω and Ω are equivalent representations of $\{(N, \mathcal{W}_k), k \in N\}$.
Recall that for any $S \subseteq N$, the *principal filter* of S is defined as $\uparrow S := \{T \subseteq N \mid T \supseteq S\}$.

Definition 1. *A normal command game Ω is a set of simple games $\{(N, \mathcal{W}_k), k \in N\}$ satisfying the two conditions:*

(i) For each $k \in N$, there exists a minimal nonempty family of nonempty subsets $S^k_1, \ldots, S^k_{l_k}$ (called the generating family of $\mathcal{W}_k$) such that $\mathcal{W}_k = \uparrow S^k_1 \cup \ldots \cup \uparrow S^k_{l_k}$.
(ii) For each $k \in N$, $S^k_1 \cap \cdots \cap S^k_{l_k} \neq \emptyset$.

Let $\mathcal{G}$ denote the set of all normal command games. [21] shows the exact relations between command games and command functions, and between command games and influence functions.

Result 4 ([21], Proposition 3). *Let $\omega \in (2^N)^{(2^N)}$. Then ω corresponds to some normal command game, i.e., $\omega \in \Psi(\mathcal{G})$, if and only if the following conditions are satisfied:*

(i) $\omega(\emptyset) = \emptyset$, $\omega(N) = N$;
(ii) ω *is isotone, i.e. it is monotone w.r.t. set inclusion;*
(iii) If $S \cap S' = \emptyset$, *then* $\omega(S) \cap \omega(S') = \emptyset$.

Suppose that $\omega \in \Psi(\mathcal{G})$. Then the (unique) corresponding command game $\{(N, \mathcal{W}_k), k \in N\}$ can be determined through its generating families $\{S_1^k, \ldots, S_{l_k}^k\}$ of $\mathcal{W}_k$ as follows:

$$\{S_1^k, \ldots, S_{l_k}^k\} = \{S \in 2^N \mid \omega(S) \ni k \text{ and } S' \subset S \Rightarrow \omega(S') \not\ni k\}. \tag{1}$$

Moreover, for any $\omega \in \Psi(\mathcal{G})$, the *kernel* $\mathcal{K}(\omega)$ of ω is the collection of minimal coalitions commanding at least one player, i.e.,

$$\mathcal{K}(\omega) := \{S \in 2^N \mid \omega(S) \neq \emptyset, \text{ and } S' \subset S \Rightarrow \omega(S') = \emptyset\}.$$

Definition 2. *Let* B *be an influence function and* Ω *be a command game. Then* B *and* Ω *are equivalent if* $F_B = \omega$.

Result 5 ([21], Theorem 2)

(i) Let B *be an influence function. Then there exists a unique normal command game* Ω *equivalent to* B *if and only if* $F_B(N) = N$. *The generating families* $\{S_1^k, \ldots, S_{l_k}^k\}$, $k \in N$, *of* Ω *are given by (1), taking* $\omega := F_B$. *The minimal boss sets and minimal approval sets are:*

$$\mathsf{Boss}_k^* = \{S_j^k \mid S_j^k \not\ni k, j = 1, \ldots, l_k\}, \quad \mathsf{App}_k^* = \{S_j^k \setminus k \mid S_j^k \ni k, j = 1, \ldots, l_k\}.$$

(ii) Let Ω *be a normal command game. Then any influence function in* $\Phi^{-1}(\omega)$ *is equivalent to* Ω, *in particular the upper inverse* $\overline{B}_\omega$ *and the lower inverse* $\underline{B}_\omega$. *Moreover, the kernel of any influence function* B *in* $\Phi^{-1}(\omega)$ *is given by*

$$\mathcal{K}(B) = \min\Big(\bigcup_{k \in N} \{S_1^k, \ldots, S_{l_k}^k\}\Big) = \mathcal{K}(\omega)$$

where min(...) means that only minimal sets are selected from the collection.

4 Modeling Opinion Dynamics by Aggregation Functions

In this section, we recall some selected results on the dynamic versions of the one-step binary model of influence (see Sect. 3) that were investigated in [8,15, 23,26] focusing on different aspects of opinion dynamics and influence; see also [20,22,24].

4.1 Aggregation Functions

Next, we recall some basic notions on aggregation functions [14].

- An n-place *aggregation function* is any mapping $A : \{0,1\}^n \to [0,1]$ satisfying (i) $A(0,\ldots,0) = 0, A(1,\ldots,1) = 1$ (boundary conditions) and (ii) if $x \leq x'$ (coordinatewise) then $A(x) \leq A(x')$ (nondecreasingness).
- We say that an n-place aggregation function A is *anonymous* if for all $x \in \{0,1\}^n$ and any permutation $\sigma : N \to N$, $A(x_1,\ldots,x_n) = A(x_{\sigma(1)},\ldots,x_{\sigma(n)})$.
- An n-place aggregation function A is *Boolean* if $A(x) \in \{0,1\}$ for all $x \in \{0,1\}^n$.
- An aggregation function A is *strict* if $A(x) = 0$ iff $x = (0,\ldots,0)$ and $A(x) = 1$ iff $x = (1,\ldots,1)$.
- We say that an n-place aggregation function A is an *ordered weighted average* $A = \mathsf{OWA}_w$ with weight vector w, i.e., $0 \leq w_i \leq 1$ for $i = 1,\ldots,n$ and $\sum_{i=1}^n w_i = 1$, if $A(x) = \sum_{i=1}^n w_i x_{\sigma(i)}$ for all $x \in \{0,1\}^n$, where $x_{\sigma(1)} \geq x_{\sigma(2)} \geq \ldots \geq x_{\sigma(n)}$ are the ordered components of x and $\sigma : N \to N$.

4.2 The General Model of Influence Based on Aggregation Functions

We recall the dynamic opinion formation model based on aggregation functions [23]. Let $N := \{1,2,...,n\}$ be a set of agents who make a 'yes' or 'no' decision on a specific proposal. Each agent has an initial opinion which may change due to influence between agents. We consider the influence process which is a stochastic process with a state at a given time defined as the set $S \subseteq N$ of agents whose opinion is 'yes'. Given S, there is a certain probability $b_{S,T}$ that after one step of influence, the set S of 'yes'-agents becomes T. We assume that the influence process is Markovian.

To each agent $i \in N$ we associate an aggregation function A_i determining how agent i modifies his opinion from opinions of all agents. Let $\mathbf{A} := (A_1,\ldots,A_n)$ denote the vector of aggregation functions. We compute $\mathbf{A}(1_S) = (A_1(1_S),\ldots,A_n(1_S))$, where 1_S is the characteristic vector of S and the output $A_i(1_S) \in [0,1]$ of agent i's aggregation function is his probability to say 'yes' after one step of influence when the current state is 1_S. If we assume that these probabilities are independent among agents, then the probability of transition from S to T is

$$b_{S,T} = \prod_{i \in T} A_i(1_S) \prod_{i \notin T} (1 - A_i(1_S))$$

which determines $\mathbf{B}$. Deterministic models correspond to Boolean aggregation functions, i.e., those satisfying $A_i(1_S) \in \{0,1\}$ for all $i \in N$.

Definition 3. *Consider an influence model based on aggregation functions* $\mathbf{A} = (A_1,\ldots,A_n)$.

1. *Agent* $j \in N$ *is* yes-influential in A_i *if* $A_i(1_j) > 0$.

2. *Agent $j \in N$ is* no-influential *in A_i if $A_i(1_{N\setminus j}) < 1$.*
3. *The* graph of yes-influence *is a directed graph $G^{\text{yes}}_{\mathbf{A}} = (N, E)$ whose set of nodes is N, and there is an arc (j, i) from j to i if j is yes-influential in A_i. The graph of no-influence $G^{\text{no}}_{\mathbf{A}}$ is defined in a similar way.*
4. *A coalition $S \subseteq N$ is* yes-influential *for i if $A_i(1_S) > 0$ and for all $S' \subset S$, $A_i(1_{S'}) = 0$.*
5. *A coalition S is* no-influential *for i if $A_i(1_{N\setminus S}) < 1$ and for all $S' \subset S$, $A_i(1_{N\setminus S'}) = 1$.*

We denote by $\mathcal{C}^{\text{yes}}_i$ and $\mathcal{C}^{\text{no}}_i$ the collections of yes- and no-influential coalitions for i. These collections are never empty, since by the boundary conditions of the aggregation functions, $A_i(1_N) = 1$ and $A_i(1_\emptyset) = 0$, and are antichains, i.e., any two sets in $\mathcal{C}^{\text{yes}}_i$ or $\mathcal{C}^{\text{no}}_i$ are incomparable w.r.t. set inclusion.

Result 6 ([23], Theorem 2). *Consider an influence process* **B** *based on aggregation functions* **A**. *Then absorbing classes are:*

(i) either singletons $\{S\}$, $S \in 2^N$;
(ii) or cyclic absorbing classes, *i.e., cycles of nonempty sets $\{S_1, \dots, S_k\}$ of any length $2 \leq k \leq \binom{n}{\lfloor n/2 \rfloor}$ (and therefore they are periodic of period k) with the condition that all sets are pairwise incomparable (by inclusion);*
(iii) or regular absorbing classes, *i.e., collections $\mathcal{C}$ of nonempty sets with the property that $\mathcal{C} = \mathcal{C}_1 \cup \cdots \cup \mathcal{C}_p$, where each subcollection $\mathcal{C}_j$ is a Boolean lattice $[S_j, S_j \cup K_j]$, $S_j \neq \emptyset$, $S_j \cup K_j \neq N$, and at least one K_j is nonempty.*

Regular absorbing classes formed by a single Boolean lattice $[S, S \cup K] := \{T \mid S \subseteq T \subseteq S \cup K\}$ are called *Boolean absorbing classes.*

Result 7 ([23], Corollary 1). *If* **A** *is Boolean, then absorbing classes are either absorbing states or cycles.*

Given **A**, the *hypergraphs $H^{\text{yes}}_{\mathbf{A}}, H^{\text{no}}_{\mathbf{A}}$ of yes-influence* and *no-influence* (graphical representations of influential coalitions) are defined as follows: For $H^{\text{yes}}_{\mathbf{A}}$, the set of nodes is N and there is a hyperarc $(C, \{i\})$ for each $C \in \mathcal{C}^{\text{yes}}_i$ (similarly for $H^{\text{no}}_{\mathbf{A}}$).

Result 8 ([23], Theorem 3). *Consider an influence process* **B** *based on aggregation functions* **A**. *A nonempty subset $S \subset N$ is a (non trivial) absorbing state if and only if it has no ingoing hyperarc in the hypergraph $(\hat{H}^{\text{yes}}_{\mathbf{A}})^* \cup \hat{H}^{\text{no}}_{\mathbf{A}}$, where $(\hat{H}^{\text{yes}}_{\mathbf{A}})^*$ is the hypergraph $\hat{H}^{\text{yes}}_{\mathbf{A}}$ with all hyperarcs inverted.*

Result 9 ([23], Theorem 4). *Consider an influence process* **B** *based on aggregation functions* **A**, *and let $[S, S \cup K]$ be strongly connected in the transition graph Γ, where $S \neq \emptyset, K \neq \emptyset, S \cup K \neq N$. It is a Boolean absorbing class if and only if the following two conditions are satisfied:*

1. *There is no ingoing hyperarc of $\hat{H}^{\text{no}}_{\mathbf{A}}$ into S.*
2. *There is no outgoing hyperarc of $\hat{H}^{\text{yes}}_{\mathbf{A}}$ from $S \cup K$.*

4.3 Anonymous Social Influence with Conformist Agents

In [8] the authors investigate the influence model with aggregation functions [23] recalled in Sect. 4.2, but assume that the influence process is modeled by ordered weighted averages (OWA aggregators, [44,45]). In other words, it is assumed that every agent $i \in N$ has an aggregation function $A_i = \mathsf{OWA}_{w^i}$. This allows to model anonymous social influence, as the OWA operators are anonymous in the sense that they only depend on how many agents share an opinion.

Definition 4. *Suppose* **B** *is obtained from an aggregation model with aggregation functions* $A_1, \ldots, A_n$. *We say that the model is* anonymous *if for all* $s, t \in \{0, 1, \ldots, n\}$,

$$\sum_{\substack{T \subseteq N: \\ |T|=t}} b_{S,T} = \sum_{\substack{T \subseteq N: \\ |T|=t}} b_{S',T} \text{ for all } S, S' \subseteq N \text{ of size } s.$$

Result 10 ([8], **Proposition 1)**

(i) An aggregation model with anonymous aggregation functions $A_1, \ldots, A_n$ *is anonymous.*
(ii) An aggregation function A *is anonymous if and only if it is an ordered weighted average.*

Result 11 ([8], **Proposition 3).** *Consider an aggregation model with aggregation functions* $A_i = \mathsf{OWA}_{w^i}, i \in N$.

(i) A state $S \subseteq N$ *of size* s *is an absorbing state if and only if* $\sum_{k=1}^{s} w_k^i = 1$ *for all* $i \in S$ *and* $\sum_{k=1}^{s} w_k^i = 0$ *otherwise.*
(ii) There does not exist any cycle in Γ.

Result 12 ([8], **Theorem 1).** *Consider an aggregation model with aggregation functions* $A_i = \mathsf{OWA}_{w^i}, i \in N$. *Then, there are no other absorbing classes than the trivial absorbing classes if and only if there exists* $\bar{k} \in \{1, \ldots, n\}$ *such that both:*

(i) For all $k = \bar{k}, \ldots, n-1$, *there are distinct agents* $i_1, \ldots, i_{k+1} \in N$ *such that*

$$\sum_{j=1}^{k} w_j^{i_l} > 0 \text{ for all } l = 1, \ldots, k+1.$$

(ii) For all $k = 1, \ldots, \bar{k}-1$, *there are distinct agents* $i_1, \ldots, i_{n-k+1} \in N$ *such that*

$$\sum_{j=1}^{k} w_j^{i_l} < 1 \text{ for all } l = 1, \ldots, n-k+1.$$

4.4 Anonymous Influence with Anti-conformist Agents

Since aggregation functions are nondecreasing by definition, [8,23] cover only positive influence (conformism). [15] instead studies a model of opinion dynamics under anonymous influence with conformist and anticonformist agents, which we recall below.

As in Sect. 4.2, we consider a society N with $|N| = n$ agents who make a 'yes' or 'no' decision on a specific issue. They have their initial opinions that can change over time due to influence among agents. The state of the society at a given time is the set $S \subseteq N$ of 'yes'-agents with $s = |S|$. The evolution of the state is ruled by a homogeneous Markov chain.

An (anonymous) aggregation rule is a mapping $p : \{0, 1, \ldots, n\} \to [0, 1]$, assigning to any $0 \leq s \leq n$, representing the number of agents saying 'yes', a quantity $p(s)$ which is the probability of saying 'yes' at next time step (and consequently, $1 - p(s)$ is the probability of saying 'no'). Three classes of aggregation rules are considered: pure conformism A^c, pure anti-conformism A^a and mixed aggregation rule A^m, i.e.,

$$A^c = \{p \mid \text{if } s' > s \text{ then } p(s') \geq p(s),\ p(0) = 0 \text{ and } p(n) = 1\}$$

$$A^a = \{p \mid \text{if } s' > s \text{ then } p(s') \leq p(s),\ p(0) = 1 \text{ and } p(n) = 0\}$$

$$A^m = \{p \mid p = \alpha q^c + (1 - \alpha) q^a \text{ with } \alpha \in]0, 1[, q^c \in A^c, q^a \in A^a\}.$$

Let p_i be agent i's anonymous aggregation rule. Supposing that the update of opinion is done independently across the agents, the probability of transition from S to T is

$$\lambda_{S,T} = \prod_{i \in T} p_i(s) \prod_{i \notin T} (1 - p_i(s)).$$

We distinguish between three types of agents i: *purely conformist* if $p_i \in A^c$, *purely anti-conformist* if $p_i \in A^a$, and *mixed agent* if $p_i \in A^m$.

The society is partitioned into $N = N^c \cup N^a \cup N^m$, where N^c (N^a), N^m is the set of purely conformist (anti-conformist), mixed agents. For simplicity, we assume that for each $i \neq j$ in N^c:

$$\min\{s \mid p_i(s) > 0\} = \min\{s \mid p_j(s) > 0\} =: l^c + 1$$

$$\min\{s \mid p_i(s) = 1\} = \min\{s \mid p_j(s) = 1\} =: n - r^c.$$

l^c is the *firing threshold* and is the (maximum) number of 'yes' for which no effect on the probability of saying 'yes' arises. r^c is the (maximum) number of 'no' for which no effect on this probability is visible, so $n - r^c$ is the *saturation threshold* beyond which there is no more change of opinion for the agent. Similarly, for each $i \neq j$ in N^a:

$$\min\{s \mid p_i(s) < 1\} = \min\{s \mid p_j(s) < 1\} =: l^a + 1$$

$$\min\{s \mid p_i(s) = 0\} = \min\{s \mid p_j(s) = 0\} =: n - r^a$$

where l^a is the firing threshold, while $n - r^a$ is the saturation threshold for anti-conformists.

We write $S \to T$ if a transition from S to T is possible ($\lambda_{S,T} > 0$), and $S \xrightarrow{1} T$ if $\lambda_{S,T} = 1$ (sure transition). Let $\mathcal{S}, \mathcal{T}$ be two nonempty collections of sets in 2^N. We define:

$$\mathcal{S} \xrightarrow{1} \mathcal{T} \quad \Leftrightarrow \quad \forall T \in \mathcal{T}, \exists S \in \mathcal{S} \text{ s.t. } \lambda_{S,T} > 0 \text{ and } \forall S \in \mathcal{S}, \forall T \notin \mathcal{T}, \lambda_{S,T} = 0.$$

For any $S \subseteq T \subseteq N$, we denote $[S,T] := \{K \subseteq N \mid S \subseteq K \subseteq T\}$. Moreover, for any $x, y \in \mathbb{N}$, $x \wedge y := \min(x,y)$ and $x \vee y := \max(x,y)$.

Result 13 **([15], Theorem 1).** *Assume that $N^m = \emptyset$, $N^a \neq \emptyset$ and $N^c \neq \emptyset$. There are twenty possible absorbing classes, grouped in the following categories:*

1. **Polarization:**
   (1) N^a if and only if $n^c \geq (n - l^c) \vee (n - l^a)$;
   (2) N^c if and only if $n^c \geq (n - r^c) \vee (n - r^a)$;
2. **Cycles:**
   (3) $N^a \xrightarrow{1} \emptyset \xrightarrow{1} N^a$ if and only if $n - l^c \leq n^c \leq r^a$;
   (4) $N^c \xrightarrow{1} N \xrightarrow{1} N^c$ if and only if $n - r^c \leq n^c \leq l^a$;
   (5) $N^a \xrightarrow{1} N^c \xrightarrow{1} N^a$ if and only if $n^c \leq l^c \wedge l^a \wedge r^c \wedge r^a$;
   (6) $\emptyset \xrightarrow{1} N^a \xrightarrow{1} N^c \xrightarrow{1} \emptyset$ if and only if $n^c \leq r^c \wedge r^a \wedge l^c$ and $n^c \geq n - r^a$;
   (7) $N^a \xrightarrow{1} N \xrightarrow{1} N^c \xrightarrow{1} N^a$ if and only if $n^c \leq l^c \wedge l^a \wedge r^c$ and $n^c \geq n - l^a$;
3. **Fuzzy cycles:**
   (8) $N^a \xrightarrow{1} [\emptyset, N^c] \xrightarrow{1} N^a$ if and only if $n^c \leq l^c \wedge l^a \wedge r^a$ and $r^c < n^c < n - l^c$;
   (9) $N^c \xrightarrow{1} [N^a, N] \xrightarrow{1} N^c$ if and only if $n^c \leq r^c \wedge r^a \wedge l^a$ and $l^c < n^c < n - r^c$;
   (10) $[\emptyset, N^c] \xrightarrow{1} [N^a, N] \xrightarrow{1} [\emptyset, N^c]$ if and only if $r^c \vee l^c < n^c \leq r^a \wedge l^a \wedge (n - l^c - 1) \wedge (n - r^c - 1)$;
4. **Fuzzy polarization:**
   (11) $[\emptyset, N^a]$ if and only if $(n - l^c) \vee (r^a + 1) \leq n^c < n - l^a$;
   (12) $[N^c, N]$ if and only if $(n - r^c) \vee (l^a + 1) \leq n^c < n - r^a$;
5. **Chaotic polarization:**
   (13) $[\emptyset, N^a] \cup [\emptyset, N^c]$ if and only if $l^c \geq n - r^a$ and $n^c \in \big(]r^c, n - l^c[\cap]l^a, n - r^c[\big) \cup \big((]l^a, n - r^a[\cup]l^c, n - r^c[) \cap]0, r^c]\big)$;
   (14) $[N^a, N] \cup [N^c, N]$ if and only if $l^a \geq n - r^c$ and $n^c \in \big(]l^c, n - r^c[\cap]r^a, n - l^c[\big) \cup \big((]r^a, n - l^a[\cup]r^c, n - l^c[) \cap]0, l^c]\big)$;
   (15) $[\emptyset, N^a] \cup \{N^c\}$ if and only if $l^c + r^c = n - 1$, $r^a \geq r^c$, $l^c > l^a$ and $l^a < n^c < (n - r^a) \wedge (n - l^c)$;
   (16) $[N^c, N] \cup \{N^a\}$ if and only if $l^c + r^c = n - 1$, $l^a \geq l^c$, $r^c > r^a$ and $r^a < n^c < (n - l^a) \wedge (n - r^c)$;
   (17) $[\emptyset, N^c] \cup \{N^a\}$ if and only if $l^a + r^a = n - 1$, $l^c \geq l^a$, $n^c < n - r^c$ and $n^c \in]r^c, n - l^c[\cup]l^c, r^c]$;
   (18) $[N^a, N] \cup \{N^c\}$ if and only if $l^a + r^a = n - 1$, $r^c \geq r^a$, $n^c < n - l^c$ and $n^c \in]l^c, n - r^c[\cup]r^c, l^c]$.
   (19) $[\emptyset, N^a] \cup [N^c, N]$ if and only if $l^c + r^c = n - 1$ and $l^a \vee r^a < n^c \leq l^c \wedge r^c$;

6. **Chaos:**
   (20) 2^N *otherwise.*

Note that the only states that can appear in the absorbing classes are $\emptyset$, N, N^a and N^c. Polarization means that the society of agents is divided into two groups: one with opinion 'yes' and another with opinion 'no'. Cycles contain the infinite repetition of a pattern with sequences of states. In fuzzy cycles, the pattern contains states and intervals of states. While fuzzy polarization is defined by an interval, chaotic polarization involves several intervals. In chaos, at each time step a state is picked at random among all possible states.

In [15] (Theorem 2), the authors also consider the mixed case ($N^m \neq \emptyset$) and identify 20 possible absorbing classes (fuzzy polarization, fuzzy cycles, chaotic polarization and chaos). The classes are similar to those in the pure case ($N^m = \emptyset$), but the sets N^a and N^c are replaced by the intervals $[N^a, N^a \cup N^m]$ and $[N^c, N^c \cup N^m]$, respectively.

4.5 Diffusion in Countable Networks

In [26] the authors study diffusion in a countably infinite society of agents interacting with their neighbors in a network, with the diffusion mechanism represented by an aggregation function. They distinguish between probabilistic and deterministic diffusion mechanisms, and consider strict as well as Boolean aggregation functions. Under Boolean aggregation functions the diffusion process becomes deterministic and we recover the model of [36] on contagion, defined as a phenomenon occurring when one of two actions can spread from a finite set of agents to the whole (countably infinite) population.

Definition 5. *A (countable) network is an undirected graph* $(\mathscr{X}, E)$*, where* $\mathscr{X}$ *is the set of agents (society), and* E *the set of edges or links, satisfying the following properties:*

1. $\mathscr{X}$ *is countably infinite;*
2. $(\mathscr{X}, E)$ *is connected;*
3. *For every agent* $x \in \mathscr{X}$*, the neighborhood of* x*, denoted by* $\Gamma(x)$*, does not contain* x*;*
4. *For every agent* $x \in \mathscr{X}$*, the size of* $\Gamma(x)$ *(degree of* x*) is bounded by a fixed integer* γ*.*

We assume that for any x, we have an order on the neighbors in $\Gamma(x)$.

At a given time, the society consists of active and inactive agents. A *configuration* of the society describes who is active and who is inactive, and can be represented either by a 0-1-valued function on $\mathscr{X}$, or by the set of active agents. The set of all possible configurations is $\Omega := \{0,1\}^{\mathscr{X}} \equiv 2^{\mathscr{X}}$. In the function representation, a configuration is a function $\omega \in \Omega$, where $\omega(x) = 1$ if x is active, and $\omega(x) = 0$ if x is inactive. For every $X \subset \mathscr{X}$, we denote by π_X the projection from Ω to $\{0,1\}^X$. Every element of $\{0,1\}^X$ is called a *partial configuration* restricted to X.

We assume that the probability for an agent x to be active at time $t+1$, given the configuration ω at time t, is obtained by aggregating the vector of statuses of all neighbors of x in the configuration ω, i.e.,

$$P(x \mid \omega) = A_x(\pi_{\Gamma(x)}(\omega)).$$

We assume that the aggregation functions are Boolean, and hence the diffusion model becomes deterministic. Assume additionally that the aggregation functions A_x are anonymous for all $x \in \mathscr{X}$. Then for every x, there exists a threshold $0 \leq \widetilde{q}_x \leq \gamma$ such that

$$A_x(1_S) = \begin{cases} 1 & \text{if } |S| \geq \widetilde{q}_x \\ 0 & \text{otherwise.} \end{cases} \tag{2}$$

corresponding to the classical threshold model [27], where the rule of diffusion with threshold $0 \leq q_x \leq 1$ for x is as follows: Given a configuration $X(t)$ at time t, $X(t+1)$ is the set of agents having a proportion of neighbors in $X(t)$ at least equal to q_x:

$$X(t+1) = \left\{ x \in \mathscr{X} \ : \ \frac{|\Gamma(x) \cap X(t)|}{|\Gamma(x)|} \geq q_x \right\}.$$

Assuming that aggregation functions have the same threshold q for all agents, we obtain the contagion model [36]. All aggregation functions A_x are then identical, up to the size of the neighborhood. The *contagion threshold* ξ is the largest q such that infection spreads over $\mathscr{X}$ from some finite group $X(0)$. By definition, if q is below the contagion threshold, the absorbing states are the trivial states $\emptyset$ and $\mathscr{X}$. Otherwise, other nontrivial absorbing classes may occur. Without imposing additional assumptions on $\mathbf{A} = (A_x)_{x \in \mathscr{X}}$, we get

Result 14 ([26], Proposition 6). *Suppose* $\mathbf{A}$ *is Boolean. Then absorbing classes are either singletons* $\{X\}$, *where* $X \in 2^{\mathscr{X}}$, *or cycles (periodic trajectories) of nonempty sets* $\{X_1, \ldots, X_k\}$ *with the condition that all sets are pairwise incomparable by inclusion.*

Note that this is related to the "period 2 property" of majority over a large class of infinite graphs [11].

5 Concluding Remarks and Future Research

In this survey, we presented some results of our research on influence and opinion dynamics in social networks. First, we recalled the one-step model of influence with binary opinions and its relation to command games. Then we recalled some results on the influence model in a dynamic setting, with a particular focus on modeling influence by aggregation functions. Despite the fact that this framework has been extensively investigated, there are still several research directions worth being explored in future research.

It would be interesting to continue studying the influence indices defined in the static framework of influence with binary opinions [17] and an ordered set of possible opinions [18]. To the best of our knowledge no axiomatic justification of these indices has been provided so far, despite their usefulness in determining the influential agents in the process of opinion formation. Apart from studying properties and finding axiomatic characterizations (i.e., by properties) of the static influence indices, it would be interesting to introduce and justify axiomatically some generalizations of the influence measures in the dynamic setting.

Another direction for follow-up research concerns the study presented in [16,21], where we compare the static model of influence with a cooperative game theoretic approach based on command games. In particular, it would be interesting to investigate possible relations between the iterated model of influence and the command games in a dynamic setting. After defining an authority distribution over an organization, creating its power transition matrix and using a Markov chain to describe the long-run authority of the organization, we could introduce the authority distribution based on the influence indices.

Moreover, in parallel to theoretical studies, conducting lab experiments on influence and opinion dynamics could be of great interest. Using various methods and the interdisciplinary approach, in particular, a complementary experimental approach, could help in testing the theoretical framework and getting a deeper insight into the influence processes.

References

1. Acemoglu, D., Ozdaglar, A.: Opinion dynamics and learning in social networks. Dyn. Games Appl. **1**, 3–49 (2011)
2. Aracena, J., Demongeot, J., Goles, E.: On limit cycles of monotone functions with symmetric connection graph. Theoret. Comput. Sci. **322**, 237–244 (2004)
3. Berge, C.: Graphs and Hypergraphs, 2nd edn. North-Holland, Amsterdam (1976)
4. Bramoullé, Y., Galeotti, A., Rogers, B.W.: The Oxford Handbook of the Economics of Networks. Oxford University Press, Oxford (2016)
5. Castellano, C., Muñoz, M.A., Pastor-Satorras, R.: Nonlinear q-voter model. Phys. Rev. E **80**, 041129 (2009)
6. Clifford, P., Sudbury, A.: A model for spatial conflict. Biometrika **60**, 581–588 (1973)
7. Davey, B.A., Priestley, H.A.: Introduction to Lattices and Orders. Cambridge University Press, Cambridge (1990)
8. Förster, M., Grabisch, M., Rusinowska, A.: Anonymous social influence. Games Econ. Behav. **82**(C), 621–635 (2013)
9. Galam, S.: Minority opinion spreading in random geometry. Eur. Phys. J. B **25**, 403–406 (2002)
10. Galam, S.: Contrarian deterministic effects on opinion dynamics: "the hung elections scenario." Phys. A **333**, 453–460 (2004)
11. Ginosar, Y., Holzman, R.: The majority action on infinite graphs: strings and puppets. Discret. Math. **215**, 59–71 (2000)
12. Goles, E., Olivos, J.: Periodic behavior of generalized threshold functions. Discret. Math. **30**, 187–189 (1980)
13. Grabisch, M., Li, F.: Anti-conformism in the threshold model of collective behavior. Dyn. Games Appl. **10**, 444–477 (2020)

14. Grabisch, M., Marichal, J.-L., Mesiar, R., Pap., E.: Aggregation functions. Number 127. In: Encyclopedia of Mathematics and its Applications. Cambridge University Press, Cambridge (2009)
15. Grabisch, M., Poindron, A., Rusinowska, A.: A model of anonymous influence with anti-conformist agents. J. Econ. Dyn. Control **109**(C), 103773 (2019)
16. Grabisch, M., Rusinowska, A.: Measuring influence in command games. Soc. Choice Welfare **33**(2), 177–209 (2009)
17. Grabisch, M., Rusinowska, A.: A model of influence in a social network. Theor. Decis. **69**(1), 69–96 (2010)
18. Grabisch, M., Rusinowska, A.: A model of influence with an ordered set of possible actions. Theor. Decis. **69**(4), 635–656 (2010)
19. Grabisch, M., Rusinowska, A.: Different approaches to influence based on social networks and simple games. In: Van Deemen, A., Rusinowska, A. (eds.) Collective Decision Making: Views from Social Choice and Game Theory. Theory and Decision Library C, vol. 43, pp. 185–209. Springer, Heidelberg (2010). https://doi.org/10.1007/978-3-642-02865-6_13
20. Grabisch, M., Rusinowska, A.: Iterating influence between players in a social network. CES Working Papers, 2010.89 (2010). https://shs.hal.science/halshs-00543840
21. Grabisch, M., Rusinowska, A.: Influence functions, followers and command games. Games Econom. Behav. **72**(1), 123–138 (2011)
22. Grabisch, M., Rusinowska, A.: Lattices in social networks with influence. In: Proceedings of the ICFCA 2011 (9th International Conference on Formal Concept Analysis), Nicosia, Cyprus (2011)
23. Grabisch, M., Rusinowska, A.: A model of influence based on aggregation functions. Math. Soc. Sci. **66**(3), 316–330 (2013)
24. Grabisch, M., Rusinowska, A.: Determining influential models. Oper. Res. Decis. **26**(2), 69–85 (2016)
25. Grabisch, M., Rusinowska, A.: A survey on nonstrategic models of opinion dynamics. Games **11**(4), 65 (2020)
26. Grabisch, M., Rusinowska, A., Venel, X.: Diffusion in large networks. J. Econ. Dyn. Control **139**(C), 104439 (2022)
27. Granovetter, M.: Threshold models of collective behavior. Am. J. Sociol. **83**, 1420–1443 (1978)
28. Gravner, J., Griffeath, D.: Cellular automaton growth on $\mathbb{Z}^2$: theorems, examples and problems. Adv. Appl. Math. **21**, 241–304 (1998)
29. Holley, R.A., Liggett, T.M.: Ergodic theorems for weakly interacting infinite systems and the voter model. Ann. Probab. **3**(4), 643–663 (1975)
30. Hoede, C., Bakker, R.: A theory of decisional power. J. Math. Sociol. **8**, 309–322 (1982)
31. Hu, X., Shapley, L.S.: On authority distributions in organizations: controls. Games Econom. Behav. **45**, 153–170 (2003)
32. Hu, X., Shapley, L.S.: On authority distributions in organizations: equilibrium. Games Econom. Behav. **45**, 132–152 (2003)
33. Jackson, M.: Social and Economic Networks. Princeton University Press, Princeton (2008)
34. Jędrzejewski, A., Sznajd-Weron, K.: Statistical physics of opinion formation: is it a SPOOF? C R Phys. **20**, 244–261 (2019)
35. Kemeny, J.G., Snell, J.L.: Finite Markov Chains. Springer, New York (1976)
36. Morris, S.: Contagion. Rev. Econ. Stud. **67**, 57–78 (2000)

37. Mossel, E., Tamuz, O.: Opinion exchange dynamics. Probab. Surv. **14**, 155–204 (2017)
38. Nowak, N., Sznajd-Weron, K.: Homogeneous symmetrical threshold model with nonconformity: independence versus anticonformity. Complexity **2019**, 5150825 (2019)
39. Poindron, A.: A general model of binary opinions updating. Math. Soc. Sci. **109**(C), 52–76 (2021)
40. Remy, E., Ruet, P., Thieffry, D.: Graphic requirements for multistability and attractive cycles in a Boolean dynamical framework. Adv. Appl. Math. **41**, 335–350 (2008)
41. Rusinowska, A., Berghammer, R., De Swart, H., Grabisch, M.: Social networks: prestige, centrality, and influence. In: de Swart, H. (ed.) RAMICS 2011. LNCS, vol. 6663, pp. 22–39. Springer, Heidelberg (2011). https://doi.org/10.1007/978-3-642-21070-9_2
42. Schelling, T.: Micromotives and Macrobehaviour. Norton, New York (1978)
43. Seneta, E.: Non-negative Matrices and Markov Chains. Springer Series in Statistics, Springer, New York (2006). https://doi.org/10.1007/0-387-32792-4
44. Yager, R.: On ordered weighted averaging aggregation operators in multicriteria decision making. IEEE Trans. Syst. Man Cybern. **18**(1), 183–190 (1988)
45. Yager, R., Kacprzyk, J.: The Ordered Weighted Averaging Operators. Kluwer Academic Publishers (1997)

Contributed Papers

Generation of Pseudo-Isomorphic Cellular Automata

Kamalika Bhattacharjee(✉) and Tarun Dittakavi

Department of Computer Science and Engineering, National Institute of Technology, Tiruchirappalli, Tiruchirappalli 620015, India
kamalika@nitt.edu

Abstract. This paper explores isomorphism in one-dimensional finite cellular automata and introduces a new concept, named *pseudo-isomorphism*. An approach for generating pseudo-isomorphic cellular automata has been described here, that works by reversing cycles in the transition diagrams. Additionally, a new mathematical notion, named *state-neighborhood relation* has been introduced and is used to determine if a particular set of cycles in the transition diagram can be reversed to generate a pseudo-isomorphic cellular automaton.

Keywords: Isomorphism · Pseudo-Isomorphism · Reversibility · Transition Diagrams · State-Neighborhood Relation

1 Introduction

Cellular automata (CAs) are dynamical systems that exhibit complex global behavior from simple local interactions. In case of a finite cellular automaton (CA), its evolution can be represented as graphs using *transition diagrams*. Two CAs are said to be isomorphic if their transition diagrams are isomorphic to each other [1]. For finite CAs, isomorphic CAs have applications in different fields such as cryptography, pattern classification, clustering, etc. [1]. In fact, isomorphism is an important property of graphs with several theoretical as well as technological advantages. It is an ongoing field of research where the latest algorithm to check whether two graphs are isomorphic takes *quasi-polynomial* time of its number of vertices [2–4]. In case of transition diagrams, the number of vertices for a d-state n-cell CA is equal to the number of configurations of the CA, that is, d^n. So, testing for isomorphism of two CAs using their transition diagrams cannot be done in time lesser than $\Omega(d^n)$. In this situation, Ref. [1] describes two synthesis algorithms to generate a set of isomorphic CAs from the transition diagram of a given n-cell CA considering *permutation* and *exchange* of the states. One of these algorithms ensure that the synthesized isomorphic CAs have the same neighborhood architecture such as the given CA, while in the other scheme this invariant is not guaranteed.

Published by Springer Nature Switzerland AG 2024
M. Gadouleau and A. Castillo-Ramirez (Eds.): AUTOMATA 2024, LNCS 14782, pp. 77–94, 2024.
https://doi.org/10.1007/978-3-031-65887-7_5

In this work, we consider another approach of generating isomorphic CAs based on the cyclic components of the transition diagram: Given a transition diagram with a number of cycles, if the direction of a set of cycles is reversed, the resulting graph can be isomorphic to the original graph. However, for this approach, if the CA is *reversible*, that is, having only disjoint directed cycles, then it creates isomorphic CAs. But, if the CAs are *irreversible*, then the resulting CAs look like the original CA, but need not be isomorphic. We name such CAs as *pseudo-isomorphic* CAs. This paper explores the concept of *pseudo-isomorphism* in CAs and defines the condition when reversing a set of cycles results in generating a CA with the same neighborhood architecture and boundary condition as the given CA.

2 Definitions

This work considers finite 1D CAs where the neighborhood vector of a cell consists of the cell itself, l cells immediately to its left and r cells immediately to its right. Here l is known as the *left radius* and r is known as the *right radius* of a cell. Each cell assumes any state from a finite set of states $\mathcal{S} = \{0, 1, \ldots, d-1\}$ and takes a rule from a *rule vector* $\mathcal{R} = \langle \mathcal{R}_0, \mathcal{R}_1, \ldots, \mathcal{R}_{n-1} \rangle$ to update its state. If $\mathcal{R}_0 = \mathcal{R}_1 = \cdots = \mathcal{R}_{n-1}$, the CA is called a *uniform CA*, otherwise it is a *non-uniform CA* [5]. In this paper, unless otherwise mentioned, a CA refers to a non-uniform finite 1D CA where all cells have the same neighborhood architecture. The boundary condition followed by a CA will be mentioned accordingly.

A finite 1D CA having n cells is arranged in the form of a linear array, where each cell is addressed by its index i $(0 \le i < n)$. For a finite 1D CA under *null boundary condition*, the missing neighbors of leftmost and rightmost cells are always considered to be null (in state 0); whereas, for *periodic boundary condition*, the first and last cells are considered as neighbors of each other. An elementary CA (ECA) is a binary ($\mathcal{S} = \{0, 1\}$) 1D CA where the neighborhood vector of a cell consists of its immediate left neighbor, the cell itself and its immediate right neighbor.

The states of all cells of a CA taken together at any point of time is known as its *configuration* at that instant. As a CA evolves over time, it hops from one configuration to another. Let $\mathcal{C}_n$ be the set of all configurations of a CA having n cells. The *global transition function* $\mathcal{G}_n : \mathcal{C}_n \to \mathcal{C}_n$ takes a configuration of the CA as its input and returns the next configuration as its output. A CA whose global transition function $\mathcal{G}_n$ is a bijection, is said to be a *reversible CA*. Otherwise it is an *irreversible CA*. A finite CA is reversible, if and only if, for every configuration $c \in \mathcal{C}_n$ there exists $k \in \mathbb{N}$ such that $\mathcal{G}_n^k(c) = c$.

A finite CA can be represented as a directed graph where each vertex represents a particular configuration and each edge represents a transition from one configuration to another. An edge from vertex $c_x = x_0x_1 \ldots x_{n-1}$ to vertex $c_y = y_0y_1 \ldots y_{n-1}$, for $c_x, c_y \in \mathcal{C}_n$, means that c_x is a predecessor of c_y. In the above notation x_i and y_i denote the state of ith cell in configurations c_x and c_y respectively. Such a graph is known as the *transition diagram* of a CA. For a finite reversible CA, the transition diagram consists entirely of disjoint directed cycles.

Two directed graphs G and H are said to be isomorphic to each other if there exists a bijection $f : V(G) \to V(H)$ from the vertex set of G to vertex set of H, such that two vertices u and v of G are adjacent if and only if the vertices $f(u)$ and $f(v)$ of H are adjacent and the direction of each edge is preserved. Two CAs are said to be isomorphic if their transition diagrams are isomorphic [1]. Figure 1 shows that the ECAs with rule vectors $\langle 9, 142, 165, 65\rangle$ and $\langle 6, 212, 90, 65\rangle$ are isomorphic to each other under periodic boundary condition.

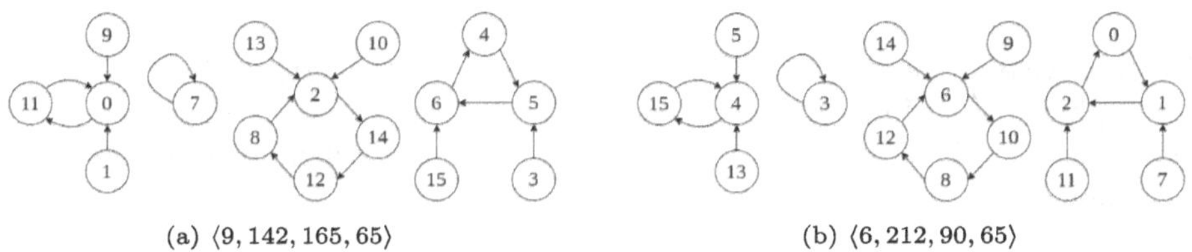

Fig. 1. Example of isomorphic CAs

In the current paper, we extend the concept of isomorphism by defining *pseudo-isomorphism* in CAs and describe a scheme for generating such pseudo-isomorphic CAs, by maintaining the invariant of same neighborhood architecture and boundary condition. Before diving into pseudo-isomorphic CAs, we define the following mathematical operations that will later be used to prove some results.

Definition 1 (Sub-Graph Removal). *Suppose G' is a sub-graph of G. The graph $G - G'$ is obtained by removing $E(G')$—the set of all edges of G'—from the graph G and then removing all the nodes of G' with in-degree and out-degree of 0. Let $E_{in}(v)$ be the set of all incoming edges and $E_{out}(v)$ be the set of all outgoing edges of a node v. Then $E(G - G') = E(G) - E(G')$ and $V(G - G') = V(G) - \{v \in G' \mid E_{in}(v) \subseteq E(G')$ and $E_{out}(v) \subseteq E(G')\}$.*

Figure 2 shows an example of this operation.

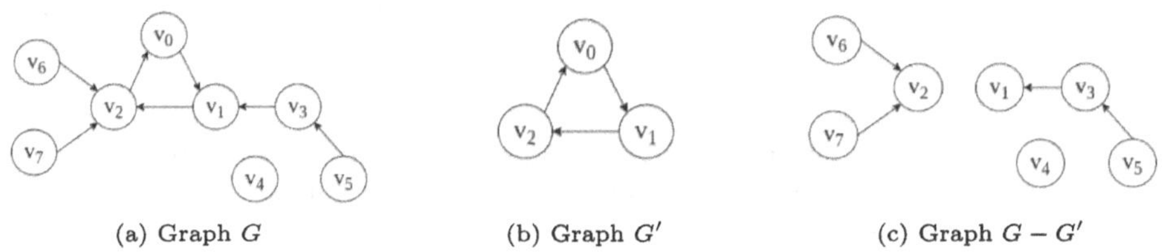

Fig. 2. Example of sub-graph removal

Definition 2 (Graph Union). *Suppose G and H are two labeled graphs. The graph $G \cup H$ contains all the nodes and edges of both G and H, that is, $V(G \cup H) = V(G) \cup V(H)$ and $E(G \cup H) = E(G) \cup E(H)$.*

Figure 3 shows an example of this operation.

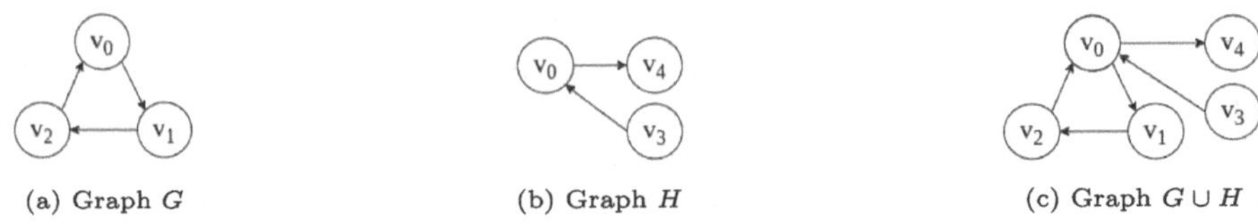

(a) Graph G (b) Graph H (c) Graph $G \cup H$

Fig. 3. Example of graph union

3 Pseudo-Isomorphic Cellular Automata

When a cycle of some graph G is reversed, the resultant graph H need not be isomorphic to G. While the truth of this statement can be easily verified for generic graphs, it is also true for transition diagrams, where the out-degree of every node is exactly 1.

(a) Graph G (b) Graph H

Fig. 4. Reversing a cycle need not result in an isomorphic graph

Figure 4 demonstrates the case where a possible transition diagram G is not isomorphic to H, which is obtained by reversing a cycle of G. Here even though G and H look almost similar, they are not isomorphic because there does not exist any bijection $f : V(G) \to V(H)$, such that there is an edge from node u to node v in G, if and only if, there is an edge from node $f(u)$ to node $f(v)$ in H. This leads us to the definition of *pseudo-isomorphism* in graphs.

Definition 3 (Pseudo-Isomorphic Graphs). *Two graphs G and H are said to be pseudo-isomorphic to each other, if G is isomorphic to H_r, where H_r is obtained by reversing zero or more cycles of H and leaving the other edges of H untouched.*

Figure 5 shows an example of pseudo-isomorphic graphs. Here graphs G and H are pseudo-isomorphic to each other, since G is isomorphic to H_r, which is obtained by reversing a cycle of H.

Lemma 1. *Isomorphism implies pseudo-isomorphism, that is, two graphs G and H that are isomorphic to each other, are pseudo-isomorphic to each other as well. But, the converse is not true, that is, two graphs G and H that are pseudo-isomorphic to each other, need not be isomorphic to each other.*

It is obvious that isomorphism implies pseudo-isomorphism. To show that pseudo-isomorphism does not imply isomorphism, it suffices to give an example

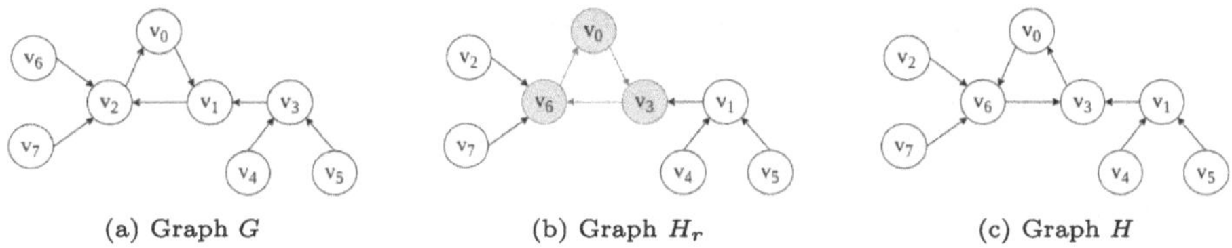

Fig. 5. Example of pseudo-isomorphic graphs

that demonstrates a case where graphs G and H are pseudo-isomorphic, but not isomorphic to each other. The example graphs given in Fig. 4 demonstrate exactly the same.

Remark 1. From the definition of pseudo-isomorphism, it is clear that whenever a set of cycles of a graph G are reversed, the resulting graph H will be pseudo-isomorphic to G. But, if the reversed cycles are separate components of their own, then the graph H will not only be pseudo-isomorphic, but will also be isomorphic to G.

Having defined pseudo-isomorphism with respect to graphs, we can apply this concept to CAs. Two CAs are said to be pseudo-isomorphic to each other, if their transition diagrams are pseudo-isomorphic to each other. Figure 6 shows that ECAs with rule vectors $\langle 51, 105, 4, 132\rangle$ and $\langle 3, 60, 236, 84\rangle$ are pseudo-isomorphic, but not isomorphic under null boundary condition. Similarly, Fig. 7 shows that ECAs with rule vectors $\langle 95, 18, 5, 111\rangle$ and $\langle 219, 3, 10, 86\rangle$ are pseudo-isomorphic, but not isomorphic under periodic boundary condition.

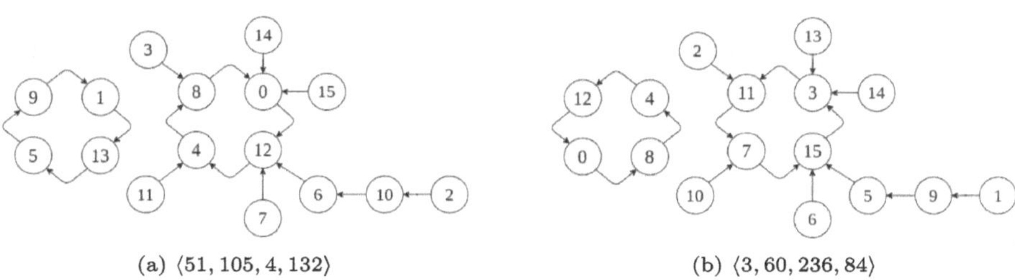

Fig. 6. Example of pseudo-isomorphic CAs under null boundary condition

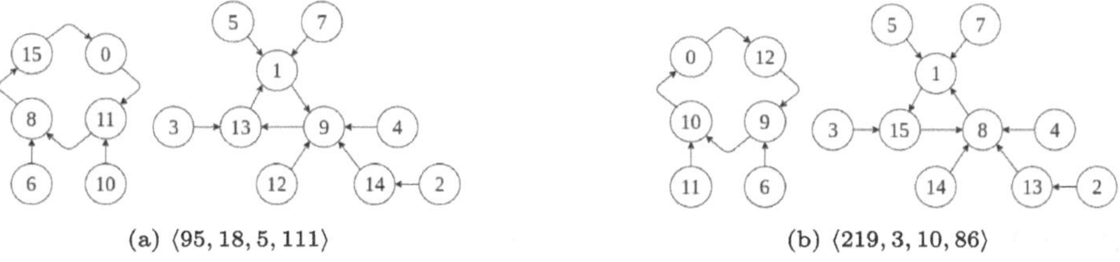

Fig. 7. Example of pseudo-isomorphic CAs under periodic boundary condition

4 State-Neighborhood Relation

To obtain pseudo-isomorphic CAs by reversing cycles, we introduce a new mathematical notion named *state-neighborhood relation* as defined below:

Definition 4 (State-Neighborhood Relation). *Consider a CA, with $\mathcal{S}$ being the finite set of states a cell can be in, l being the left radius, r being the right radius and $\mathcal{N}$ being the set of all possible neighborhood patterns a cell can have. Clearly, $\mathcal{N} = \mathcal{S}^{l+r+1}$. The state-neighborhood relation $\mathcal{SN}_i \subseteq \mathcal{S} \times \mathcal{N}$ for a cell i of the CA, is a relation from the set of states $\mathcal{S}$ to the set of neighborhood patterns $\mathcal{N}$, such that $(s_j, n_j) \in \mathcal{SN}_i$, if there exist configurations $c_1, c_2 \in \mathcal{C}$, such that $\mathcal{G}(c_1) = c_2$, the state of i in c_1 is s_j, and neighborhood of i in c_2 is n_j.*

Remark 2. Let G' be a sub-graph of the transition diagram G of a CA. The state-neighborhood relation for a cell i, restricted over G' would be $\mathcal{SN}_i|_{G'} \subseteq \mathcal{SN}_i$, such that $(s_j, n_j) \in \mathcal{SN}_i|_{G'}$, if there exist configurations $c_1, c_2 \in V(G')$, such that $\mathcal{G}(c_1) = c_2$, the state of i in c_1 is s_j, and neighborhood of i in c_2 is n_j. On the same note, $\mathcal{R}_i$ restricted over the sub-graph G' would be

$$\mathcal{R}_i|_{G'}(n_j) = \begin{cases} \mathcal{R}_i(n_j) & \text{if} \, \exists c \in V(G') \, \text{such that neighborhood of} \, i \, \text{in} \, c \, \text{is} \, n_j \\ \textit{undefined} & \text{otherwise} \end{cases}$$

Remark 3. $\mathcal{SN}_i|_G = \mathcal{SN}_i$ and $\mathcal{R}_i|_G = \mathcal{R}_i$.

Remark 4. $(\mathcal{SN}_i|_{G'})^{-1} = \{(n_j, s_j) \mid (s_j, n_j) \in \mathcal{SN}_i|_{G'}\}$.

Figure 8 shows the transition diagram of an ECA with rule vector $\langle 201, 51, 195, 204 \rangle$ under periodic boundary condition and the state-neighborhood relation $\mathcal{SN}_0$, for the first cell of the CA. Consider the successive configurations $c_1 = 0000$ and $c_2 = 1110$. The state of first cell in c_1 is 0 and its neighborhood in c_2 is 011. So $(0, 011) \in \mathcal{SN}_0$. The other elements of $\mathcal{SN}_0$ are computed similarly.

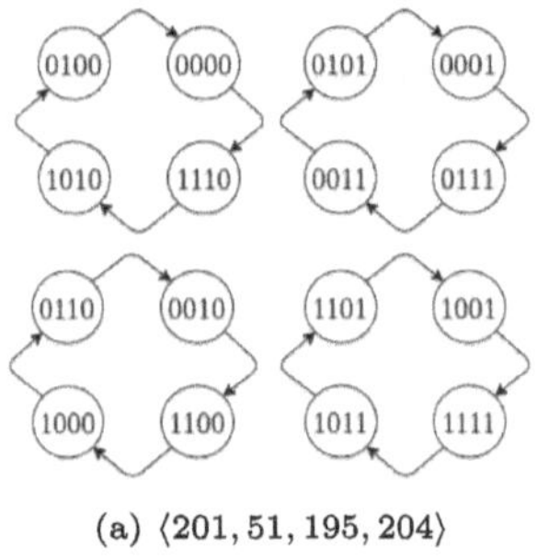

(a) $\langle 201, 51, 195, 204 \rangle$

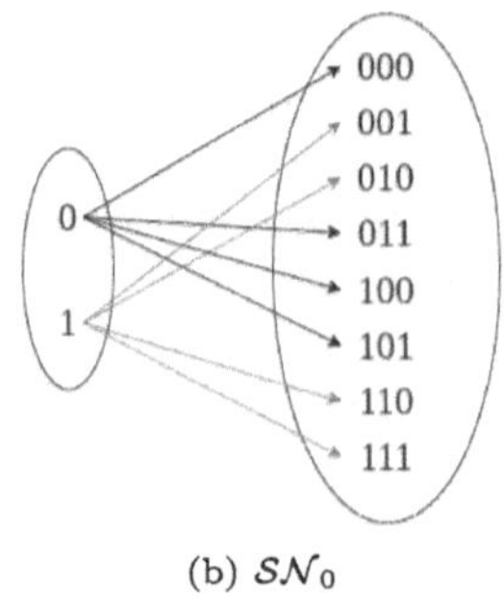

(b) $\mathcal{SN}_0$

Fig. 8. Example of state-neighborhood relation under periodic boundary condition

5 Pseudo-Isomorphic CAs by Reversing Cycles

Definition 3 says that reversing a set of cycles in the transition diagram G of a CA $\mathcal{CA}_1$ and leaving the remaining edges untouched, results in a pseudo-isomorphic transition diagram H. This transition diagram H may or may not correspond to a CA having the same neighborhood architecture and boundary condition as that of $\mathcal{CA}_1$. If it does, then the CA corresponding to H (say $\mathcal{CA}_2$) is pseudo-isomorphic to $\mathcal{CA}_1$. The transition diagram H corresponds to a CA, if every cell follows a *valid* local rule over the same neighborhood architecture and boundary condition as that of $\mathcal{CA}_1$, while updating its state by following the transitions defined in H. A cell is said to follow a *valid* local rule, under a specified neighborhood architecture and boundary condition, if there does not exist any neighborhood pattern n_j under that condition, for which the cell transitions into more than one state.

To check if a cell i follows a valid local rule or not, every node (configuration) of H needs to be visited to obtain the neighborhood of i at that node, along with the state to which i is making a transition. The rule followed by i will be valid, if no collisions are encountered for any neighborhood of i. Assuming k to be the number of cycles in the transition diagram G of the input CA, there will be a total of 2^k possible cycle reversal patterns, out of which one would correspond to G itself. Thus, a maximum of $2^k - 1$ pseudo-isomorphic CAs can be obtained by this reversing cycles algorithm. A flowchart demonstrating the high level overview of this algorithm is presented in Fig. 9.

Remark 5. The transition diagram G of a reversible CA is composed entirely of disjoint directed cycles. This implies that each cycle is a component of its own. So the transition diagram H, obtained by reversing a set of cycles of G, will be isomorphic to G. If H corresponds to a CA, then the CA corresponding to H will be isomorphic to the CA corresponding to G.

The immediate question that follows is, *when can a selected set of cycles in the transition diagram of a CA be reversed, so as to obtain a pseudo-isomorphic CA?* This can be answered by the following theorem, which uses the concept of state-neighborhood relation, introduced in the earlier section.

Theorem 1. *Consider a CA $\mathcal{CA}_1$ with n cells, having rule vector $\mathcal{R} = \langle \mathcal{R}_0, \mathcal{R}_1, \ldots, \mathcal{R}_{n-1} \rangle$. Let G be its transition diagram. Let $\mathcal{SN}_i$ be the state-neighborhood relation of the cell i and $\mathcal{SN}_i|_{G'}$ be the restriction of $\mathcal{SN}_i$ over a set of cycles G' of G. Let $\mathcal{R}_i|_{G-G'}$ be the restriction of $\mathcal{R}_i$ over the sub-graph $G - G'$. The set of cycles G' can be reversed to produce a pseudo-isomorphic CA (say $\mathcal{CA}_2$) having the same neighborhood architecture and boundary condition as that of $\mathcal{CA}_1$, if and only if, for each cell i, both the following conditions are satisfied:*

1. *$\mathcal{SN}_i|_{G'}$ is one-to-one or one-to-many, that is, there does not exist any neighborhood pattern n_j, such that $(s_a, n_j) \in \mathcal{SN}_i|_{G'}$ and $(s_b, n_j) \in \mathcal{SN}_i|_{G'}$, for states $s_a \neq s_b$.*

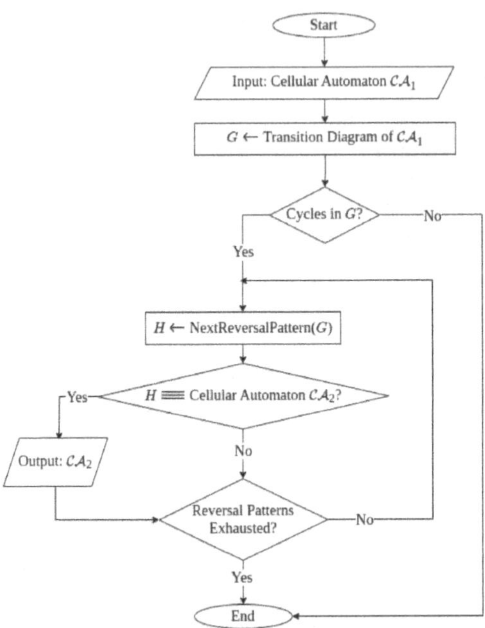

Fig. 9. Reversing cycles algorithm

2. $(\mathcal{SN}_i|_{G'})^{-1}$ *and* $\mathcal{R}_i|_{G-G'}$ *do not have any conflicts, that is, there does not exist any neighborhood pattern* n_j*, such that* $\mathcal{R}_i|_{G-G'}(n_j)$ *is defined and* $(n_j, s_a) \in (\mathcal{SN}_i|_{G'})^{-1}$*, for* $s_a \neq \mathcal{R}_i|_{G-G'}(n_j)$*.*

Proof. Let G'_r be the sub-graph that results from reversing G'. The transition diagram H obtained by reversing G' would be $H = (G - G') \cup G'_r$.

If: Consider that both the conditions stated in the theorem hold true. It needs to be shown that H would correspond to a CA having the same neighborhood architecture and boundary condition as that of $\mathcal{CA}_1$.

The local rule for cell i to transition into a new state within the sub-graph G'_r would be given by $(\mathcal{SN}_i|_{G'})^{-1}$. Since $\mathcal{SN}_i|_{G'}$ is one-to-one or one-to-many, its inverse, $(\mathcal{SN}_i|_{G'})^{-1}$, is one-to-one or many-to-one. Since $(\mathcal{SN}_i|_{G'})^{-1}$ is a one-to-one or many-to-one relation, no neighborhood will be mapped to more than one state by $(\mathcal{SN}_i|_{G'})^{-1}$, making it a valid local rule for a CA having the same neighborhood architecture and boundary condition as that of $\mathcal{CA}_1$, within the sub-graph G'_r.

Similarly, the local rule for cell i within the sub-graph $G - G'$ would be given by $\mathcal{R}_i|_{G-G'}$. Since $\mathcal{R}_i$ is a valid local rule for $\mathcal{CA}_1$, $\mathcal{R}_i|_{G-G'}$ is a valid local rule for a CA having the same neighborhood architecture and boundary condition as that of $\mathcal{CA}_1$, within the sub-graph $G - G'$.

Therefore, the local rule followed by cell i, to transition into a new state within the graph $H = (G - G') \cup G'_r$ is given by

$$\mathcal{R}'_i(n_j) = \begin{cases} (\mathcal{SN}_i|_{G'})^{-1}(n_j) & \text{within the sub-graph}\, G'_r \\ \mathcal{R}_i|_{G-G'}(n_j) & \text{within the sub-graph}\, G - G' \end{cases}$$

Since there is no conflict between $(\mathcal{SN}_i|_{G'})^{-1}$ and $\mathcal{R}_i|_{G-G'}$, there does not exist any neighborhood pattern n_j, such that $\mathcal{R}_i|_{G-G'}(n_j)$ is defined and $(n_j, s_a) \in (\mathcal{SN}_i|_{G'})^{-1}$, for $s_a \neq \mathcal{R}_i|_{G-G'}(n_j)$. So $\mathcal{R}'_i$ is a valid local rule for a CA having the same neighborhood architecture and boundary condition as that of $\mathcal{CA}_1$, within the graph $H = (G-G') \cup G'_r$. Hence, cell i does not violate the local rule property within the graph H. Hence, if both the above stated conditions hold true for every cell of the CA $\mathcal{CA}_1$, then H would emulate a CA having the same neighborhood architecture and boundary condition as that of $\mathcal{CA}_1$.

Only If: Consider that any one of the conditions stated in the theorem does not hold true for a cell i of $\mathcal{CA}_1$.

Suppose the first condition does not hold, that is, $\mathcal{SN}_i|_{G'}$ is neither one-to-one nor one-to-many. This implies that $\mathcal{SN}_i|_{G'}$ is many-to-one or many-to-many. So its inverse, $(\mathcal{SN}_i|_{G'})^{-1}$, is one-to-many or many-to-many. The local rule followed by cell i to transition into a new state within the sub-graph G'_r would be given by $(\mathcal{SN}_i|_{G'})^{-1}$. Since $(\mathcal{SN}_i|_{G'})^{-1}$ is one-to-many or many-to-many, there exists a neighborhood pattern n_j, such that $(n_j, s_a) \in (\mathcal{SN}_i|_{G'})^{-1}$ and $(n_j, s_b) \in (\mathcal{SN}_i|_{G'})^{-1}$, for states $s_a \neq s_b$. So $(\mathcal{SN}_i|_{G'})^{-1}$ is not a valid local rule for a CA having the same neighborhood architecture and boundary condition as that of $\mathcal{CA}_1$, within the sub-graph G'_r. Hence, clearly cell i violates the local rule property in the graph $H = (G - G') \cup G'_r$.

Suppose the first condition holds, but the second one does not, that is, $(\mathcal{SN}_i|_{G'})^{-1}$ and $\mathcal{R}_i|_{G-G'}$ have at least one conflict. The local rule followed by cell i to transition into a new state within the graph $H = (G-G') \cup G'_r$ is given by $\mathcal{R}'_i$, as defined previously. Since there is at least one conflict between $(\mathcal{SN}_i|_{G'})^{-1}$ and $\mathcal{R}_i|_{G-G'}$, there exists a neighborhood pattern n_j, such that $\mathcal{R}_i|_{G-G'}(n_j)$ is defined and $(n_j, s_a) \in (\mathcal{SN}_i|_{G'})^{-1}$, for $s_a \neq \mathcal{R}_i|_{G-G'}(n_j)$. So $\mathcal{R}'_i$ is not a valid local rule for a CA having the same neighborhood architecture and boundary condition as that of $\mathcal{CA}_1$ within the graph $H = (G - G') \cup G'_r$.

So if any of the above stated conditions does not hold true for any cell of $\mathcal{CA}_1$, then H would not emulate a CA having the same neighborhood architecture and boundary condition as that of $\mathcal{CA}_1$.

Remark 6. By reversing cycles of length less than 3, the obtained transition diagram H is exactly same as the transition diagram G of the input CA. So H would correspond to the input CA itself. A CA is said to have *non-trivial reversed cycle pseudo-isomorphisms*, if a pseudo-isomorphic CA having the same neighborhood architecture and boundary condition can be obtained by reversing one or more cycles of length ≥ 3.

Example 1. Consider an ECA with rule vector $\mathcal{R} = \langle 51, 201, 204, 163\rangle$ under periodic boundary condition. As per the notations used in the above theorem, G is its transition diagram, G' is a sub-graph of selected set of cycles, G'_r is the sub-graph obtained by reversing G' and H is $(G - G') \cup G'_r$. Figure 10 shows the graphs G, G' and H. Similarly, $\mathcal{SN}_i|_{G'}$, the state-neighborhood relation for each cell i, restricted over the set of cycles G' is shown in Fig. 11. It can be observed that for all i, $\mathcal{SN}_i|_{G'}$ is one-to-many and $(\mathcal{SN}_i|_{G'})^{-1}$ does not have any conflicts with $\mathcal{R}_i|_{G-G'}$. Since both the conditions stated in the theorem are true, the transition diagram $H = (G - G') \cup G'_r$ corresponds to an ECA with rule vector $\mathcal{R}' = \langle 51, 156, 204, 163\rangle$ under periodic boundary condition. Each rule $\mathcal{R}'_i$ is computed as per the formula mentioned in the proof of the theorem.

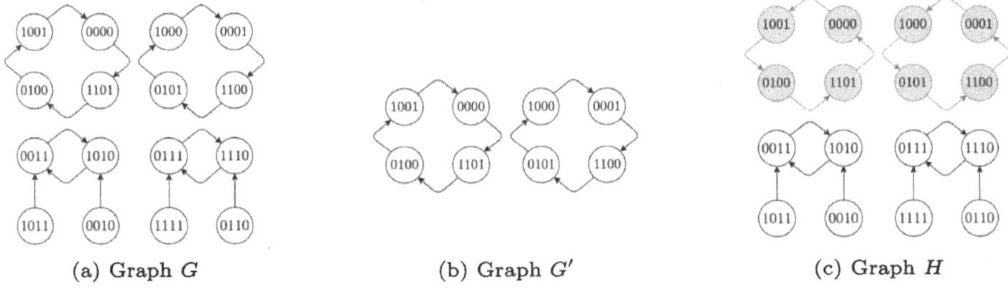

Fig. 10. G, G' and H of $\langle 51, 201, 204, 163\rangle$ under periodic boundary condition

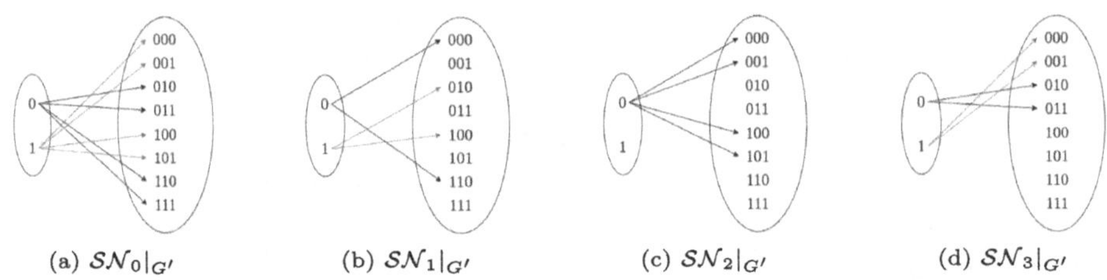

Fig. 11. $\mathcal{SN}_i|_{G'}$ for $i = 0$ to 3 of $\langle 51, 201, 204, 163\rangle$ under periodic boundary condition

Example 2. Consider an ECA with rule vector $\mathcal{R} = \langle 90, 150, 60, 90\rangle$ under null boundary condition. Its transition diagram G, a set of cycles G' of G and H computed as $(G - G') \cup G'_r$ (where G'_r is the sub-graph obtained by reversing G') are shown in Fig. 12. Similarly, $\mathcal{SN}_i|_{G'}$, the state-neighborhood relation for each cell i, restricted over the set of cycles G' is shown in Fig. 13. It can be observed that $\mathcal{SN}_0|_{G'}$ and $\mathcal{SN}_3|_{G'}$ are many-to-many relations, thereby violating the first condition of the theorem. As a result, the transition diagram $H = (G - G') \cup G'_r$ does not correspond to any ECA under null boundary condition.

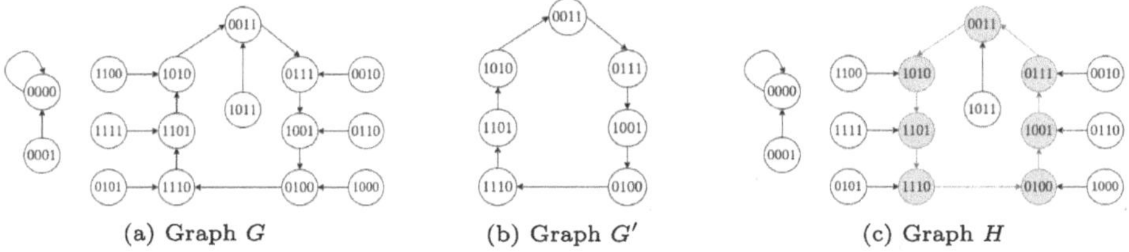

(a) Graph G (b) Graph G' (c) Graph H

Fig. 12. G, G' and H of $\langle 90, 150, 60, 90\rangle$ under null boundary condition

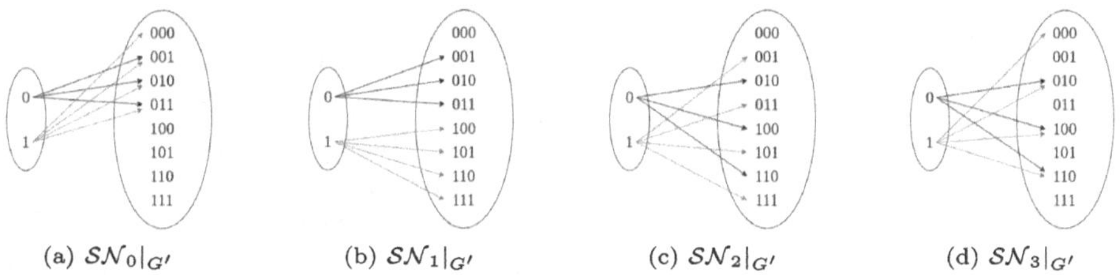

(a) $\mathcal{SN}_0|_{G'}$ (b) $\mathcal{SN}_1|_{G'}$ (c) $\mathcal{SN}_2|_{G'}$ (d) $\mathcal{SN}_3|_{G'}$

Fig. 13. $\mathcal{SN}_i|_{G'}$ for $i = 0$ to 3 of $\langle 90, 150, 60, 90\rangle$ under null boundary condition

6 Experimental Results and Observations

The algorithm for reversing cycles is used to check the number of ECAs having non-trivial reversed cycle pseudo-isomorphisms over reversible ECAs under null boundary condition. To test the algorithm, the synthesis scheme described in Ref. [6] is used to generate 1000 random reversible ECAs for $n \in \{3, 4, 5\}$. In that experiment, for ECAs of size 3, on an average, 18% of the generated reversible ECAs are found to contain non-trivial reversed cycle pseudo-isomorphisms. But the percentage quickly drops to 7% for ECAs of size 4 and to 2% for ECAs of size 5. Since these ECAs are reversible, the ECAs obtained by reversing cycles are not just pseudo-isomorphic, but are also isomorphic to the original ECA.

Figure 14 shows an example of a reversible ECA with rule vector $\langle 3, 204, 102, 17\rangle$ under null boundary condition. Isomorphic ECAs with rule vectors $\langle 3, 204, 105, 17\rangle$ and $\langle 3, 204, 150, 17\rangle$ under null boundary condition are obtained by reversing proper sub-graphs of the transition diagram, while an isomorphic ECA with rule vector $\langle 3, 204, 153, 17\rangle$ under null boundary condition is obtained by reversing the entire transition diagram itself. It is known that for an ECA with rule vector $\mathcal{R} = \langle \mathcal{R}_0, \mathcal{R}_1, \ldots, \mathcal{R}_{n-1}\rangle$ under null boundary condition, an ECA with rule vector $\mathcal{R}^{ref} = \langle \mathcal{R}^{ref}_{n-1}, \mathcal{R}^{ref}_{n-2}, \ldots, \mathcal{R}^{ref}_0\rangle$ is isomorphic to it, where $\mathcal{R}^{ref}_i$ refers to the reflection transformation [8] of $\mathcal{R}_i$. The ECAs obtained by reversing cycles may or may not include the one with rule vector $\mathcal{R}^{ref}$. For $\mathcal{R} = \langle 3, 204, 102, 17\rangle$, $\mathcal{R}^{ref} = \langle 3, 60, 204, 17\rangle$. In this case, none of the isomorphic ECAs obtained by reversing cycles corresponds to an ECA with rule vector $\mathcal{R}^{ref}$.

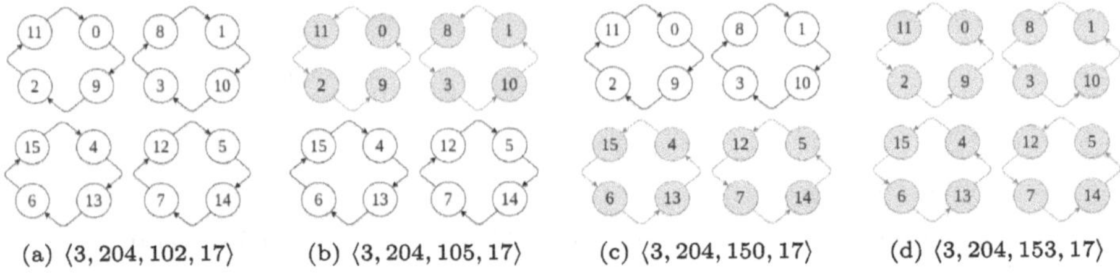

(a) $\langle 3, 204, 102, 17\rangle$ (b) $\langle 3, 204, 105, 17\rangle$ (c) $\langle 3, 204, 150, 17\rangle$ (d) $\langle 3, 204, 153, 17\rangle$

Fig. 14. Example of reversing cycles under null boundary condition

Figure 15 shows an example of a reversible ECA with rule vector $\langle 201, 51, 105, 204\rangle$ under periodic boundary condition. Isomorphic ECAs with rule vectors $\langle 198, 51, 60, 204\rangle$ and $\langle 201, 51, 195, 204\rangle$ under periodic boundary condition are obtained by reversing proper sub-graphs of the transition diagram, while an isomorphic ECA with rule vector $\langle 198, 51, 150, 204\rangle$ under periodic boundary condition is obtained by reversing the entire transition diagram itself. It is known that for an ECA with rule vector $\mathcal{R} = \langle \mathcal{R}_0, \mathcal{R}_1, \ldots, \mathcal{R}_{n-1}\rangle$ under periodic boundary condition, ECAs with rule vectors $\mathcal{R}^{conj} = \langle \mathcal{R}_0^{conj}, \mathcal{R}_1^{conj}, \ldots, \mathcal{R}_{n-1}^{conj}\rangle$, $\mathcal{R}^{ref} = \langle \mathcal{R}_{n-1}^{ref}, \mathcal{R}_{n-2}^{ref}, \ldots, \mathcal{R}_0^{ref}\rangle$ and $\mathcal{R}^{c.r.} = \langle \mathcal{R}_{n-1}^{c.r.}, \mathcal{R}_{n-2}^{c.r.}, \ldots, \mathcal{R}_0^{c.r.}\rangle$ are isomorphic to it, where $\mathcal{R}_i^{conj}$, $\mathcal{R}_i^{ref}$ and $\mathcal{R}_i^{c.r.}$ refer to the conjugation, reflection and (conjugation + reflection) transformations [8] of $\mathcal{R}_i$, respectively. The ECAs obtained by reversing cycles may or may not include those with rule vectors $\mathcal{R}^{conj}$, $\mathcal{R}^{ref}$ and $\mathcal{R}^{c.r.}$. For $\mathcal{R} = \langle 201, 51, 105, 204\rangle$, $\mathcal{R}^{conj} = \langle 108, 51, 105, 204\rangle$, $\mathcal{R}^{ref} = \langle 204, 105, 51, 201\rangle$ and $\mathcal{R}^{c.r.} = \langle 204, 105, 51, 108\rangle$. In this case, none of the isomorphic ECAs obtained by reversing cycles corresponds to those with rule vectors $\mathcal{R}^{conj}$, $\mathcal{R}^{ref}$ or $\mathcal{R}^{c.r.}$.

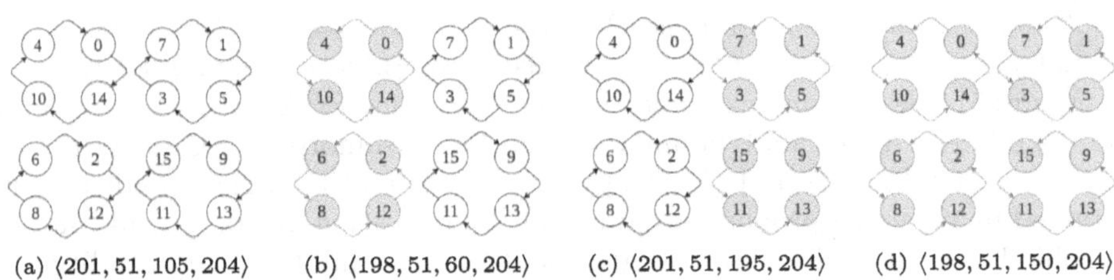

(a) $\langle 201, 51, 105, 204\rangle$ (b) $\langle 198, 51, 60, 204\rangle$ (c) $\langle 201, 51, 195, 204\rangle$ (d) $\langle 198, 51, 150, 204\rangle$

Fig. 15. Example of reversing cycles under periodic boundary condition

The synthesis scheme described in Ref. [7] is used for generating reversible ECAs under periodic boundary condition. However, not all the ECAs obtained through the scheme are found to be reversible. Out of the obtained reversible ECAs of sizes 3 and 4, under null and periodic boundary conditions, it has been observed that whenever an isomorphic ECA exists by reversing a proper subgraph G' of the transition diagram G (that is, $G' \neq G$), an isomorphic ECA also exists by reversing G as well. Figures 14 and 15 serve as examples for this statement. However, this is not always the case and a counter example has been found for the 5-cell reversible ECA with rule vector $\langle 5, 165, 204, 102, 17\rangle$ under null boundary condition. For this ECA, reversing a proper sub-graph of the transition diagram results in an isomorphic ECA with rule vector $\langle 5, 165, 204, 105, 17\rangle$, but reversing the entire transition diagram does not result in an isomorphic ECA under null boundary condition. Figure 16 demonstrates this example. Similarly, under periodic boundary condition, the reversible ECA with rule vector $\langle 51, 108, 204, 58, 105\rangle$ acts as a counter example. For this ECA, reversing a proper sub-graph of the transition diagram results in an isomorphic ECA with rule vector $\langle 51, 198, 204, 58, 105\rangle$, but reversing the entire transition diagram does not result in an isomorphic ECA under periodic boundary condition. Figure 17 demonstrates this example.

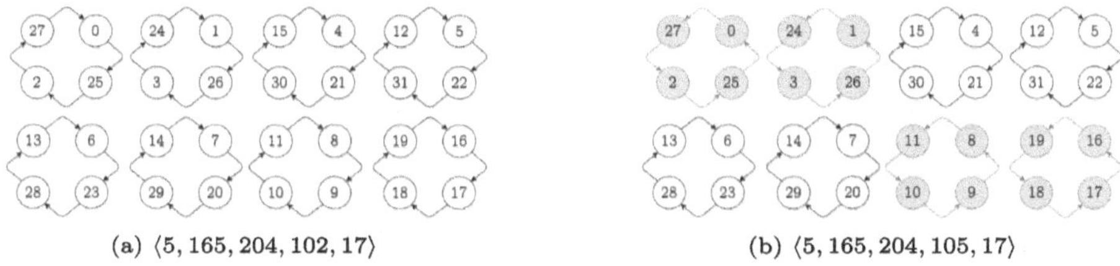

(a) $\langle 5, 165, 204, 102, 17\rangle$ (b) $\langle 5, 165, 204, 105, 17\rangle$

Fig. 16. Example of reversing cycles under null boundary condition

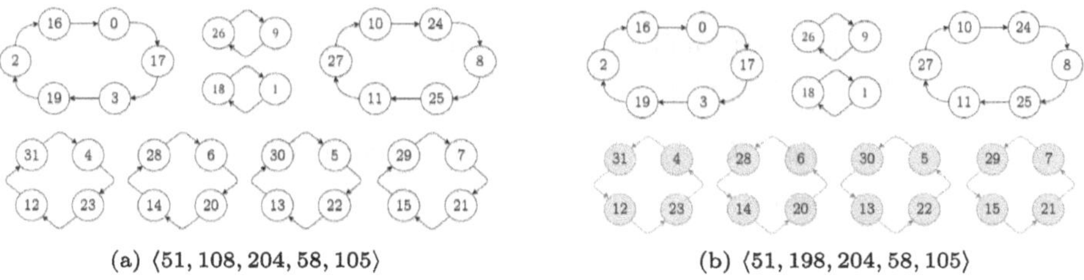

(a) $\langle 51, 108, 204, 58, 105\rangle$ (b) $\langle 51, 198, 204, 58, 105\rangle$

Fig. 17. Example of reversing cycles under periodic boundary condition

Applying the reversing cycles algorithm on uniform ECAs of sizes 4 & 5 under null boundary condition, it is found that none of them have non-trivial reversed cycle pseudo-isomorphisms. However this is not the case with uniform ECAs under periodic boundary condition. Tables 1 and 2 list the uniform ECAs of sizes 4 & 5 respectively, that have non-trivial reversed cycle pseudo-isomorphisms under periodic boundary condition.

Remark 7. On observing the transition diagrams of uniform ECAs with rule vectors $\langle 2, 2, 2, 2 \rangle$ and $\langle 16, 16, 16, 16 \rangle$ under periodic boundary condition, it has been found that they are pseudo-isomorphic as well. But they are not listed in Table 1 because one cannot be obtained from the other by just reversing a set of cycles and leaving the remaining edges untouched. As shown in Fig. 18, along with reversing a set of cycles, some non-cyclic edges need to be modified as well. Hence these cases are not covered by the reversing cycles algorithm.

(a) $\langle 2, 2, 2, 2 \rangle$ (b) $\langle 16, 16, 16, 16 \rangle$

Fig. 18. Pseudo-isomorphic CAs under periodic boundary condition

Tables 3 and 4 list the results of reversing cycles algorithm on randomly generated non-uniform ECAs of sizes 4 and 5 respectively, under null boundary condition. Tables 5 and 6 list the results of reversing cycles algorithm on randomly generated non-uniform ECAs of sizes 4 and 5 respectively, under periodic boundary condition. These tables include both reversible and irreversible ECAs.

Table 1. List of 4-cell uniform ECAs having non-trivial reversed cycle pseudo-isomorphisms under periodic boundary condition

Input CA	Pseudo-Isomorphic CA
$\langle 3, 3, 3, 3 \rangle$	$\langle 17, 17, 17, 17 \rangle$
$\langle 15, 15, 15, 15 \rangle$	$\langle 85, 85, 85, 85 \rangle$
$\langle 35, 35, 35, 35 \rangle$	$\langle 49, 49, 49, 49 \rangle$
$\langle 49, 49, 49, 49 \rangle$	$\langle 35, 35, 35, 35 \rangle$
$\langle 58, 58, 58, 58 \rangle$	$\langle 114, 114, 114, 114 \rangle$
$\langle 59, 59, 59, 59 \rangle$	$\langle 115, 115, 115, 115 \rangle$
$\langle 62, 62, 62, 62 \rangle$	$\langle 118, 118, 118, 118 \rangle$
$\langle 63, 63, 63, 63 \rangle$	$\langle 119, 119, 119, 119 \rangle$
$\langle 131, 131, 131, 131 \rangle$	$\langle 145, 145, 145, 145 \rangle$
$\langle 163, 163, 163, 163 \rangle$	$\langle 177, 177, 177, 177 \rangle$
$\langle 170, 170, 170, 170 \rangle$	$\langle 240, 240, 240, 240 \rangle$

Table 2. List of 5-cell uniform ECAs having non-trivial reversed cycle pseudo-isomorphisms under periodic boundary condition

Input CA	Pseudo-Isomorphic CA
$\langle 15, 15, 15, 15, 15\rangle$	$\langle 85, 85, 85, 85, 85\rangle$
$\langle 35, 35, 35, 35, 35\rangle$	$\langle 49, 49, 49, 49, 49\rangle$
$\langle 59, 59, 59, 59, 59\rangle$	$\langle 115, 115, 115, 115, 115\rangle$
$\langle 170, 170, 170, 170, 170\rangle$	$\langle 240, 240, 240, 240, 240\rangle$

Table 3. Some 4-cell non-uniform ECAs having non-trivial reversed cycle pseudo-isomorphisms under null boundary condition

Input CA	Reversible	Pseudo-Isomorphic CA(s)
$\langle 220, 140, 134, 49\rangle$	False	$\langle 12, 140, 137, 17\rangle$
$\langle 196, 132, 22, 49\rangle$	False	$\langle 4, 132, 25, 17\rangle$
$\langle 179, 62, 132, 19\rangle$	False	$\langle 3, 107, 132, 17\rangle$
$\langle 172, 38, 63, 68\rangle$	False	$\langle 12, 21, 243, 68\rangle$
$\langle 38, 204, 85, 89\rangle$	False	$\langle 6, 204, 102, 21\rangle$
$\langle 243, 54, 196, 188\rangle$	False	$\langle 3, 99, 196, 20\rangle$
$\langle 233, 12, 6, 17\rangle$	False	$\langle 9, 12, 9, 17\rangle$
$\langle 255, 104, 51, 198\rangle$	False	$\langle 15, 152, 51, 68\rangle$
$\langle 227, 148, 128, 25\rangle$	False	$\langle 3, 193, 128, 17\rangle$
$\langle 243, 132, 89, 155\rangle$	False	$\langle 3, 132, 86, 17\rangle$
$\langle 3, 121, 221, 147\rangle$	False	$\langle 3, 211, 221, 17\rangle$
$\langle 179, 134, 220, 108\rangle$	False	$\langle 3, 44, 220, 68\rangle$
$\langle 188, 17, 178, 236\rangle$	False	$\langle 12, 34, 43, 68\rangle$
$\langle 135, 180, 204, 25\rangle$	False	$\langle 11, 45, 204, 17\rangle$
$\langle 19, 130, 252, 229\rangle$	False	$\langle 3, 40, 252, 69\rangle$
$\langle 6, 15, 204, 20\rangle$	True	$\langle 5, 195, 204, 20\rangle$
$\langle 134, 15, 102, 208\rangle$	True	$\langle 5, 195, 170, 20\rangle$
$\langle 9, 204, 105, 17\rangle$	True	$\langle 9, 204, 102, 17\rangle$, $\langle 9, 204, 153, 17\rangle$, $\langle 9, 204, 150, 17\rangle$
$\langle 12, 51, 195, 68\rangle$	True	$\langle 12, 51, 150, 68\rangle$, $\langle 12, 51, 105, 68\rangle$, $\langle 12, 51, 60, 68\rangle$
$\langle 3, 60, 51, 17\rangle$	True	$\langle 3, 153, 51, 17\rangle$, $\langle 3, 102, 51, 17\rangle$, $\langle 3, 195, 51, 17\rangle$

Table 4. Some 5-cell non-uniform ECAs having non-trivial reversed cycle pseudo-isomorphisms under null boundary condition

Input CA	Reversible	Pseudo-Isomorphic CA(s)
⟨163, 130, 254, 173, 112⟩	False	⟨3, 40, 254, 173, 80⟩
⟨131, 134, 207, 205, 196⟩	False	⟨3, 44, 207, 205, 68⟩
⟨236, 179, 72, 86, 57⟩	False	⟨12, 179, 72, 89, 17⟩
⟨163, 147, 204, 63, 78⟩	False	⟨3, 57, 204, 63, 68⟩
⟨19, 68, 192, 169, 25⟩	False	⟨3, 68, 192, 166, 17⟩
⟨211, 57, 205, 193, 198⟩	False	⟨3, 147, 205, 193, 68⟩
⟨211, 225, 204, 6, 177⟩	False	⟨3, 180, 204, 9, 17⟩
⟨35, 28, 64, 60, 153⟩	False	⟨3, 73, 64, 60, 17⟩
⟨163, 134, 207, 203, 238⟩	False	⟨3, 44, 207, 203, 68⟩
⟨12, 54, 220, 98, 59⟩	False	⟨12, 54, 220, 146, 17⟩
⟨10, 120, 204, 57, 17⟩	True	⟨10, 120, 204, 54, 17⟩
⟨10, 15, 85, 195, 68⟩	True	⟨5, 240, 102, 15, 68⟩
⟨3, 198, 204, 89, 5⟩	True	⟨3, 108, 204, 89, 5⟩
⟨10, 180, 204, 108, 17⟩	True	⟨10, 180, 204, 156, 17⟩
⟨6, 51, 60, 51, 65⟩	True	⟨9, 51, 195, 51, 20⟩
⟨12, 156, 204, 105, 17⟩	True	⟨12, 156, 204, 102, 17⟩, ⟨12, 156, 204, 153, 17⟩, ⟨12, 156, 204, 150, 17⟩
⟨12, 204, 51, 150, 68⟩	True	⟨12, 204, 51, 195, 68⟩, ⟨12, 204, 51, 60, 68⟩, ⟨12, 204, 51, 105, 68⟩
⟨3, 150, 204, 108, 17⟩	True	⟨3, 195, 204, 108, 17⟩, ⟨3, 60, 204, 156, 17⟩, ⟨3, 105, 204, 156, 17⟩
⟨3, 57, 204, 198, 17⟩	True	⟨3, 147, 204, 198, 17⟩, ⟨3, 57, 204, 201, 17⟩, ⟨3, 147, 204, 201, 17⟩
⟨12, 51, 204, 153, 17⟩	True	⟨12, 51, 204, 150, 17⟩, ⟨12, 51, 204, 105, 17⟩, ⟨12, 51, 204, 102, 17⟩

Table 5. Some 4-cell non-uniform ECAs having non-trivial reversed cycle pseudo-isomorphisms under periodic boundary condition

Input CA	Reversible	Pseudo-Isomorphic CA(s)
⟨204, 151, 51, 55⟩	False	⟨204, 103, 51, 55⟩
⟨207, 155, 51, 131⟩	False	⟨207, 107, 51, 41⟩
⟨72, 182, 51, 57⟩	False	⟨72, 185, 51, 57⟩
⟨168130231248⟩	False	⟨152160235188⟩
⟨16, 91, 97, 31⟩	False	⟨32, 31, 81, 91⟩
⟨236, 51, 22, 136⟩	False	⟨236, 51, 67, 136⟩
⟨98, 51, 131, 236⟩	False	⟨146, 51, 41, 236⟩
⟨127, 123, 242, 84⟩	False	⟨127, 187, 182, 84⟩
⟨1, 69, 127, 159⟩	False	⟨16, 69, 127, 95⟩
⟨106, 15, 170, 165⟩	True	⟨85, 210, 90, 240⟩
⟨170, 30, 166, 240⟩	True	⟨86, 240, 170, 180⟩
⟨51, 54, 204, 198⟩	True	⟨51, 99, 204, 201⟩
⟨170, 180, 101, 15⟩	True	⟨106, 240, 85, 135⟩
⟨86, 15, 85, 75⟩	True	⟨85, 135, 101, 15⟩
⟨166, 15, 85, 165⟩	True	⟨85, 210, 90, 15⟩
⟨102, 240, 51, 51⟩	True	⟨170, 60, 51, 51⟩
⟨54, 51, 57, 204⟩	True	⟨57, 51, 57, 204⟩, ⟨54, 51, 147, 204⟩, ⟨57, 51, 147, 204⟩
⟨51, 198, 204, 54⟩	True	⟨51, 108, 204, 54⟩, ⟨51, 198, 204, 57⟩, ⟨51, 108, 204, 57⟩
⟨54, 204, 156, 51⟩	True	⟨99, 204, 156, 51⟩, ⟨54, 204, 108, 51⟩, ⟨99, 204, 108, 51⟩
⟨204, 51, 51, 195⟩	True	⟨204, 51, 51, 150⟩, ⟨204, 51, 51, 105⟩, ⟨204, 51, 51, 60⟩

Table 6. Some 5-cell non-uniform ECAs having non-trivial reversed cycle pseudo-isomorphisms under periodic boundary condition

Input CA	Reversible	Pseudo-Isomorphic CA(s)
$\langle 99, 204, 156, 51, 150\rangle$	False	$\langle 99, 204, 108, 51, 150\rangle$
$\langle 114, 204, 102, 51, 170\rangle$	False	$\langle 114, 204, 105, 51, 170\rangle$
$\langle 78, 64, 169, 51, 51\rangle$	False	$\langle 78, 64, 166, 51, 51\rangle$
$\langle 51, 204, 150, 204, 106\rangle$	False	$\langle 51, 204, 150, 204, 154\rangle$
$\langle 153, 240, 153, 204, 51\rangle$	True	$\langle 170, 195, 153, 204, 51\rangle$
$\langle 51, 150, 114, 204, 108\rangle$	True	$\langle 51, 150, 114, 204, 156\rangle$
$\langle 204, 149, 15, 51, 54\rangle$	True	$\langle 204, 149, 15, 51, 99\rangle$
$\langle 102, 204, 85, 195, 51\rangle$	True	$\langle 102, 204, 102, 15, 51\rangle$
$\langle 170, 85, 170, 85, 170\rangle$	True	$\langle 240, 240, 15, 240, 15\rangle$
$\langle 51, 147, 204, 204, 150\rangle$	True	$\langle 51, 57, 204, 204, 105\rangle$
$\langle 204, 60, 204, 85, 240\rangle$	True	$\langle 204, 60, 204, 170, 15\rangle$
$\langle 51, 150, 51, 85, 60\rangle$	True	$\langle 51, 150, 51, 153, 15\rangle$
$\langle 54, 204, 106, 240, 51\rangle$	True	$\langle 99, 204, 106, 240, 51\rangle$
$\langle 51, 57, 204, 108, 51\rangle$	True	$\langle 51, 147, 204, 156, 51\rangle$
$\langle 85, 60, 51, 156, 204\rangle$	True	$\langle 153, 15, 51, 201, 204\rangle$
$\langle 85, 170, 170, 170, 85\rangle$	True	$\langle 15, 15, 240, 240, 240\rangle$
$\langle 51, 51, 60, 204, 57\rangle$	True	$\langle 51, 51, 105, 204, 54\rangle$, $\langle 51, 51, 150, 204, 57\rangle$, $\langle 51, 51, 195, 204, 54\rangle$
$\langle 102, 204, 51, 153, 51\rangle$	True	$\langle 102, 204, 51, 60, 51\rangle$, $\langle 102, 204, 51, 195, 51\rangle$, $\langle 102, 204, 51, 102, 51\rangle$
$\langle 51, 201, 204, 108, 51\rangle$	True	$\langle 51, 156, 204, 108, 51\rangle$, $\langle 51, 201, 204, 156, 51\rangle$, $\langle 51, 156, 204, 156, 51\rangle$
$\langle 201, 204, 156, 51, 51\rangle$	True	$\langle 156, 204, 156, 51, 51\rangle$, $\langle 201, 204, 108, 51, 51\rangle$, $\langle 156, 204, 108, 51, 51\rangle$

References

1. Mukherjee, S., Vikrant, V., Bhattacharjee, K.: Isomorphism in cellular automata. In: Das, S., Martinez, G.J. (eds.) ASCAT 2023. AISC, vol. 1443, pp. 193–206. Springer, Singapore (2023). https://doi.org/10.1007/978-981-99-0688-8_15
2. Wiebking, D.: Graph isomorphism in quasipolynomial time parameterized by treewidth. In: 47th International Colloquium on Automata, Languages, and Programming (ICALP 2020). Leibniz International Proceedings in Informatics (LIPIcs), vol. 168, pp. 103:1–103:16, Schloss-Dagstuhl-Leibniz Zentrum für Informatik (2020). https://doi.org/10.4230/LIPIcs.ICALP.2020.103
3. Babai, L.: Graph isomorphism in quasipolynomial time [extended abstract]. In: Proceedings of the Forty-Eighth Annual ACM Symposium on Theory of Computing, Cambridge, MA, USA, pp. 684–697. Association for Computing Machinery (2016). https://doi.org/10.1145/2897518.2897542
4. Grohe, M., Schweitzer, P.: The graph isomorphism problem. Commun. ACM **63**(11), 128–134 (2020). https://doi.org/10.1145/3372123
5. Bhattacharjee, K., Naskar, N., Roy, S., Das, S.: A survey of cellular automata: types, dynamics, non-uniformity and applications. Nat. Comput. **19**, 433–461 (2020). https://doi.org/10.1007/s11047-018-9696-8
6. Das, S., Sikdar, B.K.: Classification of *CA* rules targeting synthesis of reversible cellular automata. In: El Yacoubi, S., Chopard, B., Bandini, S.

(eds.) ACRI 2006. LNCS, vol. 4173, pp. 68–77. Springer, Heidelberg (2006). https://doi.org/10.1007/11861201_11
7. Das, S., Sikdar, B.: Characterization of 1-D Periodic Boundary Reversible CA, Electronic Notes in Theoretical Computer Science, vol. 252, pp. 205–227 (2009). https://doi.org/10.1016/j.entcs.2009.09.022
8. Wolfram, S. : Tables of cellular automaton properties. In: Theory and Applications of Cellular Automata (Including Selected Papers 1983-1986), Advanced Series on Complex Systems 1, pp. 485–557. World Scientific Publishing (1986). https://content.wolfram.com/sw-publications/2020/07/cellular-automaton-properties.pdf

Dividing Permutations in the Semiring of Functional Digraphs

Florian Bridoux[1], Christophe Crespelle[1], Thi Ha Duong Phan[2], and Adrien Richard[1(✉)]

[1] Université Côte d'Azur, CNRS, I3S, Sophia Antipolis, France
{florian.bridoux,christophe.crespelle,adrien.richard}@univ-cotedazur.fr
[2] Institute of Mathematics, Vietnam Academy of Science and Technology, Hanoi, Vietnam
phanhaduong@math.ac.vn

Abstract. Functional digraphs are unlabelled finite digraphs where each vertex has exactly one out-neighbor. They are isomorphic classes of finite discrete-time dynamical systems. Endowed with the direct sum and product, functional digraphs form a semiring with an interesting multiplicative structure. For instance, we do not know if the following division problem can be solved in polynomial time: given two functional digraphs A and B, does A divide B? That A divides B means that there exist a functional digraph X such that AX is isomorphic to B, and many such X can exist. We can thus ask for the number of solutions X. In this paper, we focus on the case where B is a permutation, that is, a disjoint union of cycles. There is then a naïve sub-exponential algorithm to compute the number of non-isomorphic solutions X, and our main result is a polynomial algorithm when A is fixed. It uses a divide-and-conquer technique that should be useful for further developments on the division problem.

Keywords: Finite Dynamical Systems · Functional digraphs · Graph direct product

1 Introduction

A deterministic, finite, discrete-time dynamical system is a function from a finite set (of states) to itself. Equivalently, this is a *functional digraph*, that is, a finite directed graph where each vertex has a unique out-neighbor. In addition to being ubiquitous objects in discrete mathematics, such systems have many real-life applications [5]. In this paper, we consider functional digraphs up to isomorphism. An isomorphism class then corresponds to an unlabelled functional digraph, and we write $A = B$ to mean that A is isomorphic to B.

There are two natural algebraic operations to obtain larger systems from smaller ones. Given two functional digraphs A and B, the addition $A + B$ is the disjoint union of A and B, while the multiplication AB is the *direct product* of A and B: the vertex set of AB is the Cartesian product of the vertex set of A

Published by Springer Nature Switzerland AG 2024
M. Gadouleau and A. Castillo-Ramirez (Eds.): AUTOMATA 2024, LNCS 14782, pp. 95–107, 2024.
https://doi.org/10.1007/978-3-031-65887-7_6

and the vertex set of B, and the out-neighbor of (x, y) in AB is (x', y') where x' is the out-neighbor of x in A and y' is the out-neighbor of vertex y in B. Hence AB describes the parallel evolution of the dynamics described by A and B. Endowed with these two operations, the set of functional digraphs forms a semiring, first introduced in [1].

The multiplicative structure of this semiring has been studied in [2,4,6], and several important problems are highlighted in [6]. A fundamental one is the *division problem*: given two functional digraphs A and B, does A divide B, that is, does there exist a solution X to the equation $AX = B$. This problem is trivially in NP, and nothing else is know in the general case (there are better upper-bounds under some conditions, as explained above). From an applicative point of view, we can see B has an observed dynamical system, and the division problem then ask if B corresponds to the parallel evolution of A and an unknown part X; a positive answer then allows a potentially useful decomposition of B. We stress that, if a solution X exists, then it is not necessarily unique. For instance, denoting C_ℓ the (directed) cycle of length ℓ, the equation $C_2 \cdot X = C_2 + C_2$ has exactly two (non-isomorphic) solutions X, which are $X = C_2$ and $X = C_1 + C_1$; see (1). Given A and B, it is thus interesting not only to decide if A divides B, but to compute the number of solutions.

$$1 \circlearrowright 2 \cdot a \circlearrowright b \;=\; 1a \circlearrowright 2b + 1b \circlearrowright 2a \;=\; 1a \circlearrowright 2a + 1b \circlearrowright 2b \;=\; 1 \circlearrowright 2 \cdot \left(\circlearrowleft a + \circlearrowleft b \right) \qquad (1)$$

A functional digraph A contains two parts: the *cyclic part*, which is the collection of the cycles of A (these cycles are disjoint and thus form a permutation), and the *transient part*, which is obtained by deleting the cycles, and which is a disjoint union of out-trees. From a dynamical point of view, the cyclic part describes the asymptotic behavior. In this paper, we focus one this part: we study the complexity of the division problem when B is a *permutation*, that is, a disjoint union of directed cycles. This restriction has already been considered in [2] as an important step for solving polynomial equations over functional digraphs. On the other side, [6] gives a polynomial algorithm to decide if A divides B when B is a dendron, that is, B contains a unique cycle, of length 1, so that B consists of an out-tree plus a loop on the root. This result should be very useful to treat the transient part in the division problem. One may hope that efficient algorithms for the cyclic and transient parts could be combined to obtain an efficient algorithm for the general case.

If B is a permutation, there is a simple sub-exponential algorithm that computes all the solutions X of $AX = B$. It works as follows. Let $|A|$ and $|B|$ be the number of vertices in A and B, respectively ($|A|+|B|$ is the size of the instance). If $AX = B$ then A, X are permutations, and X has $n = |B|/|A|$ vertices. Now remark that isomorphic classes of permutations with n vertices are in bijection with partitions of n: a permutation with n vertices is completely described, up to isomorphism, by the sequence of the length of its cycles, which form a partition of n; and conversely, the parts of a partition of n describe the lengths of the cycles of a permutation with n vertices. For instance, $C_1 + C_3$ corresponds to the partition $1+3$ of 4. So to compute the solutions, we can enumerate the partitions of n, and check for each if the corresponding permutation X satisfies $AX = B$. This gives a sub-exponential algorithm: partitions of n can be enumerated with polynomial delay and there are at most $e^{O(\sqrt{n})}$ such partitions, the total running time.

Frustratingly, we were not able to find a faster algorithm, say running in $e^{n^{o(1)}}$, to decide if A divides B. That a polynomial algorithm exists is an interesting open problem, and [3] gives a positive answer under the condition that, in A or B, all the cycles have the same length. Here we give a polynomial algorithm that computes the number of solutions when A is fixed. The precise statement, Theorem 1 below, involves some definitions. The *support* of a permutation A is the set $L(A)$ of positive integers ℓ such that A contains C_ℓ. Given $N \subseteq \mathbb{N}$, $\text{lcm}N$ is the least common multiple of the integers in N, and $\text{div}(n)$ is the number of divisors of n.

Theorem 1. *There is an algorithm that, given two non-empty permutations A, B, computes the number of non-isomorphic permutations X satisfying $AX = B$ with time complexity*

$$O\left(|A||B|^2\left(\frac{|B|}{|A|}\right)^{\text{div}(\text{lcm}L(A))}\right). \tag{2}$$

For the proof, we introduce two operations on an instance (A, B) that we hope to be useful for further progress on the division problem. The first partitions B into $B = B_1 + B_2$ so that any solution of (A, B) is obtained by adding a solution to (A, B_1) with a solution to (A, B_2). The second reduces (A, B) into a smaller instance (A', B') so that any solution of (A, B) is obtained by multiplying the length of the cycles of a solution of (A', B') by some constant d. Repeating as much as possible these operations, we obtain a decomposition of (A, B) into few smaller instances, which can be quickly solved with a brute force approach. The solutions of (A, B) are then obtained with a simple combination of the solutions of the instances of its decomposition. This is described in Lemma 2, the main result, which easily implies Theorem 1.

The rest of the paper is devoted to the proof of Theorem 1 following this decomposition method. Before going on, let us conclude this introduction by mentioning that a natural next step concerning the division problem should consist in proving that, for every fixed functional digraph A (with possibly a non-empty transient part), there is a polynomial time algorithm that, given a functional digraph B, decides if A divides B.

2 Preliminaries

Given $N \subseteq \mathbb{N}$, we denote by $\text{lcm}N$ and $\gcd N$ the least common multiple and the greatest common divisor of the integers in N, respectively. For $n, m \in \mathbb{N}$, we set $n \vee m = \text{lcm}\{n, m\}$, and for $N, M \subseteq \mathbb{N}$ we set $N \vee M = \{n \vee m \mid n \in N, m \in M\}$. We denote by $\text{Div}(n)$ the set of divisors of n and set $\text{div}(n) = |\text{Div}(n)|$. We set

$\mathrm{Div}(N) = \cup_{n\in N}\mathrm{Div}(n)$ and $\mathrm{div}(N) = |\mathrm{Div}(N)|$. For a positive integer p, we write $p \mid N$ to means that $p \mid n$ for all $n \in N$. We set $pN = \{pn \mid n \in N\}$ and we use the rather unusual notation $N/p = \{n/p \mid n \in N, p \mid n\}$.

The unlabelled functional digraph that consists of n cycles of length ℓ is denoted by nC_ℓ. Given a permutation A and an integer ℓ, the number of cycles of length ℓ in A is denoted by $A(\ell)$. Thus $A = \sum_{\ell\geq 1} A(\ell)C_\ell$ and $|A| = \sum_{\ell\geq 1} \ell A(\ell)$, and the support $L(A)$ is the set of ℓ such that $A(\ell) > 0$. One easily check that $C_aC_b = (ab/(a \vee b))C_{a\vee b}$. One can then prove (see [2]) that the product AX of two permutations A and X satisfies: for all $\ell \geq 1$,

$$AX(\ell) = \frac{1}{\ell} \sum_{\substack{a,x\in\mathbb{N}\\ a\vee x=\ell}} aA(a)xX(x). \tag{3}$$

Let A, B be non-empty permutations. We call (A, B) an *instance*, and its *size* is $|A| + |B|$. Recall that a solution of the instance (A, B) is a permutation X such that $AX = B$ and that $|X| = |B|/|A|$ for every solution X. We denote by $\mathrm{Sol}(A, B)$ the set of non-isomorphic solutions, and $\mathrm{sol}(A, B) = |\mathrm{Sol}(A, B)|$. It is important to note that, by (3), for every permutations A, X we have

$$L(AX) = L(A) \vee L(X). \tag{4}$$

3 Support of an Instance

Let us define the *support* of an instance (A, B) as

$$L(A, B) = \{\ell \in \mathbb{N} \mid L(A) \vee \ell \subseteq L(B)\}.$$

So $L(A, B) \subseteq \mathrm{Div}(L(B))$ and

$$L(A) \vee L(A, B) \subseteq L(B). \tag{5}$$

This set $L(A, B)$ is interesting since it bounds the support of any solution:

$$\forall X \in \mathrm{Sol}(A, B), \qquad L(X) \subseteq L(A, B). \tag{6}$$

Indeed, if $AX = B$ then by (4) we have $L(A) \vee L(X) = L(B)$ and thus $L(X) \subseteq L(A, B)$. Since $L(A, B)$ bounds the support of any solution, and since any solution has obviously at most $|B|/|A|$ cycles, we obtain the following result using a brute force approach.

Lemma 1. *There is an algorithm that, given two non-empty permutations A, B, computes* $\mathrm{Sol}(A, B)$ *with time complexity* $O(|A||B|(|B|/|A|)^{|L(A,B)|})$.

Proof. Suppose that $n = |B|/|A|$ is an integer, since otherwise there is no solution. Suppose that $X \neq nC_1$ is a solution, so $X(1) < n$. For every $\ell \geq 1$, we have $\ell X(\ell) \leq n$, hence $X(\ell) < n$, and if $\ell \notin L(A, B)$ then $X(\ell) = 0$ by (6). Consequently, X corresponds to a function from $L(A, B)$ to $\{0, \ldots, n-1\}$. Hence, to find all the solutions: we enumerate the $n^{|L(A,B)|}$ such functions; we check for each, in $O(|A||B|)$, if it is a solution; and we then check if nC_1 is a solution. □

Another interesting point is that the support of an instance gives an easy to check necessary condition for the existence of a solution. Let us say that an instance (A, B) is *consistent* if $L(A) \vee L(A, B) = L(B)$. Then non-consistent instances have no solution. Indeed, if X is a solution to (A, B) then (A, B) is consistent since

$$L(B) = L(AX) \overset{(4)}{=} L(A) \vee L(X) \overset{(6)}{\subseteq} L(A) \vee L(A, B) \overset{(5)}{\subseteq} L(B).$$

Example 1. Let (A, B) be an instance with $L(A) = \{6\}$ and $L(B) = \{6, 12\}$. Then $L(A, B) = \{1, 2, 3, 4, 6, 12\}$ and thus (A, B) is consistent. Let (A, B) be an instance with $L(A) = \{6\}$ and $L(B) = \{5, 6\}$. Then $L(A, B) = \{1, 2, 3, 6\}$ and thus (A, B) is not consistent since $L(A) \vee L(A, B) = \{6\}$.

4 Decomposition Lemma

Let us say that an instance (A, B) is *basic* if $L(B) \subseteq \mathrm{Div}(\mathrm{lcm}L(A))$; this is equivalent to say that for any prime power p^α dividing some $b \in L(B)$, there exists $a \in L(A)$ such that p^α divides a. By the previous lemma, Theorem 1 holds for every basic instance (A, B) since

$$L(A, B) \subseteq \mathrm{Div}(L(B)) \subseteq \mathrm{Div}(\mathrm{lcm}L(A)).$$

The key point is that any instance (A, B) can be decomposed into at most $|B|$ basic instances, with smaller sizes, in such a way that the solutions of (A, B) can be easily reconstructed from that of the basic instances. The precise statement, Lemma 2 below, needs some definitions.

The *cycle length multiplication* of A by p, denoted $A \otimes p$, is the permutation obtained from A by multiplying by p the length of every cycle in A; in other words: for all $a \geq 1$, we have $(A \otimes p)(a) = A(a/p)$ if $p \mid a$ and $(A \otimes p)(a) = 0$ otherwise. For instance, $(2C_1 + 3C_2 + 5C_3) \otimes 3 = 2C_3 + 3C_6 + 5C_9$. Given two sets of permutations $\mathcal{A}$ and $\mathcal{B}$ we set

$$\mathcal{A} + \mathcal{B} = \{A + B \mid A \in \mathcal{A}, B \in \mathcal{B}\}, \qquad \mathcal{A} \otimes p = \{A \otimes p \mid A \in \mathcal{A}\}.$$

Lemma 2. *There is an algorithm that, given a consistent instance (A, B), computes in $O(|A||B|^2)$ a list of $k \leq |B|$ basic instances $(A_1, B_2), \ldots, (A_k, B_k)$ and positive integers $p_1, \ldots, p_k$ such that: $|A_i| = |A|$ and $\mathrm{lcm}L(A_i) \mid \mathrm{lcm}L(A)$ for all $1 \leq i \leq k$, $|B_1| + \cdots + |B_k| \leq |B|$, and*

$$\mathrm{Sol}(A, B) = (\mathrm{Sol}(A_1, B_1) \otimes p_1) + \cdots + (\mathrm{Sol}(A_k, B_k) \otimes p_k).$$

Theorem 1 is an easy consequence of Lemma 2.

Proof of Theorem 1 Assuming Lemma 2. The algorithm is as follows. First we check if (A, B) is consistent; this is done in $O(|A||B|)$. If not, then (A, B) has no solution and we output 0. Otherwise, we compute in $O(|A||B|^2)$ the $k \leq |B|$

basic instances (A_i, B_i) as in Lemma 2. Then, for all $1 \leq i \leq k$, we use the algorithm of Lemma 1 to compute in $O(|A_i||B_i|(|B_i|/|A_i|)^{|L(A_i,B_i)|})$ the number s_i of solutions of (A_i, B_i). Finally, we output the product $s_1 \cdots s_k$, which is correct by Lemma 2. Since (A_i, B_i) is basic and $\text{lcm}L(A_i)$ divides $\text{lcm}L(A)$, we have $L(A_i, B_i) \subseteq \text{Div}(\text{lcm}L(A))$. Since $|A_i| = |A|$ and $|B_i| \leq |B|$, we deduce that the computation of each s_i is done in $O(|A||B|(|B|/|A|)^{\text{div}(\text{lcm}L(A))})$, and we obtain the running time (2) since $k \leq |B|$. □

The rest of the paper is devoted to the proof of Lemma 2.

5 Instance Partitions

Let A be a permutation, and $L \subseteq \mathbb{N}$. We denote by $A[L]$ the permutations obtained from A by removing every cycle of A whose length is not in L: for all $a \geq 1$, $A[L](a) = A(a)$ if $a \in L$ and $A[L](a) = 0$ otherwise. Here is a simple sufficient condition for an instance (A, B) to be decomposable into two independent instances (when we consider partitions, parts are always non-empty).

Lemma 3. *Let (A, B) be a consistent instance. Let L_1, L_2 be a partition of $L(A, B)$, and let $B_i = B[L(A) \vee L_i]$ for $i = 1, 2$. Suppose that $L(B_1) \cap L(B_2) = \emptyset$. Then $B = B_1 + B_2$. Furthermore, (A, B_1) and (A, B_2) are consistent, and*

$$\text{Sol}(A, B) = \text{Sol}(A, B_1) + \text{Sol}(A, B_2). \tag{7}$$

Proof. We deduce from (5) that $L(B_1) = L(A) \vee L_1$ and $L(B_2) = L(A) \vee L_2$, and from that we deduce that (A, B_1) and (A, B_2) are consistent. Since $L_1 \cup L_2 = L(A, B)$ and (A, B) is consistent, we have

$$L(B_1) \cup L(B_2) = (L(A) \vee L_1) \cup (L(A) \vee L_2) = L(A) \vee L(A, B) = L(B).$$

Hence, $L(B_1), L(B_2)$ is a partition of $L(B)$ and thus $B = B_1 + B_2$.

It remains to prove (7). If X_1, X_2 are solutions of $(A, B_1), (A, B_2)$ then

$$A(X_1 + X_2) = AX_1 + AX_2 = B_1 + B_2 = B,$$

thus $X = X_1 + X_2$ is a solution of (A, B). Conversely, let X be a solution of (A, B) and let us prove that $X = X_1 + X_2$ for some solutions X_1, X_2 of $(A, B_1), (A, B_2)$. Let $X_i = X[L_i \cap L(X)]$ for $i = 1, 2$. By (6) we have $L(X) \subseteq L(A, B)$. Hence, $L(X_1) \cup L(X_2) = L(X)$. Thus $X = X_1 + X_2$ and using (4) we obtain

$$\begin{aligned} L(B) = L(AX) &= L(A) \vee L(X) \\ &= (L(A) \vee L(X_1)) \cup (L(A) \vee L(X_2)) = L(AX_1) \cup L(AX_2). \end{aligned}$$

For $i = 1, 2$, we have $L(X_i) \subseteq L_i$ and thus, using (4),

$$L(AX_i) = L(A) \vee L(X_i) \subseteq L(A) \vee L_i = L(B_i).$$

Since $L(B_1), L(B_2)$ is a partition of $L(B)$, we deduce that $L(AX_i) = L(B_i)$ for $i = 1, 2$. Hence, to prove that X_i is a solution of (A, B_i), it is sufficient to prove that $AX_i(b) = B_i(b)$ for all $b \in L(B_i)$. So let $b \in L(B_i)$. For every $a \in L(A)$ and $x \in L(X)$ with $a \vee x = b$ we have $x \in L_i$ and thus $x \in L(X_i)$. Consequently,

$$AX_i(b) = \frac{1}{b} \sum_{\substack{a \in L(A) \\ x \in L(X_i) \\ a \vee x = b}} aA(a)xX_i(x) = \frac{1}{b} \sum_{\substack{a \in L(A) \\ x \in L(X_i) \\ a \vee x = b}} aA(a)xX(x)$$

$$= \frac{1}{b} \sum_{\substack{a \in L(A) \\ x \in L(X) \\ a \vee x = b}} aA(a)xX(x) = B(b) = B_i(b).$$

□

We now prove that a non-basic instance (A, B) with $\gcd L(A, B) = 1$ is decomposable; we will then prove that, in some sense, the condition on the gcd can be suppressed, leading to a decomposition of every non-basic instance. For a positive integer n, and a prime p, let $\nu_p(n)$ be the greatest integer α such that p^α divides n.

Lemma 4. *Let (A, B) be a non-basic consistent instance with $\gcd L(A, B) = 1$. Let $b \in L(B)$ and a prime p such that $\nu_p(b) > \nu_p(a)$ for all $a \in L(A)$ (these exist since (A, B) is not basic). Let L_1 be the set of $x \in L(A, B)$ with $\nu_p(x) = \nu_p(b)$, and $L_2 = L(A, B) \setminus L_1$. Let $B_i = [L(A) \vee L_i]$ for $i = 1, 2$. Then (A, B_1) and (A, B_2) are consistent instances such that $B = B_1 + B_2$ and*

$$\text{Sol}(A, B) = \text{Sol}(A, B_1) + \text{Sol}(A, B_2).$$

Proof. Since (A, B) is consistent, there exists $a \in L(A)$ and $x \in L(A, B)$ such that $a \vee x = b$. Since $\nu_p(a) < \nu_p(b)$ we have $\nu_p(x) = \nu_p(b)$ and thus $x \in L_1$; so L_1 is not empty. Since $p \mid \gcd L_1$ and $\gcd L(A, B) = 1$, we have $L_1 \neq L(A, B)$ and thus L_2 is also non-empty.

Let $a \in L(A)$. For all $x \in L_1$, we have $\nu_p(a) < \nu_p(b) = \nu_p(x)$, thus $\nu_p(a \vee x) = \nu_p(b)$, and for all $y \in L_2$ we have $\nu_p(a), \nu_p(y) \neq \nu_p(b)$ thus $\nu_p(a \vee y) \neq \nu_p(b)$. Consequently, $L(A) \vee L_1$ is disjoint from $L(A) \vee L_2$. By Lemma 3 we have $B = B_1 + B_2$, and the instances (A, B_1) and (A, B_2) have the desired properties. □

Example 2. Let $A = C_6$ and $B = 3C_6 + 8C_{12}$. Then (A, B) is consistent but not basic, and $\gcd L(A, B) = 1$ (see Example 1). Applying Lemma 4 with $b = 12$ and $p = 2$ we obtain $L_1 = \{4, 12\}$ and $L_2 = \{1, 2, 3, 6\}$, giving $B_1 = 8C_{12}$ and $B_2 = 3C_6$. Since the support of any solution X_1 of (A, B_1) is included in L_1,

$$\begin{aligned} C_6 X_1 = 8C_{12} &\iff C_6(X_1(4)C_4 + X_1(12)C_{12}) = 8C_{12} \\ &\iff 2X_1(4)C_{12} + 6X_1(12)C_{12} = 8C_{12} \\ &\iff 2X_1(4) + 6X_1(12) = 8. \end{aligned}$$

Thus each solution X_1 corresponds to a partition of 8 with parts in $\{2, 6\}$: these are $2+6$ and $2+2+2+2+2$, giving $X_1 = C_4 + C_{12}$ and $X_1 = 4C_4$. Proceeding similarly, since the support of any solutions X_2 of (A, B_2) is included in L_2, we have $C_6X_2 = 3C_6$ iff $X_2(1)+2X_2(2)+3X_2(3)+6X_2(6) = 3$. Thus each solution X_2 corresponds to a partition of 3 with parts in $\{1, 2, 3, 6\}$: these are 3, 1+2, and 1+1+1, giving $X_2 = C_3$, $X_2 = C_1 + C_2$ and $X_2 = 3C_1$. By Lemma 4, we have $\mathrm{Sol}(A, B) = \mathrm{Sol}(A, B_1) + \mathrm{Sol}(A, B_2)$. Hence (A, B) has 6 solutions, obtained by adding a solution X_1 to (A, B_1) with a solution X_2 to (A, B_2).

6 Instance Reduction

We say that an instance (A, B) is *compact* if $\gcd L(A, B) = 1$. This condition is used in Lemma 4 to decompose non-basic instances, but in this section we show that every instance can be reduced to an "equivalent" compact instance, which can then be decomposed. For this reduction, we need two operations.

The *cycle length division* of a permutation A by a positive integer p, denoted $A \oslash p$, is the permutation obtained from A by deleting every cycle whose length is not a multiple of p, and by dividing by p the length of the remaining cycles; in other words: for all $a \geq 1$, $(A \oslash p)(a) = A(pa)$. Note that $L(A \oslash p) = L(A)/p$ and if $p \mid L(A)$ then $L(A) = pL(A \oslash p)$. For instance,

$$(2C_1 + 3C_3 + 5C_4 + 7C_6) \oslash 3 = 3C_1 + 7C_2.$$

The cycle length division $\oslash$ is the inverse of the cycle length multiplication $\otimes$.

Lemma 5. *Let A be a permutation and let p be a positive integer. Then $(A \otimes p) \oslash p = A$, and if $p \mid L(A)$ then $(A \oslash p) \otimes p = A$.*

Proof. For all $a \geq 1$, we have $((A \otimes p) \oslash p)(a) = (A \otimes p)(pa) = A(a)$. Suppose that $p \mid L(A)$ and let $a \geq 1$. If $p \nmid a$ then $A(a) = 0$ and $((A \oslash p) \otimes p)(a) = 0$ (since $p \mid L((A \oslash p) \otimes p)$). If $p \mid a$ then $((A \oslash p) \otimes p)(a) = (A \oslash p)(a/p) = A(a)$. □

The second operation is for the moment only defined when p is a prime; it will be extended to every positive integers later. The *contraction* of A by a prime p is the sum of cycle $A \boxslash p$ defined by: for all $a \geq 1$,

$$(A \boxslash p)(a) = \begin{cases} A(a) + pA(pa) & \text{if } p \nmid a \\ pA(pa) & \text{otherwise.} \end{cases} \tag{8}$$

This operation transforms each cycle of length pa into p cycles of length a (and thus keeps the number of vertices unchanged). Note that $L(A \boxslash p)$ is the set of integers a such that either $a \in L(A)$ and $p \nmid a$ or $pa \in L(A)$. For instance,

$$\begin{aligned}(2C_1 + 3C_3 + 5C_4 + 7C_6) \boxslash 3 &= 2C_1 + 9C_1 + 5C_4 + 21C_2 \\ &= 11C_1 + 5C_4 + 21C_2.\end{aligned}$$

Our interest for these two operations lies in the following property.

Lemma 6. *Let A, X be permutations. If $p \mid L(X)$ for some prime p, then*

$$(A \boxslash p)(X \oslash p) = (AX) \oslash p.$$

Proof. Suppose that $p \mid L(X)$ for some prime p, and let $A' = A \boxslash p$ and $X' = X \oslash p$. We have to prove that $A'X' = AX \oslash p$, that is, for all $\ell \geq 1$, $A'X'(\ell) = (AX \oslash p)(\ell) = AX(p\ell)$. Let us fix $\ell \geq 1$. We have

$$p\ell A'X'(\ell) = \sum_{\substack{a,x \\ a \vee x = \ell}} paA'(a)xX'(x) = \sum_{\substack{a,x \\ a \vee x = \ell}} aA'(a)pxX(px).$$

Denoting by Ω the of couples $(a, x) \in \mathbb{N}^2$ with $p \mid x$ and $a \vee \frac{x}{p} = \ell$, we obtain

$$p\ell A'X'(\ell) = \sum_{(a,x) \in \Omega} aA'(a)xX(x).$$

By splinting the sum according to the definition of A' we obtain

$$\begin{aligned} p\ell A'X'(\ell) &= \sum_{\substack{(a,x) \in \Omega \\ p \nmid a}} (aA(a) + paA(pa))xX(x) + \sum_{\substack{(a,x) \in \Omega \\ p \mid a}} paA(pa)xX(x) \\ &= \sum_{\substack{(a,x) \in \Omega \\ p \nmid a}} aA(a)xX(x) + \sum_{\substack{(a,x) \in \Omega \\ p \nmid a}} paA(pa)xX(x) + \sum_{\substack{(a,x) \in \Omega \\ p \mid a}} paA(pa)xX(x). \end{aligned}$$

Denoting by Ω' the set of $(a, x) \in \mathbb{N}^2$ with $p \mid x$, $p \mid a$ and $\frac{a}{p} \vee \frac{x}{p} = \ell$, we obtain

$$p\ell A'X'(\ell) = \sum_{\substack{(a,x) \in \Omega \\ p \nmid a}} aA(a)xX(x) + \sum_{\substack{(a,x) \in \Omega' \\ p \nmid \frac{a}{p}}} aA(a)xX(x) + \sum_{\substack{(a,x) \in \Omega' \\ p \mid \frac{a}{p}}} aA(a)xX(x).$$

If $p \nmid a$ then $a \vee \frac{x}{p} = \ell$ iff $a \vee x = p\ell$; and $\frac{a}{p} \vee \frac{x}{p} = \ell$ iff $a \vee x = p\ell$. Consequently

$$p\ell A'X'(\ell) = \sum_{\substack{a,x \\ p \mid x \\ a \vee x = p\ell}} aA(a)xX(x).$$

Since $p \mid L(X)$, if $p \nmid x$ then $X(x) = 0$, so

$$p\ell A'X'(\ell) = \sum_{\substack{a,x \\ a \vee x = p\ell}} aA(a)xX(x) = p\ell AX(p\ell).$$

Thus $A'X'(\ell) = AX(p\ell)$ for all $\ell \geq 0$, as desired. □

We obtain that every non compact instance can be reduced.

Lemma 7. *Let (A, B) be a consistent instance, and suppose $p \mid L(A, B)$ for some prime p. Then $(A \boxslash p, B \oslash p)$ is consistent with support $L(A, B)/p$, and*

$$\mathrm{Sol}(A, B) = \mathrm{Sol}(A \boxslash p, B \oslash p) \otimes p. \tag{9}$$

Proof. Let $A' = A \boxslash p$ and $B' = B \oslash p$. We first prove (9). Let X be a solution of (A, B). By (6) we have $L(X) \subseteq L(A, B)$ and since $p \mid L(A, B)$ we have $p \mid L(X)$. Hence, by Lemma 6, $A'(X \oslash p) = AX \oslash p = B \oslash p = B'$, that is, $X \oslash p$ is a solution of (A', B'). Since $p \mid L(X)$, by Lemma 5 we have $(X \oslash p) \otimes p = X$ and thus $X \in \mathrm{Sol}(A' B') \otimes p$.

We now prove the converse direction. Let X' be a solution of (A', B'), and let $X = X' \otimes p$. We have to prove that X is a solution of (A, B). By Lemma 5 we have $X \oslash p = X'$ thus $A'(X \oslash p) = B' = B \oslash p$. Since $p \mid L(X)$, by Lemma 6, we have $A'(X \oslash p) = (AX) \oslash p$. Thus $(AX) \oslash p = B \oslash p$. Since $p \mid L(A, B)$ and (A, B) is consistent, we have $p \mid L(B)$. Since $X = X' \otimes p$ we obviously have $p \mid L(X)$. Thus p divides $L(A) \vee L(X) = L(AX)$. Using Lemma 5 we obtain $AX = ((AX) \oslash p) \otimes p = (B \oslash p) \otimes p = B$. Thus X is a solution of (A, B). This proves (9).

We now prove that $L(A, B)/p \subseteq L(A', B')$. For that, we fix $x \in L(A, B)/p$, and we prove that $a \vee x$ is in $L(B')$ for any $a \in L(A')$. Indeed, if $pa \in L(A)$ then $pa \vee px = b$ for some $b \in L(B)$ and we deduce that $a \vee x = b/p \in L(B')$. If $pa \notin L(A)$, then $p \nmid a$ and $a \in L(A)$. Thus $a \vee px = b$ for some $b \in L(B)$ and since $p \nmid a$ we deduce that $a \vee x = b/p \in L(B')$.

We now prove the converse inclusion. For that, we fix $x \in L(A', B')$, and we prove that $a \vee px$ is in $L(B)$ for any $a \in L(A)$. Indeed, if $p \mid a$ then $a/p \in L(A')$ and thus $(a/p) \vee x = b$ for some $b \in L(B')$ so that $a \vee px = pb \in L(B)$. If $p \nmid a$ then $a \in L(A')$ and thus $a \vee x = b$ for some $b \in L(B')$, and since $p \nmid a$ we have $a \vee px = pb \in L(B)$.

We finally prove that (A', B') is consistent. By (5) we only have to prove that $L(B') \subseteq L(A') \vee L(A', B')$. Let $b \in L(B')$. Then $pb \in L(B)$ and since (A, B) is consistent, there is $a \in L(A)$ and $x \in L(A, B)$ with $a \vee x = pb$. Hence $x/p \in L(A', B')$. If $p \mid a$ then $(a/p) \vee (x/p) = b$ and we are done since $a/p \in L(A')$. If $p \nmid a$ then $a \vee (x/p) = b$ and we are done since $a \in L(A')$. □

Applying several times the previous lemma we obtain a compact "equivalent" instance. Let us first extend the contraction operation from primes to any positive integer, inductively as follows: $A \boxslash 1 = A$, if p is a prime then $A \boxslash p$ is defined as previously (see (8)), and if p is composite, we take the largest prime q that divides p and set

$$A \boxslash p = (A \boxslash p/q) \boxslash q.$$

Note that, for every positive integers p, q, we have

$$(A \otimes p) \otimes q = A \otimes pq, \quad (A \oslash p) \oslash q = A \oslash pq, \quad (A \boxslash p) \boxslash q = A \boxslash pq. \tag{10}$$

The first two equalities are obvious. The third results from the following easy to check commutativity property: $(A \boxslash p) \boxslash q = (A \boxslash q) \boxslash p$ when p and q are primes.

Lemma 8. *Let (A, B) be a consistent instance and $d = \gcd L(A, B)$. Then $(A \boxslash d, B \oslash d)$ is a compact consistent instance with support $L(A, B)/d$, and*

$$\mathrm{Sol}(A, B) = \mathrm{Sol}(A \boxslash d, B \oslash d) \otimes d.$$

Proof. Suppose that $d > 1$ since otherwise there is nothing to prove. Let us write d as the product of $k \geq 1$ primes, not necessarily distinct, say $d = p_1 p_2 \dots p_k$ with $p_1 \leq p_2 \leq \dots \leq p_k$. Let $A_0 = A$, $B_0 = B$ and, for $1 \leq \ell \leq k$, let $A_\ell = A_{\ell-1} \boxslash p_\ell$ and $B_\ell = B_{\ell-1} \oslash p_\ell$. By Lemma 7, (A_ℓ, B_ℓ) is a consistent instance and $\mathrm{Sol}(A_{\ell-1}, B_{\ell-1}) = \mathrm{Sol}(A_\ell, B_\ell) \otimes p_\ell$. By (10) we have $A_k = A \boxslash d$, $B_k = B \boxslash d$, $L(A_k, B_k) = L(A, B)/d$ and $\mathrm{Sol}(A, B) = \mathrm{Sol}(A_k, B_k) \otimes d$. Since $L(A_k, B_k) = L(A, B)/d$, we obviously have $\gcd L(A_k, B_k) = 1$. $\square$

Example 3. The support of $(C_6, 8C_{12})$ is $\{4, 12\}$. We have $C_6 \boxslash 4 = (C_6 \boxslash 2) \boxslash 2 = 2C_3 \boxslash 2 = 2C_3$, and $8C_{12} \oslash 4 = 8C_3$. By Lemma 8, $\mathrm{Sol}(C_6, 8C_{12}) = \mathrm{Sol}(2C_3, 8C_3) \otimes 4$. Since the support of $(2C_3, 8C_3)$ is $\{1, 3\}$,

$$\begin{aligned} 2C_3X' = 8C_3 &\iff 2C_3(X'(1)C_1 + X'(3)C_3) = 8C_3 \\ &\iff 2X'(1)C_3 + 6X'(3)C_3 = 8C_3 \\ &\iff 2X'(1) + 6X'(3) = 8. \end{aligned}$$

Thus each solution X' corresponds to a partition of 8 with parts in $\{2, 6\}$: these are $2 + 6$ and $2 + 2 + 2 + 2 + 2$, giving $X' = C_1 + C_3$ and $X' = 4C_1$. Hence the solutions of $(C_6, 8C_{12})$ are $(C_1 + C_3) \otimes 4 = C_4 + C_{12}$ and $(4C_1) \otimes 4 = 4C_4$, which is consistent with the direct computation given in Example 2.

7 Proof of Lemma 2

We start with a definition. Let (A, B) be a consistent instance. A *decomposition* of (A, B) is a list $\mathcal{L}$ of triples (A_i, B_i, p_i), $1 \leq i \leq k$, such that

- (A_i, B_i) is a compact and consistent instance, and p_i is a positive integer,
- $|A_i| = |A|$ and $\mathrm{lcm} L(A_i)$ divides $\mathrm{lcm} L(A)$,
- $|B_1| + \dots + |B_k| \leq |B|$,
- $\mathrm{Sol}(A, B) = (\mathrm{Sol}(A_1, B_1) \otimes p_1) + \dots + (\mathrm{Sol}(A_k, B_k) \otimes p_k)$.

We call k the *length* of $\mathcal{L}$; note that by the third point, $k \leq |B|$. Furthermore, we say that $\mathcal{L}$ is *basic* if (A_i, B_i) is basic for all $1 \leq i \leq k$. We will prove that we can compute in $O(|A||B|^2)$ a basic decomposition, which clearly proves Lemma 2. For that we first prove that if (A, B) has a non-basic decomposition, we can obtain a longer decomposition by partitioning a non-basic instance (Lemma 4) and then contracting its parts (Lemma 8).

Lemma 9. *There is an algorithm that, given a consistent instance (A, B) and a non-basic decomposition $\mathcal{L}$ of (A, B) of length k, computes in $O(|A||B|)$ a decomposition $\mathcal{L}'$ of (A, B) of length $k + 1$.*

Proof. The algorithm is as follows. Let $(A_1, B_1, p_1), \dots, (A_k, B_k, p_k)$ be the triples of $\mathcal{L}$. Since $\mathcal{L}$ is not basic, we find in $O(|A||B|)$ a non-basic instance (A_i, B_i). Since (A_i, B_i) is compact and consistent, by Lemma 4, we can compute in $O(|A||B|)$ two consistent instances (A_i, B_{i1}) and (A_i, B_{i2}) such that $B_i = B_{i1} + B_{i2}$ and

$$\mathrm{Sol}(A_i, B_i) = \mathrm{Sol}(A_i, B_{i1}) + \mathrm{Sol}(A_i, B_{i2}).$$

For $j = 1, 2$, we compute in $O(|A||B|)$ the integer $p_{ij} = \gcd L(A_i, B_{ij})$ and the permutations $A_{ij} = A_i \boxslash p_{ij}$ and $B'_{ij} = B_{ij} \oslash p_{ij}$. Finally, we output the list $\mathcal{L}'$ of length $k+1$ obtained from $\mathcal{L}$ by deleting (A_i, B_i, p_i) and adding $(A_{i1}, B'_{i1}, p_i p_{i1})$ and $(A_{i2}, B'_{i2}, p_i p_{i2})$. So the running time is $O(|A||B|)$.

Let us prove that $\mathcal{L}'$ is a decomposition. By Lemma 8, (A_{ij}, B'_{ij}) is compact and consistent. Furthermore, $|A_{ij}| = |A_i| = |A|$ and since A_{ij} is a contraction of A_i, each member of $L(A_{ij})$ divides some member of $L(A_i)$, thus $\mathrm{lcm} L(A_{ij})$ divides $\mathrm{lcm} L(A_i)$, which divides $\mathrm{lcm} L(A)$. Thus $\mathrm{lcm} L(A_{ij})$ divides $\mathrm{lcm} L(A)$. Next, since $|B'_{i1}| + |B'_{i2}| \leq |B_{i1}| + |B_{i2}| = |B_i|$, the third point of the definition of a decomposition is preserved. Finally, by Lemma 8, $\mathrm{Sol}(A_i, B_{ij}) = \mathrm{Sol}(A_{ij}, B'_{ij}) \otimes p_{ij}$. Consequently,

$$\begin{aligned}\mathrm{Sol}(A_i, B_i) \otimes p_i &= (\mathrm{Sol}(A_i, B_{i1}) \otimes p_i) + (\mathrm{Sol}(A_i, B_{i2}) \otimes p_i) \\ &= (\mathrm{Sol}(A_{i1}, B'_{i1}) \otimes p_i p_{i1}) + (\mathrm{Sol}(A_{i2}, B'_{i2}) \otimes p_i p_{i2})\end{aligned}$$

and this proves that the last point of the definition of a decomposition is preserved. So $\mathcal{L}'$ is indeed a decomposition of (A, B).

Iterating the previous lemma, we get the following, which implies Lemma 2.

Lemma 10. *There is an algorithm that, given a consistent instance (A, B), computes in $O(|A||B|^2)$ a basic decomposition of (A, B).*

Proof. The algorithm constructs recursively a list $\mathcal{L}_1, \ldots, \mathcal{L}_{|B|}$ of decompositions of (A, B), where the length of $\mathcal{L}_r$ is at most r, and output $\mathcal{L}_{|B|}$. First we compute $\mathcal{L}_1 = \{(A \boxslash d, B \oslash d, d)\}$ where $d = \gcd L(A, B)$ in $O(|A||B|)$; by Lemma 8, $\mathcal{L}_1$ is a decomposition of length one. Now, suppose that the decomposition $\mathcal{L}_r$ of length $k \leq r < |B|$ has already been computed. If $\mathcal{L}_r$ is basic, we set $\mathcal{L}_{r+1} = \mathcal{L}_r$. Otherwise, using Lemma 9, we compute in $O(|A||B|)$ a decomposition $\mathcal{L}_{r+1}$ of length $k+1$. Hence the running time is $O(|A||B|^2)$. It remains to prove that $\mathcal{L}_{|B|}$ is basic. If $\mathcal{L}_r = \mathcal{L}_{r+1}$ for some $r < |B|$ then $\mathcal{L}_r$ is basic and $\mathcal{L}_s = \mathcal{L}_r$ for all $r < s \leq |B|$ thus $\mathcal{L}_{|B|}$ is basic. Otherwise, $\mathcal{L}_1, \ldots, \mathcal{L}_{|B|}$ are all distinct thus the length of $L_{|B|}$ is $|B|$. If $L_{|B|}$ is not basic, by Lemma 9, (A, B) has a decomposition of length $|B| + 1$, a contradiction. Thus $\mathcal{L}_{|B|}$ is basic. □

Example 4. Let $A = C_6$ and $B = 3C_6 + 8C_{12}$. Combining Example 2 and 3, we get that the basic decomposition of (A, B) is $(2C_3, 8C_3, 4), (C_6, 3C_6, 1)$ and so $\mathrm{Sol}(A, B) = (\mathrm{Sol}(2C_3, 8C_3) \otimes 4) + \mathrm{Sol}(C_6, 3C_6)$.

Acknowledgments. This work has been funded by the HORIZON-MSCA-2022-SE-01 project 101131549 "Application-driven Challenges for Automata Networks and Complex Systems (ACANCOS)".

References

1. Dennunzio, A., Dorigatti, V., Formenti, E., Manzoni, L., Porreca, A.E.: Polynomial equations over finite, discrete-time dynamical systems. In: Mauri, G., El Yacoubi, S., Dennunzio, A., Nishinari, K., Manzoni, L. (eds.) ACRI 2018. LNCS, vol. 11115, pp. 298–306. Springer, Cham (2018). https://doi.org/10.1007/978-3-319-99813-8_27

2. Dennunzio, A., Formenti, E., Margara, L., Riva, S.: An algorithmic pipeline for solving equations over discrete dynamical systems modelling hypothesis on real phenomena. J. Comput. Sci. **66**, 101932 (2023)
3. Dennunzio, A., Formenti, E., Margara, L., Riva, S.: A note on solving basic equations over the semiring of functional digraphs. *arXiv preprint* arXiv:2402.16923 (2024)
4. Gaze-Maillot, C., Porreca, A.E.: Profiles of dynamical systems and their algebra. *arXiv preprint* arXiv:2008.00843 (2020)
5. Jarrah, A.S., Laubenbacher, R.: Finite dynamical systems: a mathematical framework for computer simulation. In: Konaté, D. (ed.) Mathematical Modeling, Simulation, Visualization and e-Learning, pp. 343–358. Springer, Heidelberg (2007). https://doi.org/10.1007/978-3-540-74339-2_21
6. Naquin,É., Gadouleau, M.: Factorisation in the semiring of finite dynamical systems. *arXiv preprint* arXiv:2210.11270 (2022)

On the Minimal Memory Set of Cellular Automata

Alonso Castillo-Ramirez[1(✉)] and Eduardo Veliz-Quintero[2]

[1] Centro Universitario de Ciencias Exactas e Ingenierías, Universidad de Guadalajara, Guadalajara, Mexico
alonso.castillor@academicos.udg.mx

[2] Centro Universitario de los Valles, Universidad de Guadalajara, Guadalajara, Mexico
eduardo.veliz9236@alumnos.udg.mx

Abstract. For a group G and a finite set A, a cellular automaton (CA) is a transformation $\tau : A^G \to A^G$ defined via a finite memory set $S \subseteq G$ and a local map $\mu : A^S \to A$. Although memory sets are not unique, every CA admits a unique *minimal memory set*, which consists on all the essential elements of S that affect the behavior of the local map. In this paper, we study the links between the minimal memory set and the *generating patterns* $\mathcal{P}$ of μ; these are the patterns in A^S that are not fixed when the cellular automaton is applied. In particular, we show that when $|S| \geq 2$ and $|\mathcal{P}|$ is not a multiple of $|A|$, then the minimal memory set must be S itself. Moreover, when $|\mathcal{P}| = |A|$, $|S| \geq 3$, and the restriction of μ to these patterns is well-behaved, then the minimal memory set must be S or $S \setminus \{s\}$, for some $s \in S \setminus \{e\}$. These are some of the first general theoretical results on the minimal memory set of a cellular automaton.

Keywords: Cellular automata · minimal memory set · local map · generating patterns

1 Introduction

Cellular automata (CA) are transformations of a discrete space defined by a fixed local rule that is applied homogeneously and in parallel in the whole space; they have been used in discrete complex systems modeling, and are relevant in several areas of mathematics, such as symbolic dynamics [7] and group theory [3].

More formally, let G be a group and let A be a finite set. A function $x : G \to A$ is called a *configuration*, and the set of all configurations is denoted by A^G. When S is a finite subset of G, a function $p : S \to A$ is called a *pattern* (or a *block*) over S, and the set of all patterns over S is denoted by A^S. A *cellular automaton* is a transformation $\tau : A^G \to A^G$ defined via a finite subset $S \subseteq G$, called a *memory set* of τ, and a *local map* $\mu : A^S \to A$ such that

$$\tau(x)(g) = \mu((g^{-1} \cdot x)|_S), \quad \forall x \in A^G, g \in G,$$

Published by Springer Nature Switzerland AG 2024
M. Gadouleau and A. Castillo-Ramirez (Eds.): AUTOMATA 2024, LNCS 14782, pp. 108–119, 2024.
https://doi.org/10.1007/978-3-031-65887-7_7

where $g^{-1} \cdot x \in A^G$ is the *shift* of x by g^{-1} defined by

$$(g^{-1} \cdot x)(h) := x(gh), \quad \forall h \in G.$$

Intuitively, applying τ to a configuration $x \in A^G$ is the same as applying the local map $\mu : A^S \to A$ homogeneously and in parallel using the shift action of G on A^G. Local maps $\mu : A^S \to A$ are also known in the literature as *block maps*. In their classical setting, CA are studied when $G = \mathbb{Z}^d$, for $d \geq 1$, and $A = \{0, 1\}$ (e.g., see [6]).

Cellular automata do not have a unique memory set. With the above notation, for any finite superset $S' \supseteq S$, we may define $\mu' : A^{S'} \to A$ by $\mu'(z) := \mu(z|_S)$, for all $z \in A^{S'}$, and it follows that μ' is also a local map that defines τ. Hence, any finite superset of a memory set of τ is also a memory set of τ. However, cellular automata do have a unique *minimal memory set* (MMS), which is the intersection of all the memory sets admitted by τ [3, Sec. 1.5]. Equivalently, the minimal memory set of τ is the memory set of smallest cardinality admitted by τ, and it consists of all the *essential* elements of G required to define a local defining map for τ.

So far, there are no general theoretical results about the minimal memory set of a cellular automaton. It is known that it does not behave well with composition: although a memory set of a composition of two cellular automata with memory sets T and S is the product ST, the minimal memory set of the composition may be a proper subset of ST [4, Ex. 1.27]. Similarly, there are no nontrivial results about the minimal memory set of the inverse of an invertible cellular automaton.

Every cellular automaton $\tau : A^G \to A^G$ admits a memory set S such that $e \in S$, where e is the identity of the group G. Let $\mu : A^S \to A$ be the corresponding local map that defines τ. The behavior of μ may be characterized by the set of patterns $\mathcal{P} \subseteq A^S$ and a function $f : \mathcal{P} \to A$ such that

$$\mu(p) = f(p) \neq p(e), \ \forall p \in \mathcal{P}, \quad \text{and} \quad \mu(z) = z(e), \ \forall z \in A^S \setminus \mathcal{P}.$$

In other words, $\mathcal{P}$ is the set of patterns in which μ does not act as the projection to $e \in S$; this means, that the cellular automaton τ fixes a configuration $x \in A^G$ if and only if no element of $\mathcal{P}$ appears as a subpattern in x. In such a situation, we say that the pair $(\mathcal{P}, f)$ *generates* the local map $\mu : A^S \to A$. We say that the function $f : \mathcal{P} \to A$ is *well-behaved* if

$$\forall p, q \in \mathcal{P}, \quad p(e) = q(e) \ \Leftrightarrow \ f(p) = f(q).$$

When $A = \{0, 1\}$, the function $f : \mathcal{P} \to A$ is always well-behaved because $f(p)$ must be equal to the complement of $p(e)$.

This approach of characterizing CA by patterns has been proved to be useful in the study of various algebraic and dynamical properties. In [2], it was shown that CA generated by a single pattern $p \in A^S$ are often idempotent, like in the case when p is a constant or symmetrical pattern. In [1,5], various dynamical properties were examined for the so-called *Coven* CA; in our terminology, these are CA generated by two distinct patterns $p, q \in A^S$ such that $p|_{S \setminus \{e\}} = q|_{S \setminus \{e\}}$. Remarkably, Coven CA were the first nontrivial class of cellular automata in which the exact computation of the topological entropy was obtained (see [8, p. 1]).

In this paper, we study the connection between the minimal memory set of a cellular automaton and the set of patterns generating its local map. It has been already shown in [2, Lemma 1] that if $\mu : A^S \to A$ is generated by only one pattern, then its minimal memory set is S itself. Here, we establish the following main result.

Theorem 1. *Let G be a group and let A be a finite set with $|A| \geq 2$. Let $S \subseteq G$ be a finite subset such that $e \in S$, $|S| \geq 2$, and let $\mu : A^S \to A$ be a local map. Denote by* $\mathrm{mms}(\mu)$ *the minimal memory set of the cellular automaton defined by μ. Suppose that the pair $(\mathcal{P}, f)$ generates μ. Then:*

1. *If $|\mathcal{P}| \neq |A|^{|S|} - |A|^{|S|-1}$, then $e \in \mathrm{mms}(\mu)$.*
2. *If $|\mathcal{P}|$ is not a multiple of $|A|$, then $\mathrm{mms}(\mu) = S$.*
3. *If $|S| \geq 3$, f is well-behaved and $|\mathcal{P}| = |A|$, then $\mathrm{mms}(\mu) = S$ or $\mathrm{mms}(\mu) = S \setminus \{s\}$, for some $s \in S \setminus \{e\}$.*

In contrast, if $|\mathcal{P}| = |A|^{|S|} - |A|^{|S|-1}$, there are examples in which the minimal memory set of μ may be any proper subset of S, including the empty set with corresponds to the constant cellular automata (see Example 5). As an application, the previous theorem may be used to improve the brute force algorithm that obtains the minimal memory set of a cellular automaton.

The structure of this paper is as follows. In Sect. 2, we set up notation, and present some basic properties on the minimal memory set of a cellular automaton. In Sect. 3, we present results on the links between the generating set of patterns of a local map $\mu : A^S \to A$ and its minimal memory set, including the proof of Theorem 1.

2 Basic Results

Let G be a group, and let A be a finite set. For the rest of the paper, we shall assume that $|A| \geq 2$, and that $\{0, 1\} \subseteq A$. The *configuration space* A^G is the set of all functions of the form $x : G \to A$.

Definition 1. *The* shift action *of G on A^G is a function $\cdot : G \times A^G \to A^G$ defined by*

$$(g \cdot x)(h) := x(g^{-1}h), \quad \forall x \in A^G, g, h \in G.$$

The shift action is indeed a group action in the sense that $e \cdot x = x$, for all $x \in A^G$, where e is the identity element of G, and $g \cdot (h \cdot x) = gh \cdot x$, for all $x \in A^G$, $g, h \in G$ (see [3, p. 2]).

When $G = \mathbb{Z}$, the configuration space $A^{\mathbb{Z}}$ may be identified with the set of bi-infinite sequences

$$x = \dots x_{-2} x_{-1} x_0 x_1 x_2 \dots$$

for all $x \in A^{\mathbb{Z}}$, where $x_k := x(k) \in A$. The shift action of $\mathbb{Z}$ on $A^{\mathbb{Z}}$ is equivalent to left and right shifts of the bi-infinite sequences. For example,

$$1 \cdot x = \dots x_{-3}x_{-2}x_{-1}x_0x_1 \dots$$

For any $k \in \mathbb{Z}$, the bi-infinite sequence $k \cdot x \in A^{\mathbb{Z}}$ is centered at x_{-k}.

Definition 2 (Def. 1.4.1 in [3]). *A* cellular automaton *is a transformation* $\tau : A^G \to A^G$ *such that there exists a finite subset* $S \subseteq G$*, called a* memory set *of* τ*, and a* local map $\mu : A^S \to A$*, such that*

$$\tau(x)(g) = \mu((g^{-1} \cdot x)|_S), \quad \forall x \in A^G, g \in G.$$

A local map $\mu : A^S \to A$ is also known as a *block map.* We say that a cellular automaton $\tau : A^G \to A^G$ *admits* a memory set $S \subseteq G$ if there exists a local map $\mu : A^S \to A$ that defines τ.

The famous Curtis-Hedlund-Lyndon Theorem (see [3, Theorem 1.8.1]) establishes that a function $\tau : A^G \to A^G$ is a cellular automaton if and only if τ is *G-equivariant* in the sense that $\tau(g \cdot x) = g \cdot \tau(x)$, for all $g \in G$, $x \in A^G$, and τ is continuous in the *prodiscrete topology* of A^G (which is the product topology of the discrete topology of A).

Example 1. Let $G := \mathbb{Z}$ and $S := \{-1, 0, 1\} \subseteq G$. The relationship between a cellular automaton $\tau : A^G \to A^G$ with local defining map $\mu : A^S \to A$ is described as follows:

$$\tau(\dots x_{-1}x_0x_1 \dots) = \dots \mu(x_{-2}, x_{-1}, x_0)\mu(x_{-1}, x_0, x_1)\mu(x_0, x_1, x_2) \dots$$

In this setting, it is common to define a local map $\mu : A^S \to A$ via a table that enlists all the elements of A^S, which are identified with tuples in A^3. For example,

$z \in A^S$	111	110	101	100	011	010	001	000
$\mu(z) \in A$	0	1	1	0	1	1	1	0

When $A = \{0, 1\}$, cellular automata that admit a memory set $S = \{-1, 0, 1\} \subseteq \mathbb{Z}$ are known as *elementary cellular automata* (ECA) [6, Sec. 2.5], and they are labeled with a *Wolfram number*, which is the decimal number corresponding to the second row of the defining table of $\mu : A^S \to A$ considered as a binary number. The Wolfram number of the ECA given by the above table is 110, as the binary number of the second row of the table is 1101110.

We write $\mu \sim \nu$ if the local maps $\mu : A^S \to A$ and $\nu : A^T \to A$ define the same cellular automaton. This defines an equivalence relation, and it holds that

$$\mu \sim \nu \quad \Leftrightarrow \quad \mu(x|_S) = \nu(x|_T), \; \forall x \in A^G.$$

If two local maps $\mu : A^S \to A$ and $\nu : A^T \to A$ define the same cellular automaton $\tau : A^G \to A^G$, then the local map $\lambda : A^{S \cap T} \to A$ defined by

$$\lambda(z) := \mu(z|_S) = \nu(z|_T), \quad \forall z \in A^{S \cap T},$$

also defines $\tau : A^G \to A^G$ (see [3, Prop. 1.5.1]). This means that the intersection of any two memory sets for τ is also a memory set for τ.

Definition 3. *The* minimal memory set *(MMS) of a cellular automaton $\tau : A^G \to A^G$, denoted by* $\mathrm{mms}(\tau)$ *is the intersection of all the memory sets admitted by τ. The minimal memory set of a local map $\mu : A^S \to A$, denoted by* $\mathrm{mms}(\mu)$, *is the minimal memory set of the cellular automaton defined by μ.*

Clearly, if $\mu \sim \nu$, then $\mathrm{mms}(\mu) = \mathrm{mms}(\nu)$. It is not hard to show that the MMS of a cellular automaton $\tau : A^G \to A^G$ is the memory set of smallest cardinality admitted by τ, and that τ admits a memory set S if and only if $\mathrm{mms}(\tau) \subseteq S$ (see [3, Prop. 1.5.2]).

In the sequel, for each $s \in S$, it will be convenient to consider the function $\mathrm{Res}_s : A^S \to A^{S \setminus \{s\}}$ defined by

$$\mathrm{Res}_s(z) := z|_{S \setminus \{s\}}, \quad \forall z \in A^S.$$

Definition 4. *We say that an element $s \in S$ is* essential *for a local map $\mu : A^S \to A$ if there exist $z, w \in A^S$ such that* $\mathrm{Res}_s(z) = \mathrm{Res}_s(w)$ *but $\mu(z) \neq \mu(w)$.*

Proposition 1 (c.f. Exercise 1.24 in [4]). *Let $\mu : A^S \to A$ be a local map. Then,*

$$\mathrm{mms}(\mu) = \{s \in S : s \textit{ is essential for } \mu\}.$$

Proof. Let $S_0 := \mathrm{mms}(\mu)$. As S is a memory set for the cellular automaton defined by μ, we must have $S_0 \subseteq S$. Suppose that $s \in S$ is not essential for μ. Define $\mu' : A^{S \setminus \{s\}} \to A$ by $\mu'(y) := \mu(\hat{y})$, for all $y \in A^{S \setminus \{s\}}$, where $\hat{y} \in A^S$ is any extension of y. The function μ' is well-defined because s is not essential for μ, so for all $z, w \in A^S$ with $\mathrm{Res}_s(z) = \mathrm{Res}_s(w)$ we have that $\mu(z) = \mu(w)$. Moreover, $\mu \sim \mu'$, so $S_0 \subseteq S \setminus \{s\}$. Hence, $s \notin S_0$.

Conversely, suppose there is $s \in S \setminus S_0$. Let $\mu_0 : A^{S_0} \to A$ be the local map associated with S_0 that defines the same cellular automaton as μ. If s is essential for μ, there exist $z, w \in A^S$ such that $\mathrm{Res}_s(z) = \mathrm{Res}_s(w)$ but $\mu(z) \neq \mu(w)$. However, $z|_{S \setminus \{s\}} = w|_{S \setminus \{s\}}$ implies that $\mu_0(z|_{S_0}) = \mu_0(w|_{S_0})$, as $s \notin S_0$. This contradicts that $\mu \sim \mu_0$. Therefore, s is not essential for μ. □

Example 2. Let $G := \mathbb{Z}$, $A := \{0, 1\}$ and $S := \{-1, 0, 1\}$. Consider the elementary cellular automaton $\tau : A^{\mathbb{Z}} \to A^{\mathbb{Z}}$ defined by the local map $\mu : A^S \to A$ described by the following table:

$z \in A^S$	111	110	101	100	011	010	001	000
$\mu(z) \in A$	0	1	1	0	0	1	1	0

This has Wolfram number 102. In this case, the element $-1 \in S$ is not essential for μ; this may be deduced by crossing out the coordinate corresponding to -1 in the tuples of A^S, and observing that there are no contradictions in the images of $x_0 x_1 \in A^{\{0,1\}}$. With this, we may obtain a reduced table corresponding to a local defining map $\mu' : A^{\{0,1\}} \to A$ for τ:

$z \in A^{\{0,1\}}$	11	10	01	00
$\mu'(z) \in A$	0	1	1	0

Now, we may check that 0 and 1 are both essential for μ' (for example, $\text{Res}_0(11) = \text{Res}_0(01)$ and $\mu(11) = 0 \neq 1 = \mu(01)$), so

$$\text{mms}(\mu) = \text{mms}(\mu') = \{0, 1\}.$$

Example 3. In the case of the local map $\mu : A^S \to A$ with Wolfram number 110 given by Example 1, we may check that all the elements of $S = \{-1, 0, 1\}$ are essential for μ, so $\text{mms}(\mu) = S$.

3 Cellular Automata Generated by Patterns

For the rest of the paper, assume that S is a finite subset of G such that $e \in S$.

Definition 5. *We say that a pair* $(\mathcal{P}, f)$ generates *a local map* $\mu : A^S \to A$ *if*

$$\mathcal{P} := \{z \in A^S : \mu(z) \neq z(e)\},$$

and $f : \mathcal{P} \to A$ *is the restriction of* μ *to* $\mathcal{P}$.

In other words, $\mathcal{P}$ is the set of patterns on which $\mu : A^S \to A$ does not act as the projection to e. Observe that if $(\mathcal{P}, f)$ generates μ, then

$$\mu(z) = \begin{cases} f(z) & \text{if } z \in \mathcal{P} \\ z(e) & \text{if } z \notin \mathcal{P} \end{cases}, \quad \forall z \in A^S.$$

Moreover, $\mu : A^S \to A$ is equal to the projection to e (which means that the cellular automaton defined by μ is the identity function) if and only if $\mathcal{P} = \emptyset$. It follows by definition that every local map $\mu : A^S \to A$ has a unique generating pair $(\mathcal{P}, f)$.

Remark 1. If $A = \{0, 1\}$, for any $\mathcal{P} \subseteq A^S$, there is a unique choice for the function $f : \mathcal{P} \to A$ because of the condition that $f(p) = \mu(p) \neq p(e)$, for all $p \in \mathcal{P}$. Explicitly, f must be defined by $f(p) := p(e)^c$, where $p(e)^c$ denotes the complement of $p(e)$. Hence, in this situation, we simply say that the set of patterns $\mathcal{P} \subseteq A^S$ generates $\mu : A^S \to A$.

Example 4. Let $G := \mathbb{Z}$, $S := \{-1, 0, 1\}$ and $A := \{0, 1\}$.

1. Let $\mu : A^S \to A$ be the local map with Wolfram number 110 given by Example 1. Then μ is generated by the set of patterns $\mathcal{P} = \{111, 101, 001\}$.
2. Let $\mu : A^S \to A$ and $\mu' : A^{\{0,1\}} \to A$ be the local maps with Wolfram number 102 given by Example 2. Then μ is generated by the set of patterns $\{111, 101, 011, 001\}$ and μ' is generated by the set of patterns $\{11, 01\}$.

A fundamental object in symbolic dynamics is a *subshift*, which may be defined as a closed (in the prodiscrete topology) G-*equivariant* subset X of A^G, in the sense that $g \cdot x \in X$ for all $g \in G$, $x \in X$. Equivalently, any subshift $X \subseteq A^G$ may be defined via a (possibly infinite) set of *forbidden patterns* (see Ex. 1.39 and 1.47 in [4]). In our setting, for $\mathcal{P} \subseteq A^S$, we shall consider the subshift $X_{\mathcal{P}} \subseteq A^G$ defined by the forbidden patterns $\mathcal{P}$:

$$X_{\mathcal{P}} := \{x \in A^G : (g \cdot x)|_S \notin \mathcal{P}, \forall g \in G\}.$$

This is a *subshift of finite type*, since the set of forbidden patterns is a finite set.

Lemma 1 (c.f. Exercise 1.61 in [4]). *Let $\tau : A^G \to A^G$ be a cellular automaton with memory set $S \subseteq G$, with $e \in S$, and local defining map $\mu : A^S \to A$. If $(\mathcal{P}, f)$ generates μ, then*

$$\mathrm{Fix}(\tau) := \{x \in A^G : \tau(x) = x\} = X_{\mathcal{P}}.$$

Proof. Let $x \in X_{\mathcal{P}}$. Then, $(g \cdot x)|_S \notin \mathcal{P}$, for all $g \in G$, so it follows that

$$\tau(x)(g) = \mu((g^{-1} \cdot x)|_S) = (g^{-1} \cdot x)(e) = x(g), \quad \forall g \in G.$$

Therefore, $x \in \mathrm{Fix}(\tau)$. Conversely, suppose that $x \notin X_{\mathcal{P}}$, so there exists $g \in G$ such that $(g \cdot x)|_S \in \mathcal{P}$. Then,

$$\tau(x)(g) = \mu((g^{-1} \cdot x)|_S) = f(g^{-1} \cdot x) \neq (g^{-1} \cdot x)(e) = x(g).$$

This shows that $\tau(x) \neq x$, so $x \notin \mathrm{Fix}(\tau)$. □

We now turn our attention to the minimal memory set of a local map $\mu : A^S \to A$ generated by a pair $(\mathcal{P}, f)$. In the following example, we examine in detail the links between the generating patterns and minimal memory sets for elementary cellular automata.

Example 5. Let $A := \{0, 1\}$ and $S := \{-1, 0, 1\} \subseteq \mathbb{Z}$. Table 1, which was obtained by direct computations, shows the sizes of the minimal memory sets of local maps $\mu : A^S \to A$ according to the sizes of their generating set of patterns $\mathcal{P} \subseteq A^S$.

Since $|A^S| = 8$, there are $\binom{8}{k}$ local maps generated by $k =: |\mathcal{P}|$ different patterns. When $k = 0$, cellular automaton must be the identity, while when $k = 8$, the cellular automaton must be the rule that exchanges 0's and 1's (ECA 51). The richest variety of minimal memory sets appears when $k = 4$, including the constant cellular automata (ECA 0 and 255) whose minimal memory set is the empty set $\emptyset$. The symmetry that appears in the possible sizes of MMS in Table 1 may be explained by Proposition 3 (2).

Table 1. Generating patterns and minimal memory set of ECA.

$\lvert\mathcal{P}\rvert$	0	1	2	3	4	5	6	7	8
No. local maps	1	8	28	56	70	56	28	8	1
Size of MMS	1	3	3 or 2	3	$0, 1, 2,$ or 3	3	3 or 2	3	1

The minimal memory set of a local map $\mu : A^S \to A$ may be more easily characterized in terms of a generating pair $(\mathcal{P}, f)$ when the function $f : \mathcal{P} \to A$ only depends on the projection to e and acts as a permutation of A. Hence, we introduce the following definition.

Definition 6. *Suppose that* $(\mathcal{P}, f)$ *generates a local map* $\mu : A^S \to A$. *We say that* $f : \mathcal{P} \to A$ *is* well-behaved *if, for all* $p, q \in \mathcal{P}$, $p(e) = q(e)$ *if and only if* $f(p) = f(q)$.

Remark 2. If $A = \{0, 1\}$, then $f : \mathcal{P} \to A$ is always well-behaved because, as explained in Remark 1, $f(p) = p(e)^c$. Clearly, $p(e) = q(e)$ if and only if $p(e)^c = q(e)^c$.

In the following lemmas, we shall analyze when $s \in S$ is essential for a local map $\mu : A^S \to A$ generated by a pair $(\mathcal{P}, f)$. The two distinctive cases will be when $s \neq e$ and $s = e$.

Recall that for $s \in S$, we define $\mathrm{Res}_s : A^S \to A^{S \setminus \{s\}}$ by $\mathrm{Res}_s(z) = z|_{S \setminus \{s\}}$. For $\mathcal{P} \subseteq A^S$, denote $\mathcal{P}^c := A^S \setminus \mathcal{P}$.

Lemma 2. *Suppose that* $(\mathcal{P}, f)$ *generates a local map* $\mu : A^S \to A$. *Let* $s \in S \setminus \{e\}$.

1. *If there exist* $p \in \mathcal{P}$ *and* $z \in \mathcal{P}^c$ *such that* $\mathrm{Res}_s(p) = \mathrm{Res}_s(z)$, *then* s *is essential for* μ.
2. *If* s *is essential for* μ *and* f *is well-behaved, then there exist* $p \in \mathcal{P}$ *and* $z \in \mathcal{P}^c$ *such that* $\mathrm{Res}_s(p) = \mathrm{Res}_s(z)$.

Proof. For point (1), observe that $z(e) = p(e)$ because $\mathrm{Res}_s(p) = \mathrm{Res}_s(z)$ and $s \neq e$. Then,

$$\mu(z) = z(e) = p(e) \neq f(p) = \mu(p).$$

It follows that s is essential for μ.

For point (2), suppose that for all $p \in \mathcal{P}$ and $z \in A^S$ such that $\mathrm{Res}_s(p) = \mathrm{Res}_s(z)$, we have $z \in \mathcal{P}$. Take arbitrary $z_1, z_2 \in A^S$ such that $\mathrm{Res}_s(z_1) = \mathrm{Res}_s(z_2)$. We have two cases:

- **Case** $z_1 \in \mathcal{P}$: By assumption, we must have $z_2 \in \mathcal{P}$. As f is well-behaved and $z_1(e) = z_2(e)$, then $f(z_1) = f(z_2)$. Then,

$$\mu(z_1) = f(z_1) = f(z_2) = \mu(z_2).$$

– **Case** $z_1 \notin \mathcal{P}$: By assumption, we must have $z_2 \notin \mathcal{P}$. Then,

$$\mu(z_1) = z_1(e) = z_2(e) = \mu(z_2).$$

This contradicts that s is essential for μ. □

Proposition 2. *Suppose that* $(\mathcal{P}, f)$ *generates a local map* $\mu : A^S \to A$ *and that* $|\mathcal{P}|$ *is not a multiple of* $|A|$. *Then every* $s \in S \setminus \{e\}$ *is essential for* μ.

Proof. Fix $s \in S \setminus \{e\}$. By Lemma 2 (1), it is enough if we show that there exist $p \in \mathcal{P}$ and $z \in \mathcal{P}^c$ such that $\text{Res}_s(p) = \text{Res}_s(z)$. If no such pair exists, it means that $\mathcal{P}$ may be written as a partition of preimages under $\text{Res}_s : A^S \to A^{S \setminus \{s\}}$:

$$\mathcal{P} = \bigsqcup_{i=1}^{n} \text{Res}_s^{-1}(y_i),$$

for some $y_i \in A^{S \setminus \{s\}}$, $i \in \{1, 2 \dots, n\}$. However,

$$|\text{Res}_s^{-1}(y_i)| = |A|, \quad \forall i \in \{1, 2 \dots, n\}.$$

Hence, $|\mathcal{P}| = n|A|$ is a multiple of $|A|$, which contradicts the hypothesis. □

Now we shall try to determine when $e \in S$ is essential for a local map $\mu : A^S \to A$ generated by $(\mathcal{P}, f)$.

Lemma 3. *Suppose that* $(\mathcal{P}, f)$ *generates a local map* $\mu : A^S \to A$.

1. *If there exist* $z, w \in \mathcal{P}^c$ *such that* $z \neq w$ *and* $\text{Res}_e(z) = \text{Res}_e(w)$, *then* $e \in S$ *is essential for* μ.
2. *Suppose that* f *is well-behaved and that there exist* $p, q \in \mathcal{P}$ *such that* $p \neq q$ *and* $\text{Res}_e(p) = \text{Res}_e(q)$. *Then,* $e \in S$ *is essential for* μ.

Proof. For part (1), observe that $z(e) \neq w(e)$ because $z \neq w$ and $\text{Res}_e(z) = \text{Res}_e(w)$. Since $z, w \in \mathcal{P}^c$, we have

$$\mu(z) = z(e) \neq w(e) = \mu(w).$$

It follows that e is essential for μ.

For part (2), we also have $p(e) \neq q(e)$. As f is well-behaved, then $f(p) \neq f(q)$, so

$$\mu(p) = f(p) \neq f(q) = \mu(q).$$

This shows that e is essential for μ. □

Corollary 1. *Suppose that* $(\mathcal{P}, f)$ *generates a local map* $\mu : A^S \to A$, *with* f *well-behaved,* $|S| \geq 2$ *and* $|A| \geq 3$. *Then* e *is essential for* μ.

Proof. First, $A^{S \setminus \{e\}} \neq \emptyset$ because $|S| \geq 2$. For any $y \in A^{S \setminus \{e\}}$, the set $\text{Res}_e^{-1}(y)$ has size $|A| \geq 3$. Hence, we must have that either $|\text{Res}_e^{-1}(y) \cap \mathcal{P}| \geq 2$ or $|\text{Res}_e^{-1}(y) \cap \mathcal{P}^c| \geq 2$. It follows from Lemma 3 that e is essential for μ.

Corollary 2. *Suppose that $(\mathcal{P}, f)$ generates a local map $\mu : A^S \to A$, and that $A = \{0,1\}$. Then, $e \in S$ is essential for μ if and only if there exist $z, w \in \mathcal{P}^c$, or $z, w \in \mathcal{P}$, such that $z \neq w$ and $\mathrm{Res}_e(z) = \mathrm{Res}_e(w)$.*

Proof. The converse implication follows by Lemma 3. Suppose that e is essential for μ. By definition, there exist $z, w \in A^S$ such that $\mathrm{Res}_e(z) = \mathrm{Res}_e(w)$ and $\mu(z) \neq \mu(w)$. Note that $z(e) \neq w(e)$ (as otherwise, $z = w$). We will show that we must have that either $z, w \in \mathcal{P}^c$ or $z, w \in \mathcal{P}$. For a contradiction, suppose that $z \in \mathcal{P}$ and $w \in \mathcal{P}^c$. Then, $\mu(w) = w(e)$ and, by Remark 1, we have $\mu(z) = f(z) = z(e)^c$. However, since $z(e) \neq w(e)$ and $A = \{0,1\}$, we must have that $w(e) = z(e)^c$. This contradicts that $\mu(z) \neq \mu(w)$. □

Proposition 3. *Let $\mathcal{P} \subseteq A^S$. Let $f : \mathcal{P} \to A$ and $g : \mathcal{P}^c \to A$ be two well-behaved functions. Suppose that $(\mathcal{P}, f)$ generates $\mu : A^S \to A$ and that $(\mathcal{P}^c, g)$ generates $\mu' : A^S \to A$.*

1. *$s \in S \setminus \{e\}$ is essential for μ if and only if $s \in S \setminus \{e\}$ is essential for μ'.*
2. *If $A = \{0,1\}$, then $\mathrm{mms}(\mu) = \mathrm{mms}(\mu')$.*

Proof. For part (1), we use Lemma 2. It follows that $s \in S \setminus \{e\}$ is essential for μ if and only if there is $p \in \mathcal{P}$ and $z \in \mathcal{P}^c$ such that $\mathrm{Res}_s(p) = \mathrm{Res}_s(z)$, which holds if and only if s is essential for μ'. Part (2) follows by Corollary 2. □

Remark 3. When $A = \{0,1\}$, the local map $\mu' : A^S \to A$ is different from what is known in the literature as the *complementary rule*, which is induced by the group-theoretic conjugation by the invertible cellular automaton that exchange 0's and 1's (ECA 51). For example, the complementary rule of the ECA 110 is the ECA 137; however, the cellular automaton generated by the complementary patterns of the ones that generate ECA 110 is the ECA 145 (which is the result of only composing on one side by ECA 51).

Lemma 4. *Suppose that $(\mathcal{P}, f)$ generates a local map $\mu : A^S \to A$, with $|S| \geq 2$. If e is not essential for μ, then*

$$|\mathcal{P}| = |A|^{|S|} - |A|^{|S|-1}.$$

Proof. As e is not essential for μ, by Lemma 3 (1) we have that all $z, w \in \mathcal{P}^c$, $z \neq w$, satisfy $\mathrm{Res}_e(z) \neq \mathrm{Res}_e(w)$. This means that $\mathrm{Res}_e : \mathcal{P}^c \to A^{S \setminus \{e\}}$ is an injective function, with $A^{S \setminus \{e\}} \neq \emptyset$ because $|S| \geq 2$. Hence $|\mathcal{P}^c| \leq |A|^{|S|-1}$, which is equivalent to $|\mathcal{P}| \geq |A|^{|S|} - |A|^{|S|-1}$.

On the other hand, that e is not essential for μ, implies that μ is constant on $\mathrm{Res}_e^{-1}(y)$ for all $y \in A^{S \setminus \{e\}}$. Hence, for all $y \in A^{S \setminus \{e\}}$, there exists a unique $\hat{y} \in \mathcal{P}^c$ such that $\hat{y} \in \mathrm{Res}_e^{-1}(y)$ (namely, if $\mu(w) = a \in A$ for all $w \in \mathrm{Res}_e^{-1}(y)$, let $\hat{y} \in \mathrm{Res}_e^{-1}(y)$ be such that $\hat{y}(e) = a$; it follows by the definition of $\mathcal{P}$ that $\mathcal{P}^c \cap \mathrm{Res}_e^{-1}(y) = \{\hat{y}\}$). This implies that there is an injective function $A^{S \setminus \{e\}} \to \mathcal{P}^c$ given by $y \mapsto \hat{y}$, so $|A|^{|S|-1} \leq |\mathcal{P}^c|$. Therefore, $|\mathcal{P}| \leq |A|^{|S|} - |A|^{|S|-1}$, and the result follows. □

Corollary 3. *Suppose that $(\mathcal{P}, f)$ generates a local map $\mu : A^S \to A$, where $|S| \geq 2$ and $|\mathcal{P}|$ is not a multiple of $|A|$. Then,*

$$\text{mms}(\tau) = S.$$

Proof. By Proposition 2, every $s \in S \setminus \{e\}$ is essential for μ. It follows by Lemma 4 that $e \in S$ is also essential for μ, because $|\mathcal{P}| \neq |A|^{|S|} - |A|^{|S|-1}$. □

The following result is Lemma 1 in [2], which is an immediate consequence of Corollary 3.

Corollary 4. *Let $S \subseteq G$ be a finite subset such that $e \in S$ and $|S| \geq 2$. Let $\mu : A^S \to A$ be a local map generated by $(\mathcal{P}, f)$ with $|\mathcal{P}| = 1$. Then,*

$$\text{mms}(\mu) = S.$$

Proposition 4. *Let $S \subseteq G$ be a finite subset such that $e \in S$ and $|S| \geq 3$. Suppose that $(\mathcal{P}, f)$ generates a local map $\mu : A^S \to A$, with f well-behaved and $|\mathcal{P}| = |A|$. Then,* $\text{mms}(\mu) = S \setminus \{s\}$, *for some $s \in S \setminus \{e\}$, or* $\text{mms}(\mu) = S$.

Proof. We divide the proof in two cases.

- **Case 1:** There exists $s \in S \setminus \{e\}$ such that for all $p, q \in \mathcal{P}$ we have $\text{Res}_s(p) = \text{Res}_s(q)$. Since $|\mathcal{P}| = |A|$, there is no $z \in \mathcal{P}^c$ such that $\text{Res}_s(z) = \text{Res}_s(p)$ for some $p \in \mathcal{P}$. By Lemma 2 (2), s is not essential for μ. Now we can consider $\mu' : A^{S \setminus \{s\}} \to A$ defined by $\mu'(z) := \mu(\hat{z})$, for all $z \in A^{S \setminus \{s\}}$, where $\hat{z} \in A^S$ is any extension of z (this is well-defined because s is not essential for μ). Then μ' is generated by $(\{\text{Res}_s(p)\}, f')$, for any $p \in \mathcal{P}$, where $f'(\text{Res}_s(p)) = f(p)$. Since $\mu \sim \mu'$, and μ' is generated by a single pattern over $A^{S \setminus \{s\}}$ with $|S \setminus \{s\}| \geq 2$, it follows from Corollary 4 that
$$\text{mms}(\mu) = \text{mms}(\mu') = S \setminus \{s\}.$$
- **Case 2:** For all $s \in S \setminus \{e\}$ there exist $p, q \in \mathcal{P}$ such that $\text{Res}_s(p) \neq \text{Res}_s(q)$. Observe that $\text{Res}_s^{-1}(\text{Res}_s(p))$ has size $|A| = |\mathcal{P}|$ and $q \in \mathcal{P} \cap \text{Res}_s^{-1}(\text{Res}_s(p))^c$, so it is not possible that $\text{Res}_s^{-1}(\text{Res}_s(p)) = \mathcal{P}$. Therefore, there exists $z \in \mathcal{P}^c$ such that $z \in \text{Res}_s^{-1}(\text{Res}_s(p))$, which means that $\text{Res}_s(z) = \text{Res}_s(p)$. It follows from Lemma 2 (1) that s is essential for μ. Now, since $|S| \geq 3$, then $|\mathcal{P}| = |A| < |A|^{|S|} - |A|^{|S|-1}$. Hence, it follows from Lemma 4 that $e \in S$ is essential for μ.

□

The proof of Theorem 1 follows from Lemma 4, Corollary 3, and Proposition 4.

Acknowledgments. The second author was supported by CONAHCYT *Becas nacionales para estudios de posgrado*, Government of Mexico. We sincerely thank all the comments and suggestions made by the anonymous reviewers of this paper, especially for fixing Case 2 in the proof of Proposition 4.

References

1. Blanchard, F., Maass, A.: Dynamical behaviour of Coven's aperiodic cellular automata. Theoret. Comput. Sci. **163**(1–2), 291–302 (1996)
2. Castillo-Ramirez, A., Magaña-Chavez, M.G., Veliz-Quintero, E.: Idempotent cellular automata and their natural order, Theoret. Comput. Sci. **1009**, 114698 (2024). https://doi.org/10.1016/j.tcs.2024.114698
3. Ceccherini-Silberstein, T., Coornaert, M.: Cellular Automata and Groups. Springer Monographs in Mathematics, Springer, Heidelberg (2010). https://doi.org/10.1007/978-3-031-43328-3
4. Ceccherini-Silberstein, T., Coornaert, M.: Exercises in Cellular Automata and Groups. Springer Monographs in Mathematics, Springer, Cham (2023). https://doi.org/10.1007/978-3-031-10391-9
5. Coven, E.M.: Topological entropy of block maps. Proc. Am. Math. Soc. **78**(4), 590–594 (1980)
6. Kari, J.: Theory of cellular automata: a survey. Theoret. Comput. Sci. **334**, 3–33 (2005). https://doi.org/10.1016/j.tcs.2004.11.021
7. Lind, D., Marcus, B.: An Introduction to Symbolic Dynamics and Coding, 2nd edn. Cambridge University Press, Cambridge (2021)
8. Lind, D.: Entropies of automorphisms of a topological Markov shift. Proc. Am. Math. Soc. **99**(3), 589–595 (1987)

Roots in the Semiring of Finite Deterministic Dynamical Systems

François Doré[1], Kévin Perrot[2], Antonio E. Porreca[2], Sara Riva[3], and Marius Rolland[2(✉)]

[1] Université Côte d'Azur, CNRS, I3S, Nice, France
[2] Aix-Marseille Université, CNRS, LIS, Marseille, France
marius.rolland@lis-lab.fr
[3] Univ. Lille, CNRS, Centrale Lille, UMR 9189 CRIStAL, 59000 Lille, France

Abstract. Finite discrete-time dynamical systems (FDDS) model phenomena that evolve deterministically in discrete time. It is possible to define sum and product operations on these systems (disjoint union and direct product, respectively) giving a commutative semiring. This algebraic structure led to several works employing polynomial equations to model hypotheses on phenomena modelled using FDDS. To solve these equations, algorithms for performing the division and computing k-th roots are needed. In this paper, we propose two polynomial algorithms for these tasks, under the condition that the result is a connected FDDS. This ultimately leads to an efficient solution to equations of the type $AX^k = B$ for connected X. These results are some of the important final steps for solving more general polynomial equations on FDDS.

Keywords: discrete dynamical systems · root of graph direct product

1 Introduction

Finite discrete-time dynamical systems (FDDS) are pairs (X, f) where X is a finite set of states and $f : X \to X$ is a transition function (where no ambiguity arises, we will usually denote (X, f) simply as X). These systems emerge from the analysis of concrete models such as Boolean networks [10,11] and are applied to biology [1,16,17] to represent, for example, genetic regulatory networks or epidemic models. We can find them also in chemistry [7], to represent the evolution over discrete time of chemical reactions, or information theory [9].

We can identify dynamical systems with their transition graph, which have uniform outgoing degree one (these are also known as functional digraphs). Their general shape is a collection of cycles with a finite number of directed trees (with arcs pointing towards the root, *i.e.*, in-trees) anchored to them by the root. The nodes inside the cycles are periodic states, while the others are transient states.

The set $(\mathbb{D}, +, \times)$ of FDDS taken up to isomorphism with the disjoint union as a *sum* operation (corresponding to the alternative execution of two systems) and the *direct product* [12] (corresponding to synchronous execution) is a commutative semiring [2]. However, this semiring is not factorial, *i.e.*, a FFDS admits,

Published by Springer Nature Switzerland AG 2024
M. Gadouleau and A. Castillo-Ramirez (Eds.): AUTOMATA 2024, LNCS 14782, pp. 120–132, 2024.
https://doi.org/10.1007/978-3-031-65887-7_8

in general, multiple factorizations into irreducibles. For this reason, the structure of product is more complex compared to other semirings such as the natural numbers, and its understanding remains limited. We are still unable to characterize or efficiently detect the FDDS obtained by parallel execution of smaller FDDS.

Some literature analyzes this problem limited to periodic behaviours, *i.e.*, to FDDS with permutations as their transition function [3,4,8]. Studying these restricted FDDS is justified by the fact that they correspond to the stable, asymptotic behaviour of the system. However, transient behaviour is more vast and various when modelling phenomena such as those from, for example, biology or physics. FDDS with a single fixed point have also been investigated [14] focusing more on the transient behaviours. Nevertheless, we cannot investigate general FDDS through a simple combination of these two techniques.

A direction for reducing the complexity of the decomposition problem is finding an efficient algorithm for equations of the form $AX = B$, *i.e.*, for dividing FDDS. The problem is trivially in NP, but we do not know its exact complexity (*e.g.*, NP-hard, GI, or P). However, [5] proved that we can solve these equations in polynomial time if A and B are certain classes of *permutations*, *i.e.*, FDDS without transient states. Nevertheless, the complexity of more general cases is unknown even for permutations.

Another direction is to propose an efficient algorithm for the computation of roots over FDDS. Since [14], we are aware of the uniqueness of the solution of k-th roots, but once again we do not know the exact complexity of the problem beyond a trivial NP upper bound.

In this paper, we will exploit the notion of unroll introduced in [14] to address the division and the root problems in the specific case where X is connected (*i.e.*, the graph of X contains just one connected component). More precisely, we start by showing that we can compute in polynomial time a FDDS X such that $AX = B$, if any exists. We also show that we can compute in polynomial time, given an FDDS A and a strictly positive integer k, a connected FDDS X such that $X^k = A$, if any exists. These two last contributions naturally lead to a solution to the more general equation $AX^k = B$.

2 Definitions

In the following, we will refer to the in-trees constituting the transient behaviour of FDDS just as *trees* for simplicity. An FDDS has a set of weakly connected components, each containing a unique cycle. In the following, we will refer to FDDS with only one component as *connected*.

In literature, two operations over FDDS have been considered: the *sum* (the disjoint union of the components of two systems) and the *product* (direct product [12] of their transition graphs). Let us recall that, given two digraphs $A = (V, E)$ and $B = (V', E')$, their product $A \times B$ is a digraph where the set of nodes is $V \times V'$ and the set of edges is $\{((v, v'), (u, u')) \mid (v, u) \in E, (v', u') \in E'\}$. When applied to the transition graphs of two connected FDDS with cycle lengths respectively

p and p', this operation generates $\gcd(p,p')$ components with cycles of length $\mathrm{lcm}(p,p')$ [2,12].

Let us recall the notion of unroll of dynamical systems introduced in [14]. We will denote trees and forests using bold letters (in lower and upper case respectively) to distinguish them from FDDS.

Definition 1 (Unroll). *Let A be an FDDS (X,f). For each state $u \in X$ and $k \in \mathbb{N}$, we denote by $f^{-k}(u) = \{v \in X \mid f^k(v) = u\}$ the set of k-th preimages of u. For each u in a cycle of A, we call the* unroll tree of A in u *the infinite tree $\mathbf{t}_u = (V,E)$ having vertices $V = \{(s,k) \mid s \in f^{-k}(u), k \in \mathbb{N}\}$ and edges $E = \{((v,k),(f(v),k-1))\} \subseteq V^2$. We call* unroll of A, *denoted $\mathcal{U}(A)$, the set of its unroll trees.*

Unroll trees have exactly one infinite branch on which the trees representing transient behaviour hook and repeat periodically. Remark that the forest given by the unroll of a connected FDDS may contain isomorphic trees and this results from symmetries in the original graph.

This transformation from an FDDS to its unroll has already proved successful in studying operations (particularly the product operation) at the level of transient behaviours. Indeed, the sum (disjoint union) of two unrolls corresponds to the unroll of the sum of the FDDS; formally, $\mathcal{U}(A)+\mathcal{U}(A') = \mathcal{U}(A+A')$. For the product, it has been shown that it is possible to define an equivalent product over unrolls for which $\mathcal{U}(A) \times \mathcal{U}(A') = \mathcal{U}(A \times A')$. Here and in the following, the equality sign will denote graph isomorphism.

Let us formally define the product of trees to be applied over the unroll of two FDDS. Since it is known that the product distributes over the different trees of the two unrolls [6], it suffices to define the product between two trees. Intuitively, this product is the direct product applied layer by layer. To define it, we let *depth*(v) be the distance of the node from the root of the tree.

Definition 2 (Product of trees). *Consider two trees $\mathbf{t}_1 = (V_1,E_1)$ and $\mathbf{t}_2 = (V_2,E_2)$ with roots r_1 and r_2, respectively. Their* product *is the tree $\mathbf{t}_1 \times \mathbf{t}_2 = (V,E)$ such that $V = \{(v,u) \in V_1 \times V_2 \mid depth(v) = depth(u)\}$ and $E = \{((v,u),(v',u')) \mid (v,u) \in V, (v,v') \in E_1, (u,u') \in E_2\}$.*

In the following, we use a total order $\leq$ on finite trees introduced in [14], which is compatible with the product, that is, if $\mathbf{t}_1 \leq \mathbf{t}_2$ then $\mathbf{t}_1\mathbf{t} \leq \mathbf{t}_2\mathbf{t}$ for all tree $\mathbf{t}$. Let us briefly recall that this ordering is based on a vector obtained from concatenating the incoming degrees of nodes visited through a BFS. During graph traversal, child nodes (preimages in our case), are sorted recursively according to this very order, resulting in a deterministic computation of the vector.

We will also need the notion of *depth* for finite trees and forests. The depth of a finite tree is the length of its longest branch. For a forest, it is the maximum depth of its trees. In the case of unrolls, which have infinite paths, we can adopt the notion of depth of a dynamical system (that is, the largest depth among the

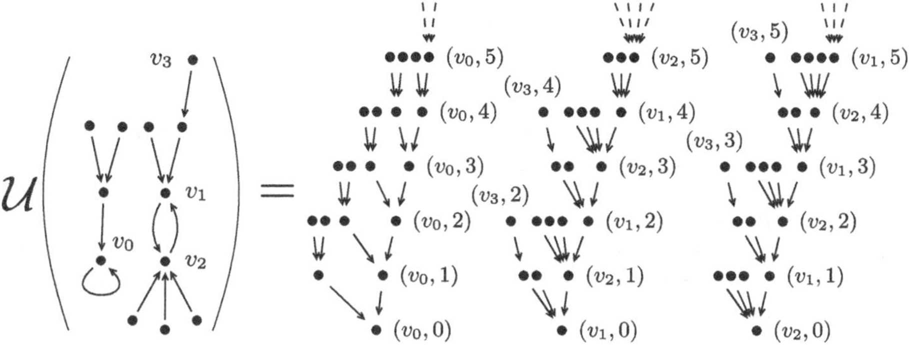

Fig. 1. The unroll $\mathcal{U}(A)$ of a disconnected FDDS A. Only the first 6 levels of $\mathcal{U}(A)$ are shown. Both the FDDS and its unroll have depth 2.

trees rooted in one of its periodic states). For an unroll tree $\mathbf{t}$, its depth is the depth of a connected FDDS A such that $\mathbf{t} \in \mathcal{U}(A)$. See Fig. 1.

We now recall three operations defined in [14] that will be useful later. Given a forest $\mathbf{F}$, we denote by $\mathcal{D}(\mathbf{F})$ the multi-set of trees rooted in the predecessors of the roots of $\mathbf{F}$. Then, we denote by $\mathcal{R}(\mathbf{F})$ the tree such that $\mathcal{D}(\mathcal{R}(\mathbf{F})) = \mathbf{F}$. Intuitively, this second operation connects the trees to a new common root. Finally, given a positive integer k, we denote $\mathcal{C}(\mathbf{t}, k)$ the induced sub-tree of $\mathbf{t}$ composed by the vertices with a depth less or equal to k. Let us generalize the same operation applied to a forest $\mathbf{F} = \mathbf{t}_1 + ... + \mathbf{t}_n$ as $\mathcal{C}(\mathbf{F}, k) = \mathcal{C}(\mathbf{t}_1, k) + ... + \mathcal{C}(\mathbf{t}_n, k)$.

3 Complexity of FDDS Division with Connected Quotient

In this section we establish an upper bound to the complexity of division over FDDS. More formally, our problem is to decide if, given two FDDS A and B, there exists a connected FDDS X such that $AX = B$. To achieve this, we will initially prove that cancellation holds over unrolls, *i.e.*, that $\mathbf{EX} = \mathbf{EY}$ implies $\mathbf{X} = \mathbf{Y}$ for unrolls $\mathbf{E}, \mathbf{X}, \mathbf{Y}$. Later, we will extend the algorithm proposed in [14, Figure 6] to handle more general unrolls (rather than just those consisting of a single tree), ultimately leading to our result.

We begin by considering the case of forests containing a finite number of finite trees; we will refer to them as *finite tree forests.* We will later generalise the reasoning to forests such as unrolls.

Lemma 1. *Let* $\mathbf{A}$, $\mathbf{X}$, *and* $\mathbf{B}$ *be finite tree forests. Then,* $\mathbf{AX} = \mathbf{B}$ *if and only if* $\mathcal{R}(\mathbf{A})\mathcal{R}(\mathbf{x}) = \mathcal{R}(\mathbf{B})$.

Proof. ($\Leftarrow$) Assume $\mathcal{R}(\mathbf{A})\mathcal{R}(\mathbf{X}) = \mathcal{R}(\mathbf{B})$. Then, $\mathcal{D}(\mathcal{R}(\mathbf{A})\mathcal{R}(\mathbf{X})) = \mathcal{D}(\mathcal{R}(\mathbf{B})) = \mathbf{B}$. Moreover, since $\mathcal{R}(\mathbf{A})$ and $\mathcal{R}(\mathbf{X})$ are finite trees, by [14, Lemma 7] we have:

$$\mathcal{D}(\mathcal{R}(\mathbf{A})\mathcal{R}(\mathbf{X})) = \mathcal{D}(\mathcal{R}(\mathbf{A}))\mathcal{D}(\mathcal{R}(\mathbf{X})) = \mathbf{AX}.$$

($\Rightarrow$) We can show the other direction by a similar reasoning. □

Thanks to this lemma, we can generalise Lemma 21 of [14] as follows.

Lemma 2. *Let* $\mathbf{A}$, $\mathbf{X}$, *and* $\mathbf{Y}$ *be finite tree forests. Then* $\mathbf{AX} = \mathbf{AY}$ *if and only if* $\mathcal{C}(\mathbf{X}, depth(\mathbf{A})) = \mathcal{C}(\mathbf{Y}, depth(\mathbf{A}))$.

Proof. ($\Leftarrow$) By the definition of tree product, all nodes of $\mathbf{X}$ (resp., $\mathbf{Y}$) of depth larger than $depth(\mathbf{A})$ do not impact the product $\mathbf{AX}$ (resp., $\mathbf{AY}$). Thus, we have $\mathbf{AX} = \mathbf{A}\mathcal{C}(\mathbf{X}, depth(\mathbf{A}))$ and $\mathbf{AY} = \mathbf{A}\mathcal{C}(\mathbf{Y}, depth(\mathbf{A}))$. Since $\mathcal{C}(\mathbf{X}, depth(\mathbf{A})) = \mathcal{C}(\mathbf{Y}, depth(\mathbf{A}))$, we conclude that $\mathbf{AX} = \mathbf{AY}$.

($\Rightarrow$) Suppose $\mathbf{AX} = \mathbf{AY}$. By Lemma 1, we have $\mathcal{R}(\mathbf{A})\mathcal{R}(\mathbf{X}) = \mathcal{R}(\mathbf{A})\mathcal{R}(\mathbf{Y})$. Since $\mathcal{R}(\mathbf{A})$, $\mathcal{R}(\mathbf{X})$, and $\mathcal{R}(\mathbf{Y})$ are finite trees, we deduce [14, Lemma 21]

$$\mathcal{C}(\mathcal{R}(\mathbf{x}), depth(\mathcal{R}(\mathbf{A}))) = \mathcal{C}(\mathcal{R}(\mathbf{Y}), depth(\mathcal{R}(\mathbf{A}))) \tag{1}$$

For all forest $\mathbf{F}$ and $d > 0$, we have that $\mathcal{D}(\mathcal{C}(\mathbf{F}, d))$ is the multiset containing the subtrees rooted on the predecessors of the roots of $\mathcal{C}(\mathbf{F}, d)$. It is therefore the same multiset as that which is composed of the subtrees rooted on the predecessors of the roots of $\mathbf{F}$ cut at depth $d-1$. It follows that $\mathcal{C}(\mathcal{D}(\mathbf{F}), d-1) = \mathcal{D}(\mathcal{C}(\mathbf{F}, d))$. In particular, for $\mathbf{F} = \mathcal{R}(\mathbf{X})$ and $d = depth(\mathbf{A}) + 1 = depth(\mathcal{R}(\mathbf{A}))$, we have

$$\mathcal{D}(\mathcal{C}(\mathcal{R}(\mathbf{X}), depth(\mathcal{R}(\mathbf{A})))) = \mathcal{C}(\mathbf{X}, depth(\mathbf{A})).$$

Likewise, $\mathcal{D}(\mathcal{C}(\mathcal{R}(\mathbf{Y}), depth(\mathcal{R}(\mathbf{A})))) = \mathcal{C}(\mathbf{Y}, depth(\mathbf{A}))$. By applying $\mathcal{D}(\cdot)$ to both sides of (1), we conclude $\mathcal{C}(\mathbf{X}, depth(\mathbf{A})) = \mathcal{C}(\mathbf{Y}, depth(\mathbf{A}))$. □

Lemma 2 is a sort of cancellation property subject to a depth condition. The first step to prove cancellation over unrolls is proving the equivalence between the notion of divisibility of unrolls and divisibility over deep enough finite cuts.

Proposition 1. *Let* A, X, *and* B *be FDDS with* α *equal to the number of unroll trees of* $\mathcal{U}(B)$. *Let* $n \geq \alpha + depth(\mathcal{U}(B))$. *Then*

$$\mathcal{U}(A)\mathcal{U}(X) = \mathcal{U}(B) \; if \; and \; only \; if \; \mathcal{C}(\mathcal{U}(A), n)\mathcal{C}(\mathcal{U}(X), n) = \mathcal{C}(\mathcal{U}(B), n)$$

To prove Proposition 1, we can apply the same reasoning of [14, Lemma 38].

We remark that the cut operation over $\mathcal{U}(B)$ at a depth n generates a forest where the size of each tree is in $\mathcal{O}(m^2)$ and the total size is in $\mathcal{O}(m^3)$ with m the size of B (*i.e.*, the number of nodes), since the chosen n is at most m. Now, we can prove the main result of this section.

Theorem 1. *For unrolls* $\mathbf{A}$, $\mathbf{X}$, $\mathbf{Y}$ *we have* $\mathbf{AX} = \mathbf{AY}$ *if and only if* $\mathbf{X} = \mathbf{Y}$.

Proof. Let α be the number of trees in $\mathbf{AX}$ and $n \geq \alpha + depth(\mathbf{AX})$ be an integer. By Proposition 1, $\mathbf{AX} = \mathbf{AY}$ if and only if $\mathcal{C}(\mathbf{A}, n)\mathcal{C}(\mathbf{X}, n) = \mathcal{C}(\mathbf{A}, n)\mathcal{C}(\mathbf{Y}, n)$. In addition, by Lemma 2, $\mathcal{C}(\mathbf{A}, n)\mathcal{C}(\mathbf{X}, n) = \mathcal{C}(\mathbf{A}, n)\mathcal{C}(\mathbf{Y}, n)$ if and only if $\mathcal{C}(\mathbf{X}, n) = \mathcal{C}(\mathbf{Y}, n)$. By Proposition 1, the theorem follows. □

Let us introduce the notion of *periodic pattern* of an unroll tree. Recall that an unroll tree $\mathbf{t}$ has exactly one infinite branch on which the trees $(\mathbf{t}_0, \mathbf{t}_1, \ldots)$ representing transient behaviour hook and repeat periodically. Let p be a positive integer. A periodic pattern with period p of $\mathbf{t}$ is a sequence of p finite trees $(\mathbf{t}_0, \ldots, \mathbf{t}_{p-1})$ rooted on the infinite branch such that, for all $i \in \mathbb{N}$ we have $\mathbf{t}_i = \mathbf{t}_{i \bmod p}$. Let us point out that the idea here is to obtain a set of trees such that we represent all different behaviours repeating in all unroll trees, obtaining a finite representation.

For connected FDDS, since its period p is the number of trees in its unroll, we can reconstruct the FDDS itself from a periodic pattern $(\mathbf{t}_0, \ldots, \mathbf{t}_{p-1})$ of one of its unroll trees $\mathbf{t}_u$ by adding edges between $\mathbf{t}_i$ and $\mathbf{t}_{(i+1) \bmod p}$ for all i. We call this operation the *roll of* $\mathbf{t}_u$ *of period* p. The following lemma shows that we can recover the periodic pattern of an unroll tree from a deep enough cut.

Lemma 3. *Let A be a connected FDDS of period p, $\mathbf{t}$ be an unroll tree of $\mathcal{U}(A)$, and $n \geq p + depth(\mathcal{U}(A))$. Let $(v_n, \ldots, v_0)$ be a directed path in $\mathcal{C}(\mathbf{t}, n)$ such that $depth(v_n) = n$ and v_0 is the root of the tree. Then, nodes $v_p, \ldots, v_0$ necessarily come from the infinite branch of $\mathbf{t}$.*

Proof. We assume, by contradiction, that at least one of the nodes $v_p, \ldots, v_0$ does not come from the infinite branch of $\mathbf{t}$. Let v_a be the node of $(v_{p-1}, \ldots, v_0)$ with maximal depth coming from the infinite branch of $\mathbf{t}$; there always is at least one of them, namely the root v_0. We have $depth(v_n) \leq depth(v_a) + depth(\mathbf{t})$. However, we assumed $depth(v_a) < p$, thus $depth(v_n) < p + depth(\mathbf{t})$. Since, $depth(v_n) = n$, we have $n < p + depth(\mathbf{t}) = p + depth(\mathcal{U}(A))$ which is a contradiction. □

We can finally describe a division algorithm for FDDS working under the hypothesis that the quotient is connected.

Algorithm 1. *Given two FDDS A and B, where $\mathcal{U}(B)$ has α trees, we can compute X such that X is a connected FDDS and $AX = B$ (if any exists) by*

1. *cutting $\mathcal{U}(A)$ and $\mathcal{U}(B)$ at depth $n = \alpha + depth(\mathcal{U}(B))$*
2. *computing $\mathbf{x}$ with the division algorithm [14] to divide the trees $\mathcal{R}(\mathcal{C}(\mathcal{U}(B), n))$ by $\mathcal{R}(\mathcal{C}(\mathcal{U}(A), n))$*
3. *computing the connected FDDS X as the roll of period p of any tree of $\mathcal{D}(\mathbf{x})$, where p is equal to the number of trees in $\mathcal{D}(\mathbf{x})$*
4. *and verifying if X multiplied by A is isomorphic to B.*

Since the depth where we cut is large enough, Proposition 1, Lemma 1 and the correctness of the division algorithm of [14] imply that the tree $\mathbf{x}$ computed in Step 2 of Algorithm 1 satisfies $\mathcal{C}(\mathcal{U}(A), n)\mathcal{D}(\mathbf{x}) = \mathcal{C}(\mathcal{U}(B), n)$. By the definition of unroll, since we only search for connected FDDS, if $\mathcal{D}(\mathbf{x})$ is the cut of an unroll then the rolls of each tree of $\mathcal{D}(\mathbf{x})$ at period p are isomorphic. Furthermore, Lemma 3 ensures that we can roll each tree in $\mathcal{D}(\mathbf{x})$. However, $\mathcal{D}(\mathbf{x})$ is not necessarily the cut of an unroll and it is possible that there exists an FDDS X such that $\mathcal{D}(\mathbf{x}) = \mathcal{C}(\mathcal{U}(X), n)$ but $AX \neq B$ (an example can be seen in Fig. 2). As a consequence, Step 4 of Algorithm 1 is mandatory to ensure its correctness.

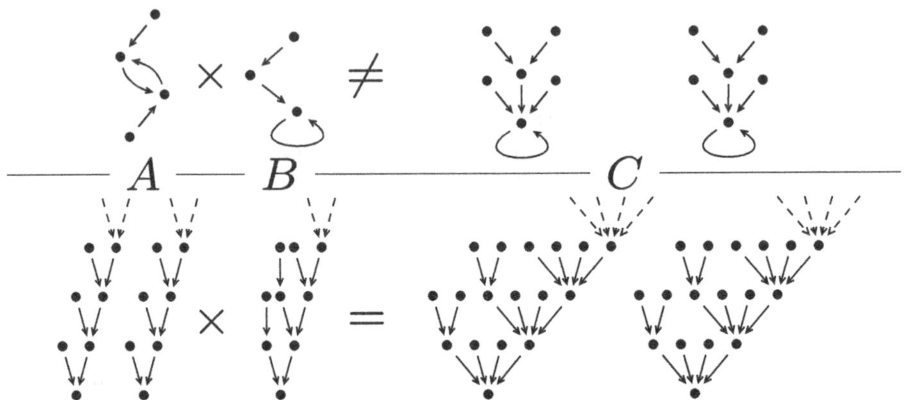

Fig. 2. Three FDDSs A, B and C such that $AB \neq C$ but $\mathcal{U}(A)\mathcal{U}(B) = \mathcal{U}(C)$. Here the symbol $\times$ denotes the product of FDDSs on the top, and of forests on the bottom.

Theorem 2. *Algorithm 1 runs in $\mathcal{O}(m^9)$ time, where m is the size of its inputs.*

Proof. The cuts of depth n of the unrolls of A and B can be computed in $\mathcal{O}(m^3)$ time and the size of the result is $\mathcal{O}(m^3)$. In fact, we can construct $\mathcal{C}(\mathcal{U}(A), n)$ and $\mathcal{C}(\mathcal{U}(B), n)$ backwards from their roots up to depth n; the size of $\mathcal{C}(\mathcal{U}(A), n)$ is bounded by the size of $\mathcal{C}(\mathcal{U}(B), n)$, which is $\mathcal{O}(m^3)$. By analysing the division tree algorithm in Fig. 6 of [14], we can check that it can be executed in cubic time. Moreover, since its inputs have size $\mathcal{O}(m^3)$, Step 2 of Algorithm 1 requires $\mathcal{O}(m^9)$ time. The roll procedure of a tree can be computed by a traversal, requiring $\mathcal{O}(m^2)$ time. Finally, the product of two FDDS is quadratic-time on its input but linear-time on its output. However, in our case, the size of the output of AX is bounded by the size of B; hence, the product can be computed in $\mathcal{O}(m)$ time. Finally, the isomorphism test requires $\mathcal{O}(m)$ [13]. □

4 Complexity of Computing k-th Roots of Unrolls

The purpose of this section is to study the problem of computing connected roots on FDDS, particularly on transients. Let $\mathbf{A} = \mathbf{t}_1 + \ldots + \mathbf{t}_n$ be a forest and k a positive integer. Then $\mathbf{A}^k = \sum_{k_1+\ldots+k_n=k} \binom{k}{k_1,\ldots,k_n} \prod_{i=1}^{n} \mathbf{t}_i^{k_i}$; furthermore, since the sum of forests is their disjoint union, each forest (in particular $\mathbf{A}^k$) can be written as a sum of trees in a unique way (up to reordering of the terms). The injectivity of k-th roots, in the semiring of unrolls, has been proved in [14]. Here, we study this problem from an algorithmic and complexity point of view, and find a polynomial-time upper bound for the computation of k-th roots.

We begin by studying the structure of a forest of finite trees raised to the k-th power. Indeed, if we suppose $\mathbf{X} = \mathbf{t}_1 + \ldots + \mathbf{t}_n$ with $\mathbf{t}_i \leq \mathbf{t}_{i+1}$, we want to be able to identify the smallest tree of $\mathbf{X}^k$ from the product $\mathbf{t}_i \times \prod_{j=1}^{n} \mathbf{t}_j$. Moreover, we want to be able to identify it for all $\mathbf{t}_i$.

Hereafter, we consider $\mathbf{a}^0$ to be equivalent to the simple oriented path with length equivalent to the depth of $\mathbf{a}$ (the same is true for forests).

Lemma 4. *Let* $\mathbf{X}$ *be a forest of the form* $\mathbf{X} = \mathbf{t}_1 + \ldots + \mathbf{t}_n$ *(with* $\mathbf{t}_i \leq \mathbf{t}_{i+1}$*) and* k *a positive integer. For any tree* $\mathbf{t}_i$ *of depth* d_i *in* $\mathbf{X}$*, the smallest tree* $\mathbf{t}_s$ *of depth* d_i *with factor* $\mathbf{t}_i$ *in* $\mathbf{X}^k$ *is isomorphic to* $\mathbf{t}_m^{k-1}\mathbf{t}_i$*, where* $\mathbf{t}_m$ *is the smallest tree of* $\mathbf{X}$ *with depth at least* d_i*.*

Proof. Let us assume that the smallest tree $\mathbf{t}_s$ of depth d_i with factor $\mathbf{t}_i$ in $\mathbf{X}^k$ is not isomorphic to $\mathbf{t}_m^{k-1}\mathbf{t}_i$. Two cases are possible. Either $\mathbf{t}_s$ contains a third factor other than $\mathbf{t}_m$ and $\mathbf{t}_i$, or it is of the form $\mathbf{t}_m^{k-k_i}\mathbf{t}_i^{k_i}$, with $k_i > 1$.

In the former case, let us suppose that there exists $a \in \{1, \ldots, i-1\} \setminus \{m\}$ and $k_a > 0$ such that $\mathbf{t}_a \neq \mathbf{t}_m$ and $\mathbf{t}_s$ is isomorphic to $\mathbf{t}_i^{k_i}\mathbf{t}_a^{k_a}\mathbf{t}_m^{k_m}$. Remark that, according to [14, Lemma 10], the smallest tree of depth d_i with factor $\mathbf{t}_i$ in $\mathbf{X}^k$ necessarily has all its factors of depth at least d_i. For this reason, we can assume $depth(\mathbf{t}_a) \geq d_i$ without loss of generality. However, since $\mathbf{t}_m < \mathbf{t}_a$, we have $\mathbf{t}_m^{k_m+1}\mathbf{t}_a^{k_a-1} < \mathbf{t}_m^{k_m}\mathbf{t}_a^{k_a}$. Thus, we have that $\mathbf{t}_i^{k_i}\mathbf{t}_m^{k_m+1}\mathbf{t}_a^{k_a-1} < \mathbf{t}_i^{k_i}\mathbf{t}_m^{k_m}\mathbf{t}_a^{k_a}$. This brings us into contradiction with the minimality of $\mathbf{t}_s$.

In the second case, we assume that $\mathbf{t}_s$ is isomorphic to $\mathbf{t}_m^{k-k_i}\mathbf{t}_i^{k_i}$ with $k_i > 1$. By hypothesis, we have $\mathbf{t}_i \geq \mathbf{t}_m$. If we consider the case of $\mathbf{t}_m < \mathbf{t}_i$, we have $\mathbf{t}_m^{k-k_i+1}\mathbf{t}_i^{k_i-1} < \mathbf{t}_m^{k-k_i}\mathbf{t}_i^{k_i}$. Once again, this is in contradiction with the minimality of $\mathbf{t}_s$. In the case of $\mathbf{t}_m = \mathbf{t}_i$, we have $\mathbf{t}_m^{k-k_i+1}\mathbf{t}_i^{k_i-1} = \mathbf{t}_m^{k-k_i}\mathbf{t}_i^{k_i}$. But we supposed $\mathbf{t}_s$ not isomorphic to $\mathbf{t}_m^{k-1}\mathbf{t}_i$. This concludes the proof. □

Before describing an algorithmic technique for computing roots over unrolls (*i.e.*, forests), we need a last technical lemma.

Lemma 5. *Let* $\mathbf{x}$ *and* $\mathbf{a}$ *be two finite trees such that* $\mathbf{x}^k = \mathbf{a}$*, and* k *a positive integer. Then,* $\mathcal{D}(\mathbf{a}) = \mathcal{D}(\mathbf{x})^k$*.*

Proof. Since $\mathbf{x}$ is a tree, for all $i \leq k$, $\mathbf{x}^i$ is also a tree. According to [14, Lemma 7], we have $\mathcal{D}(\mathbf{a}) = \mathcal{D}(\mathbf{x}^k) = \mathcal{D}(\mathbf{x})^k$. □

We now introduce an algorithmic procedure to compute the roots over forests based on an induction over decreasing depths in which, each time, we reconstruct part of the solution considering the smallest tree with at least a specific depth (according to Lemmas 4 and 5).

Theorem 3. *Given a forest* $\mathbf{A}$ *and* k *a strictly positive integer, we can compute* $\mathbf{X}$ *such that* $\mathbf{X}^k = \mathbf{A}$ *with Algorithm 2.*

In Algorithm 2, the main idea is to extract iteratively the minimal tree among the tallest ones in $\mathbf{A}$(*i.e.*,$\mathbf{t}_s$). This tree will be used to reconstruct one of the trees of $\mathbf{X}$(*i.e.*,$\mathbf{t}_i$). This can be done in two ways according to two possible scenarios. In the first case, $\mathbf{t}_s$ is smaller than the smallest one already reconstructed (*i.e.*,$\mathbf{t}_m$) raised to the power k. If this is the case, we compute a new tree in $\mathbf{X}$ through a recursive call to our `root` function. In the second case, the extracted tree is greater than $\mathbf{t}_m^k$. This means, by Lemma 4, that it is a product of the smallest

Algorithm 2. `root`

Require: $\mathbf{A}$ a forest, k an integer
1: **if** $\mathbf{A}$ is a path **then**
2:     **return** $\mathbf{A}$
3: **end if**
4: $\mathbf{R} \leftarrow \varnothing$
5: $\mathbf{t}_m \leftarrow \varnothing$
6: $\mathbf{F} \leftarrow \mathbf{A}$
7: **while** $\mathbf{F} \neq \varnothing$ **do**
8:     $\mathbf{F} \leftarrow \mathbf{A} \setminus \mathbf{R}^k$.
9:     $\mathbf{t}_s \leftarrow \min\{\mathbf{t} \mid \mathbf{t} \in \mathbf{F}, \mathit{depth}(\mathbf{t}) = \mathit{depth}(\mathbf{F})\}$
10:     **if** $\mathbf{t}_m = \varnothing$ **or** $\mathbf{t}_m^k > \mathbf{t}_s$ **then**
11:         $\mathbf{t}_i \leftarrow \mathcal{R}(\mathtt{root}(\mathcal{D}(\mathbf{t}_s), k))$
12:         $\mathbf{t}_m \leftarrow \mathbf{t}_i$
13:     **else**
14:         $\mathbf{t}_i \leftarrow \mathtt{divide}(\mathbf{t}_s, \mathbf{t}_m^{k-1})$
15:     **end if**
16:     **if** $\mathbf{t}_i = \bot$ **or** $(\mathbf{R} + \mathbf{t}_i)^k \nsubseteq \mathbf{A}$ **then**
17:         **return** $\bot$
18:     **end if**
19:     $\mathbf{R} \leftarrow \mathbf{R} + \mathbf{t}_i$
20: **end while**
21: **return** $\mathbf{R}$

reconstructed (*i.e.*, $\mathbf{t}_m$) one and a new one (*i.e.*, $\mathbf{t}_i$). In this case, the latter can be computed by the `divide` algorithm of [14]. After the reconstruction of a tree $\mathbf{t}_i$ of $\mathbf{X}$, we remove from $\mathbf{A}$ all the trees obtainable from products of already computed trees in $\mathbf{X}$. This allows us to extract progressively shorter trees $\mathbf{t}_s$ from $\mathbf{A}$ and to compute consequently shorter trees of $\mathbf{X}$. When we remove all trees in $\mathbf{A}$ obtainable from trees $\mathbf{t}_i$ with depth at least d_i in $\mathbf{X}$, this leaves us only trees with depth at most d_i. Since for each depth, the number of trees of this depth is finite, the algorithm necessarily halts.

Let us consider an example. In Fig. 3, in order to compute the left side from the right one, the first tree considered is $\mathbf{t}_1^2$, the single tallest one. The latter can be used to compute $\mathbf{t}_1$ recursively. Next, the smallest one among the remaining ones is $\mathbf{t}_0^2$, which is smaller than $\mathbf{t}_1^2$. Thus, we can compute $\mathbf{t}_0$ again through recursion. Finally, the last tree extracted, after removing the trees with exclusively $\mathbf{t}_0$ and $\mathbf{t}_1$ as factors, is $\mathbf{t}_0\mathbf{t}_2$. Since this time $\mathbf{t}_0^2$ is smaller, we can get the third and final tree $\mathbf{t}_2$ by dividing it by the smallest computed tree yet.

Theorem 4. *Algorithm 2 runs in $\mathcal{O}(m^3)$ time if k is at most $\lfloor \log_2 m \rfloor$, where m is the size of* $\mathbf{A}$.

Proof. If $\mathbf{A}$ is a path, then the algorithm halts in linear time $\mathcal{O}(m)$ on line 2.

Otherwise, there exists a level i of $\mathbf{A}$ containing $\beta \geq 2$ nodes. In order to justify the upper bound on k, suppose $\mathbf{R}^k = \mathbf{A}$. Then, level i of $\mathbf{R}$ contains $\sqrt[k]{\beta}$

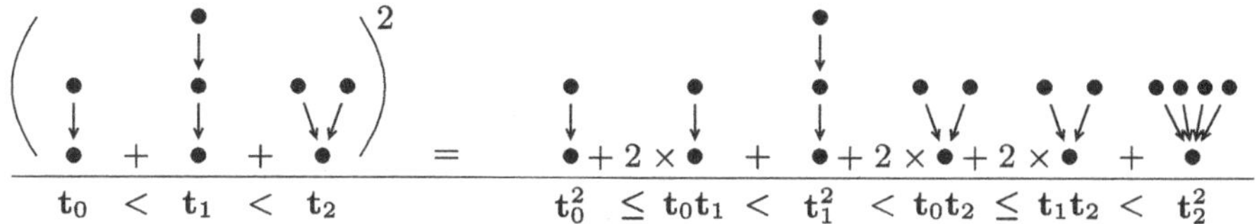

Fig. 3. Order of the trees in the square of a forest.

nodes. The smallest integer greater than 1 having a k-th root is 2^k, thus $\beta \geq 2^k$. Since $\beta \leq m$, we have $k \leq \lfloor \log_2 m \rfloor$.

Lines 1–6 take linear time $\mathcal{O}(m)$. The while loop of lines 7–20 is executed, in the worst case, once per tree of the k-th root $\mathbf{R}$, *i.e.*, a number of times equal to the k-th root of the number of trees in $\mathbf{A}$. Line 7 takes $\mathcal{O}(1)$ time. The product of trees requires linear time in its output size. Consequently, $\mathbf{R}^k$ can be computed in $\mathcal{O}(m \log m)$ time. Moreover, since we can remove $\mathbf{R}^k$ from $\mathbf{A}$ in quadratic time, we deduce that line 8 takes $\mathcal{O}(m^2)$ time. Since the search of $\mathbf{t}_s$ consists of a simple traversal, we deduce that line 9 takes $\mathcal{O}(m)$ time. Line 10 takes $\mathcal{O}(m \log m)$ time for computing $\mathbf{t}_m^k$. If no recursive call is made, line 14 is executed in time $\mathcal{O}(m_s^3)$, where m_s is the size of $\mathbf{t}_s$. The runtime of lines 16–20 is dominated by line 16, which takes $\mathcal{O}(m^2)$ as line 8.

Since each tree $\mathbf{t}_s$ in $\mathbf{A}$ is used at most once, we have $\sum m_s^3 \leq m^3$; as a consequence, the most expensive lines of the algorithm (namely, 8, 14, and 16) have a total runtime of $\mathcal{O}(m^3)$ across all iterations of the while loop.

We still need to take into account the recursive calls of line 11. By taking once again into account the bound $\sum m_s^3 \leq m^3$, the total runtime of these recursive calls is also $\mathcal{O}(m^3)$. We conclude that Algorithm 2 runs in time $\mathcal{O}(m^3)$. □

Corollary 1. *Let* $\mathbf{A}$ *be a forest. Then, it is possible to decide in polynomial time if there exists a forest* $\mathbf{X}$ *and an integer* $k > 1$ *such that* $\mathbf{X}^k = \mathbf{A}$.

Proof. Since k is bounded by the logarithm of the size of $\mathbf{A}$ and, according to Theorem 4, we can compute the root in $\mathcal{O}(m^3)$, we can test all k (up to the bound) and check if there exists a $\mathbf{X}$ such that $\mathbf{X}^k = \mathbf{A}$ in $\mathcal{O}(m^3 \log m)$, where m denotes once again the size of $\mathbf{A}$. □

According to Corollary 1, we easily conclude that the corresponding enumeration problem of finding all solutions $\mathbf{X}$ (for all powers k) is in EnumP, since the verification of a solution can be done in polynomial time and the size of a solution is polynomial in the size of the input. Moreover, the problem is in the class DelayP since the time elapsed between the computation of one solution (for a certain k) and the next is polynomial. We refer the reader to [15] for more information about enumeration complexity classes.

Now that we have a technique to compute the root of forests, let us think in terms of unrolls of FDDS. Consider an FDDS A and its unroll $\mathbf{A} = \mathcal{U}(A)$. According to Proposition 1, we can compute the FDDS X such that $A = X^k$ by considering the forest $\mathbf{F} = \mathcal{C}(\mathbf{A}, n)$ where α is the number of trees in $\mathbf{F}$ and

$n = \alpha + depth(\mathbf{A})$. Again, this depth allows us to ensure that all the transient dynamics of the dynamical system are represented in the different trees. Applying the root algorithm on $\mathbf{F}$, we obtain the result of the root as a forest of finite trees. However, this is just a candidate solution for the corresponding problem over the initial FDDS (for the same reasoning as in the case of division). In order to test the result of the root algorithm, as before, we realised the roll of one tree in the solution to period p with p as the number of trees in the result. Then to decide if X is truly the k-th root of A, we verify if $X^k = A$ where X is the result of the roll operation. That is possible because the algorithm is designed to study connected solutions. Indeed, the following holds.

Corollary 2. *Let A be a FDDS, it is possible to decide if there exists a connected FDDS X and an integer $k > 1$ such that $X^k = A$ in polynomial time.*

By combining the division algorithm with the root algorithm, we are now able to study equations of the form $AX^k = B$. Given FDDS A and B and $k > 0$, we can first compute the result $\mathbf{Y}$ of the division of $\mathcal{C}(\mathcal{U}(B), n)$ by $\mathcal{C}(\mathcal{U}(A), n)$, where α is the number of trees in $\mathcal{U}(B)$ and $n = \alpha + depth(B)$. Then, we compute the k-th root $\mathbf{X}$ of $\mathbf{Y}$. After that, we make the roll of one tree of $\mathbf{X}$ in period p, with p the number of trees in $\mathbf{X}$. Then, using the roll result X, we just need to verify if $AX^k = B$. Once again, the solutions found by this method are only the connected ones, and further non-connected solutions are also possible.

5 Conclusions

In this article we have proven the cancellation property for products of unrolls and established that the division of FDDSs is polynomial-time when searching for connected quotients only. Furthermore, we have proven that calculating the k-th root of a FDDSs is polynomial-time if the solution is connected. Finally, we have shown that solving equations of the form $AX^k = B$ is polynomial if X is connected. However, numerous questions remain unanswered.

The main direction for further investigation involves removing the connectivity condition. Although the cancellation property of unrolls we proved and the new polynomial-time algorithm for the division suggest that the primary challenge for FDDS division lies in the cycles rather than the transients, the same cannot be said for the computation of the k-th root of FDDS. Another intriguing direction is solving general polynomial equations $P(X_1, \ldots, X_n) = B$ with a constant right-hand side B. While this appears to be at least as challenging as division, some specific cases, such as when the polynomial is injective, could yield more direct results. Furthermore, the results of this work can improve the state of the art of the solution of $P(X_1, \ldots, X_n) = B$ where polynomial P is a sum of univariate monomials [4]. Indeed, a technique to solve (and enumerate the solutions) of this type of equation in a finite number of systems of equations of the form $AX^k = B$ has been introduced. Thus, our result, which is more efficient than previously known techniques, can have a positive impact on the complexity of the proposed pipeline. It would also be interesting to investigate whether our techniques also apply to finding nontrivial solutions to equations of the form $XY = B$ with X and Y connected, which would make it possible to improve our knowledge of the problem of irreducibility.

Acknowledgment. SR was supported by the French Agence Nationale pour la Recherche (ANR) in the scope of the project "REBON" (grant number ANR-23-CE45-0008), and KP, AEP and MR by the EU project MSCA-SE-101131549 "ACANCOS".

References

1. Bernot, G., Comet, J.P., Richard, A., Chaves, M., Gouzé, J.L., Dayan, F.: Modeling and analysis of gene regulatory networks. In: Cazals, F., Kornprobst, P. (eds.) Modeling in Computational Biology and Biomedicine, pp. 47–80. Springer, Heidelberg (2012). https://doi.org/10.1007/978-3-642-31208-3_2
2. Dennunzio, A., Dorigatti, V., Formenti, E., Manzoni, L., Porreca, A.E.: Polynomial equations over finite, discrete-time dynamical systems. In: Mauri, G., El Yacoubi, S., Dennunzio, A., Nishinari, K., Manzoni, L. (eds.) ACRI 2018. LNCS, vol. 11115, pp. 298–306. Springer, Cham (2018). https://doi.org/10.1007/978-3-319-99813-8_27
3. Dennunzio, A., Formenti, E., Margara, L., Montmirail, V., Riva, S.: Solving equations on discrete dynamical systems. In: Cazzaniga, P., Besozzi, D., Merelli, I., Manzoni, L. (eds.) CIBB 2019. LNCS, vol. 12313, pp. 119–132. Springer, Cham (2020). https://doi.org/10.1007/978-3-030-63061-4_12
4. Dennunzio, A., Formenti, E., Margara, L., Riva, S.: An algorithmic pipeline for solving equations over discrete dynamical systems modelling hypothesis on real phenomena. J. Comput. Sci. **66**, 101932 (2023)
5. Dennunzio, A., Formenti, E., Margara, L., Riva, S.: A note on solving basic equations over the semiring of functional digraphs. arXiv e-prints (2024). https://arxiv.org/abs/2402.16923
6. Doré, F., Formenti, E., Porreca, A.E., Riva, S.: Decomposition and factorisation of transients in functional graphs. Theoret. Comput. Sci. **999**, 114514 (2024)
7. Ehrenfeucht, A., Rozenberg, G.: Reaction systems. Fund. Inform. **75**, 263–280 (2007)
8. Formenti, E., Régin, J.-C., Riva, S.: MDDs boost equation solving on discrete dynamical systems. In: Stuckey, P.J. (ed.) CPAIOR 2021. LNCS, vol. 12735, pp. 196–213. Springer, Cham (2021). https://doi.org/10.1007/978-3-030-78230-6_13
9. Gadouleau, M., Riis, S.: Graph-theoretical constructions for graph entropy and network coding based communications. IEEE Trans. Inf. Theory **57**(10), 6703–6717 (2011)
10. Gershenson, C.: Introduction to random Boolean networks. arXiv e-prints (2004). https://doi.org/10.48550/arXiv.nlin/0408006
11. Goles, E., Martìnez, S.: Neural and Automata Networks: Dynamical Behavior and Applications. Kluwer Academic Publishers (1990)
12. Hammack, R., Imrich, W., Klavžar, S.: Handbook of Product Graphs. Discrete Mathematics and Its Applications, 2nd edn. CRC Press (2011)
13. Hopcroft, J.E., Wong, J.K.: Linear time algorithm for isomorphism of planar graphs (preliminary report). In: Proceedings of the Sixth Annual ACM Symposium on Theory of Computing, pp. 172–184 (1974)

14. Naquin, E., Gadouleau, M.: Factorisation in the semiring of finite dynamical systems. Theoret. Comput. Sci. **998**, 114509 (2024)
15. Strozecki, Y.: Enumeration complexity: incremental time, delay and space. HDR thesis, Université de Versailles Saint-Quentin-en-Yvelines (2021)
16. Thomas, R.: Boolean formalization of genetic control circuits. J. Theor. Biol. **42**(3), 563–585 (1973)
17. Thomas, R., D'Ari, R.: Biological Feedback. CRC Press (1990)

Asynchronous Cellular Systems that Solve the Parity Problem

Nazim Fatès(✉)

Université de Lorraine, CNRS, Inria, LORIA, 54000 Nancy, France
nazim.fates@loria.fr

Abstract. We present stochastic cellular automata that classify the parity of initial conditions. The model is an interacting particles system where cells are updated by pairs, randomly chosen at each time step. A first rule is proposed, with a symmetry between 0's and 1's. We show that it classifies the parity of the initial configurations thanks to a non-biased random walk of the frontiers between 0's and 1's. We present an analysis of the classification time, as well as numerical simulations, to establish that the classification time scales quadratically with the number of cells. In a second time, breaking the state symmetry, we propose an improvement of this rule with the simultaneous use of two classifying systems.

Keywords: asynchronous cellular automata · interacting particle systems · parity classification

1 Introduction

Cellular automata are an original model of computation where parallelism and locality are primordial. They are formed of elementary computing units, the cells, which are arranged on a grid of arbitrary dimension, and which interact according to a local rule. The cells change their state at a discrete times, either synchronously if a global clock is present, or asynchronously when the updating times are independent. Although they have the same computing power as Turing machines, it is not yet well understood how to program cellular automata in order to obtain a given behaviour, especially when we aim to use a small number of states and only simple interaction rules.

With their parallel and local mode of operation, cellular automata and their derived models form a fertile field of research; they invite us to think differently about computational processes. In this research field, two main families of problems exist: in the direct problems, one analyses the properties of a rule or a set of rules, while in the *inverse problems*, one seeks to find the rules that display a given behaviour, often a computational task. The *parity problem* is an inverse problem: given a finite one-dimensional cellular system with binary states and spatially periodic conditions (cycles), find a rule which determines the parity of

M. Gadouleau and A. Castillo-Ramirez (Eds.): AUTOMATA 2024, LNCS 14782, pp. 133–145, 2024.
https://doi.org/10.1007/978-3-031-65887-7_9

the number of 1's contained in this initial configuration. More precisely, it is a consensus problem: if the parity of the initial configuration is even, all the cells should agree on 0 and remain in this state, while they should all agree on 1 if this number is odd [1].

A deterministic solution to the problem was proposed by Betel and al. [2]. These authors designed a clever way to achieve the classification of the initial conditions by constructing a rule which alternatively tries to attain the all-1 and the all-0 fixed points with internal "signals" that travel back and forth. The difficulty to overcome is that such signals need to be encoded within the system itself, without the use of additional states. The rule they proposed has a radius of four, which means that each cell decides its next state according to the state of the four nearest cells on the left and on the right, plus its own state. In order to be encoded, this rule can be given as a sequence of 512 bits, a 156-digit code, or, more compactly, as a list of 10 sub-rules with wildcards, that is, states than can take any value indifferently[1]

In a different context, Ruivo and de Oliveira proposed to solve the parity problem with a simple rule, namely the Elementary Cellular Automaton 150, with a particular asynchronous updating [3]. With this local rule, each cell simply applies an XOR operation on its own state and the state of its left and right neighbours. The cells are updated according to the parity of their position on the line: all the even cells are updated synchronously and then all the odd cells, which means that a global synchronisation of the transitions is still required. These authors and their coauthors also tackled a more general case where the dynamical systems were defined on various types of graphs [4, 5].

In this work, we revisit this problem with a model which uses *independent random updates* of pairs of cells. This means that this is an *interacting particle system*: at each time step, a pair of adjacent cells is chosen randomly and uniformly and then the state of the two cells of the pair is simultaneously updated. Our aim is to explore to which extent the introduction of randomness in the updating scheme can allow us to simplify the construction of a solution. We will first present a formal framework to define the problem and a first solution and, in a second step, we study the convergence properties of this rule with a worst-case analysis. We also present an improvement of the classification process by using simultaneously two different rules. We then present numerical simulations for the average case and conclude with a few words of perspective.

2 Presentation of the Model

We deal with a finite system of n cells arranged with periodic boundary conditions, that is, they form a ring. The set of cells is thus denoted by $\mathcal{L} = (\mathbb{Z}/n\mathbb{Z})$.

We assume that cells have a binary state in $Q = \{0, 1\}$. The state of the system at a given time is called a *configuration*; for a configuration x, the state of cell $i \in \mathcal{L}$ is denoted by x_i. The set of configurations is denoted by $\mathcal{E}_n = Q^{\mathcal{L}}$.

[1] The solution that was initially published is possibly altered by a mistake, which nevertheless does not compromise the whole construction [private communications].

We say that the parity $P(x)$ of a configuration x is even or odd if the number of 1's it contains is even or odd, respectively. We will write $P(x) = |x|_1 \mod 2$, where $|x|_1$ denotes the number of 1's in x. We also call a 1-region (resp. a 0-region) a set of contiguous cells in state 1 (resp. 0) which is maximal (with respect to the inclusion).

We now present our first model for solving the parity problem. Let $(U_t)_{t \in \mathbb{N}}$ be a series of independent identically distributed random variables that draw uniformly a pair of adjacent cells in $\mathcal{L}$. These random variables represent the *updating method*, here, the pair of cells which is selected for being updated at each time step. For the sake of simplicity we will identify the random variable U_t and its realisation and simply consider that $U_t = \{i, i+1\}$ represents the fact that the cells i and $i+1$ are updated at time t.

Starting from a given configuration $x \in \mathcal{E}_n$, the evolution of the system is stochastic; let $(x^t)_{t \in \mathbb{N}}$ be the series of random configurations that will be obtained from x, with the initial condition $x^0 = x$. We now introduce the *balanced rule*: For $\{i, i+1\} = U(t)$,

$$(x_i^{t+1}, x_{i+1}^{t+1}) = \begin{cases} (1 - x_i^t, 1 - x_{i+1}^t) & \text{if } x_{i-1}^t \neq x_i^t \text{ or } x_{i+1}^t \neq x_{i+2}^t, \\ (x_i^t, x_{i+1}^t) & \text{otherwise;} \end{cases}$$

and $\forall i \in \mathcal{L}, i \notin U_t \implies x_i^{t+1} = x_i^t$.

In words, the cells that are not updated keep their state and the state of the two cells selected for an update will be flipped only if there is a difference of state between the left updated cell and its left neighbour or between the right updated cell and its right neighbour. These patterns, which trigger a flip, are called *active neighbourhood patterns*, the other ones are *passive*. There are four passive neighbourhood patterns: 0000, 0011, 1100, and 1111 ; the twelve other patterns are active. The model has two fixed points $\mathbf{0} = 0^{\mathcal{L}}$ or $\mathbf{1} = 1^{\mathcal{L}}$; these uniform configurations represent the ouput of the classification process.

Definition 1. *The classification time $T(x)$ corresponds to the number of time steps needed to attain one of the configurations $\mathbf{0}$ or $\mathbf{1}$ starting from a configuration x, that is,*

$$T(x) = \min\{t \in \mathbb{N} : x^t \in \{\mathbf{0}, \mathbf{1}\}\}.$$

The average classification time of x is denoted by $\mathbb{E}\{T(x)\}$.

Definition 2. *A configuration x is* well classified *if $T(x)$ is finite and $x^{T(x)} = (P(x))^{\mathcal{L}}$, that is, x^T is equal to $\mathbf{0}$ (resp. $\mathbf{1}$) if the parity of x is even (resp. odd).*

In our model, we update one pair of cells at each time step. However, this introduces an artificial slowing down factor of the order of n. For example if the only possible transformation of the pair would be to replace a 10 by a 01, then a 1 surrounded by 0's would travel to the right at the average speed of $1/n$. In order to allow a fair comparison between the synchronous and asynchronous models, we prefer to handle a *rescaled* time where one time step corresponds to n random updates.

For a given ring size $n \in \mathbb{N}$, we will evaluate a rule with its *rescaled worst expected classification time* $\tau(n)$, that is, the highest value of the average rescaled classification time:

$$\tau(n) = \max_{\{x \in \mathcal{E}_n\}} \mathbb{E}\{T(x)/n\} = \frac{1}{n} \cdot \max_{\{x \in \mathcal{E}_n\}} \mathbb{E}\{T(x)\}.$$

For simplicity, we will drop the adjective *rescaled* as it will be clear from the context if we are dealing with the rescaled time (τ) or with the number of updates (T).

Fig. 1. Two space-time diagrams showing the evolution of the system. Cells with state 0 and 1 are depicted in white and blue (or black), respectively. The successive configurations attained by the system are packed from left to right. (top): the initial number of 1's is even (bottom): the initial number of 1's is odd.

Note that for the sake of coherence, we only consider odd ring sizes. Indeed, if we take an even ring size, a problem might occur with the all-1 configuration: as it can be considered as an initial condition, the system should then converge to all-0, but at the same time it is supposed to be a fixed point by construction because it is an answer for the initial configurations which are classified as odd. The use of odd ring sizes allow us to avoid this paradox.

Also note that the model presented above is somehow minimal: since the system has no external memory, the parity needs to be preserved through time, which means that we cannot do less than updating cells by pairs. Here, the pairs are chosen randomly at each time step without any memory and the neighbourhood of each pair of cell is limited to the left and right neighbouring cells of the cells which are updated.

3 Properties of the Balanced Rule

Figure 1 depicts two sample evolutions of the system for $n = 11$ cells. These space-time diagrams were selected to display cases of rapid convergence towards a fixed point, however, this convergence takes more time in general. Let us now analyse the convergence properties of this rule and study this behaviour analytically.

Proposition 1. *Every configuration of odd size is almost surely well classified.*

Proof. The proof of this property is quite simple since $(x^t)_{t\in\mathbb{N}}$ is a Markov chain: it is sufficient to examine the reachability relationships in this chain.

First, we can observe that the application of the local rule conserves the parity of a configuration.

Second, we show that the fixed point $\mathbf{0}$ (resp. $\mathbf{1}$) is reachable from every even (resp. odd) configuration. To see why, let us consider an arbitrary configuration x different from $\mathbf{0}$ with an even number of 1's. Let us show that x can reach a configuration y where the number of 1's has decreased by two, that is, $|y|_1 = |x|_1 - 2$.

(a) This is immediate if the x contains a 11. Indeed, it necessarily contains the pattern 011, as x differs from $\mathbf{1}$, which implies that it contains either a 0110 or a 0111 and in both cases the flip on the two central 1's apply.

(b) If all the 1's of x are isolated, that is, if x does not contain a pattern 11, then we can choose an arbitrary 1 and flip the pairs 01 from the right to the left until we reach a configuration which contains a 11. Indeed, this is always possible since both 0010 and 1010 are active neighbourhoods.

By recurrence, we can show that the fixed point $\mathbf{0}$ is reachable from any even configuration. Since this is a fixed point, it implies that all the even configurations different from $\mathbf{0}$ are transient. By exchanging 0's and 1's, the same property can be established for odd configurations and the fixed point $\mathbf{1}$ (we are on a ring of odd size). These two properties imply that all the configurations will be almost surely well classified.

Conjecture 1. The worst expected classification time scales quadratically with the ring size, that is, we have $\tau(n) = \Theta(n^2)$ for $n \in 2\mathbb{N}+1$.

The justification of this conjecture is that the density almost follows a non-biased random walk until it hits the fixed point. We say *almost* because since a configuration can reach only one fixed point (which corresponds to its parity), the evolution of the density cannot be strictly non-biased. In particular, for a ring size $n = 2k+1$, when the number of ones is equal to $2k$, the density can only decrease.

To study more precisely the conjecture, we will proceed in two steps: (a) first we obtain a lower bound by calculating precisely the classification time of configurations from a given set, then (b) we give some evidence why it is not straightforward to establish a quadratic upper bound.

Lemma 1. *The worst expected classification time scales at least quadratically with the ring size, that is, we have $\tau(n) = \Omega(n^2)$, for $n \in 2\mathbb{N}+1$.*

Proof. For a ring size $n = 2k+1$ and $k > 3$, let us consider the set of *even* initial configurations $z_i = 1^{2i}0^{n-2i}$ for $i \in \{0, \dots, k\}$. As the rule cannot increase the

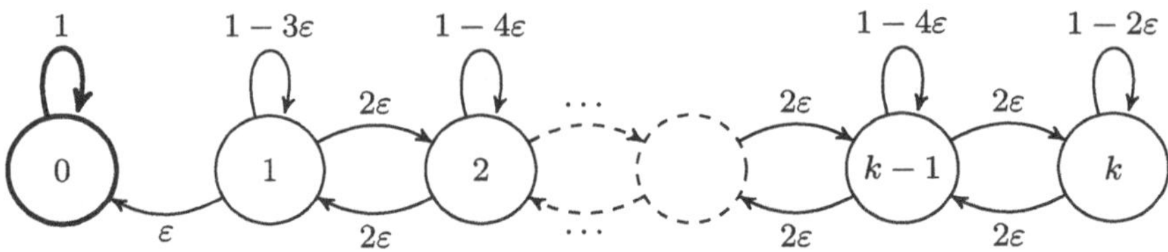

Fig. 2. Representation of the Markov chain which describes the evolution of the balanced rule from configuration $1^{2i}0^{n-2i}$. The state of the Markov chain is the number of 11 pairs. The quantity ϵ is equal to $1/n$.

number of 1-regions, all the configurations reached by the system during its evolution will be equivalent up to shift to an element of $\{z_i\}_i$, up to shifts. Let $(x^t)_{t\in\mathbb{N}}$ denote the stochastic process that describes the evolution of the system and let $X_t = \frac{|x^t|_1}{2}$ denote the number of 11 pairs at a given time t.

Clearly (X_t) is a Markov chain; it has one absorbing state $X_t = 0$, which corresponds to $x^t = \mathbf{0}$, the end of the classification process. Let us evaluate the average time needed to converge to this absorbing state when we start from z_i.

For $i = 1$, we have $x^t =$ 0000110000... (up to shifts) and $X_t = 1$, there are three positions where an update will change the configuration, (a) the two positions with the active neighbourhoods 0001 and 1000 give $X_{t+1} = 2$, and (b) the position with the active neighbourhood 0110, which will transform x^t into $\mathbf{0}$ and the classification ends. The cases (a) and (b) happen with probabilities $2/n$ and $1/n$, respectively.

For $1 < i \leq k - 1$, there are four possibilities to modify a configuration equivalent to z_i: (a) the active neighbourhood is 0001 or 1000, in which case we increase by one $X_{t+1} = X_t + 1$, or (b) the updated neighbourhood is 0111 or 1110, in which case we decrease by one $X_{t+1} = X_t - 1$. The cases (a) and (b) both happen with probability $2/n$.

The special configuration z_k has the form 01^{2k} and in this case the only possible transformation is to turn a 11 into a 00, in which case we reach a configuration equivalent to z_{k-1}. This happens with probability $2/n$.

The transitions of the Markov chain are represented on Fig. 2. Let us denote by T_i the classification time starting from a configuration which has $2i$ contiguous cells in state 1's, that is, an equivalent of z_i up to shifts.

For a state that is not a fixed point, we calculate the convergence time of this state as the weighted sum of the convergence time of the states that are reachable from this state, to which we add one, as the time needed to make the transition. This is a classical technique which is sometimes called the step forward method (see e.g. Ref. [6]). We thus find that the sequence (T_i) obeys the following set of equations: (i) $T_0 = 0$,

$$(ii)\ T_1 = 1 + \frac{1}{n}T_0 + \frac{n-3}{n}T_1 + \frac{2}{n}T_2,$$

$$(iii)\ T_i = 1 + \frac{2}{n}T_{i-1} + \frac{n-4}{n}T_i + \frac{2}{n}T_{i+1} \text{ for all } i \in \{2,\ldots,k-1\}, \text{and,}$$

$$(iv)\ T_k = 1 + \frac{2}{n}T_{k-1} + \frac{n-2}{n}T_k.$$

Using the rescaled time $\tau_i = T_i/n$, the system is simplified into: (i) $\tau_0 = 0$,
(ii) $1 + \tau_0 - 3\tau_1 + 2\tau_2 = 0$,
(iii) $1 + 2\tau_{i-1} - 4\tau_i + 2\tau_{i+1} = 0$ for all $i \in \{2,\ldots,k-1\}$, and
(iv) $1 + 2\tau_{k-1} - 2\tau_k = 0$.

Solving this system yields $\tau_i = \frac{(i+1)k}{2} - \frac{i(i-1)}{4}$ for $i \in \{1,\ldots,k\}$. In particular, for k tending to infinity, we have:

$$\tau_k \sim k^2/4, \text{ and since } k \sim n/2, \text{this yields } \tau_k = \Theta(n^2),$$

which gives us a lower bound with a quadratic scaling in the ring size n.

We have established the classification time for configurations with one region, let us see what happens in the general case.

If we take an even configuration with only two 1-regions, if the length of these regions is even, then it is not difficult to show that the convergence is also quadratic. Indeed, the length of these regions will increase by two or decrease by two and this length will always remain even. So each region will eventually disappear and the system will converge to the all-zero fixed point, as it should. Using martingale techniques, one can show that this will happen in average in a time which is quadratic in the ring size [6]. However, a problem arises with regions of odd size, especially those regions which are separated by an odd number of cells. Consider for instance the configuration 0^k0011111000000011100^k, with k large enough. The central region of 0's has a length of 7. The two 1-regions can grow or shrink their size, but, unfortunately, they cannot merge in the central region because the length of this region always remains odd. So when the two regions will be separated by only one 0, they will "bounce" against each other and reduce their size. So the convergence can only happen if the 1-regions merge on the other size of the ring, or if an odd region shrinks to a size of 1 and then moves left or right, which will make the central region have an even size.

We believe that this effect, although slowing down the process, will not modify qualitatively its dynamics, and this why we think that it has a quadratic convergence time. The positive side of the "bouncing phenomenon" is that it lead us to consider another method that avoids this inconvenient. This will be exposed in the next section

4 Joint Classifications of Even and Odd Configurations

In the case where we can duplicate the state of the initial configurations that we want to classify, we now propose to use *two separate systems* to determine the class of the input configuration: the first system will converge only if the configuration is even and the second if the configuration is odd. We thus modify the rule above and define, informally, the *even classifier* (resp. the *odd classifier*) as a modification of the balanced rule where the transition $\mathtt{00} \to \mathtt{11}$ (resp. $\mathtt{11} \to \mathtt{00}$) are inhibited. In other words, in the even classifier, 1-regions shrink but never expand, and equivalently for 0-regions in the odd classifier. This will make the even and odd classifiers respectively converge only for even and odd configurations, otherwise they will evolve without reaching a fixed point.

Formally, for $q \in \{\mathtt{0}, \mathtt{1}\}$, for a configuration $x \in \mathcal{E}_n$, we take the same definitions as above, with U the updating method; we keep:

$$\forall i \in \mathcal{L}, i \notin U_t \implies x_i^{t+1} = x_i^t$$

and, for $\{i, i+1\} = U(t)$, we now define that,

if (a) $x_{i-1}^t \neq x_i^t$ or $x_{i+1}^t \neq x_{i+2}^t$, and (b) $(x_i^t, x_{i+1}^t) \neq (q, q)$ then

$$(x_i^{t+1}, x_{i+1}^{t+1}) = (1 - x_i^t, 1 - x_{i+1}^t),$$

otherwise

$$(x_i^{t+1}, x_{i+1}^{t+1}) = (x_i^t, x_{i+1}^t).$$

The even and odd rules are then defined for $q = \mathtt{0}$ and $q = \mathtt{1}$, respectively ; the even rule makes the number of 1's a non-increasing function of time while the odd rule makes it non-decreasing.

Theorem 1. *For the even (resp. odd) rule, the worst expected classification time of the even (resp. odd) configurations of odd size scales quadratically with the ring size, that is,* $\tau(n) = \Theta(n^2)$.

We prove this claim in three steps: (a) prove the convergence of the configurations, (b) establish a lower bound by calculating precisely the classification time for a given set of configurations, and then (c) give a quadratic upper bound with martingale techniques.

Proof. Without loss of generality, let us show that the even rule correctly classifies the even configurations.

(a) Convergence. The number of 1's can only decrease by pairs and regions of 1's cannot appear, nor can they merge if they are not reduced to isolated 1's. This means that after a finite number of steps, each region of 1's with an even length will disappear, and the region of 1's with an odd length will form an isolated 1. We will thus attain a configuration formed of an even number of isolated 1's. Then, it can be seen that the random movements of these 1's will create pairs of 1's, which will progressively disappear until the systems reaches the fixed point **0**.

(b) Lower bound. For a ring size $n = 2k+1$ and $k \geq 2$, consider the configurations $z_i = \mathtt{10}^i\mathtt{10}^{i-1}$ as the initial conditions of the system. The configurations z_i contain two isolated 1's. As long as these 1's are not adjacent, they will move with a non-biased random walk.

To determine their movements, we choose to keep track of their respective position and call them the first and second 1 ; we then define X_t as the number of cells between the first and second 1. (X_t) is a random variable that takes its values between 0 and $n-2$; let T_k be the number of steps needed to attain one of the boundaries 0 or $n-2$ starting from z_k. Note that once the pattern 11 has appeared, nothing can happen except the disappearance of the pair of 1, which happens with a probability $1/n$. It thus takes n updates in average to reach **0**, that is, we need only one time step with the rescaling time.

The transitions of the Markov chain are represented on Fig. 3. Using the step forward method, we obtain a set of equations similar to the ones of asynchronous Elementary Cellular Automata (ECA) 178 [6]: (i) $T_0 = 0$; (ii) $T_{n-2} = 0$ and

$$(iii)\ T_i = 1 + \frac{2}{n}T_{i-1} + \frac{n-4}{n}T_i + \frac{2}{n}T_{i+1} \text{ for all } i \in \{1, \dots, n-3\};$$

which gives us $T_i = \frac{n}{4}i(n-2-i)$.

This yields a rescaled time $\tau_i = T_i/n = 4i(n-2-i)$, with a maximum time of $\tau_k = 4k(n-2-k) = \Theta(n^2)$. Since the rescaled classification time of z_k is equal to $\tau_k + 1$, it thus scales quadratically with the ring size.

Note that other equivalent possibilities exist to calculate the convergence time of this system: for instance, one may simply model the distance between the two 1's or use a transformation of the configuration (see below).

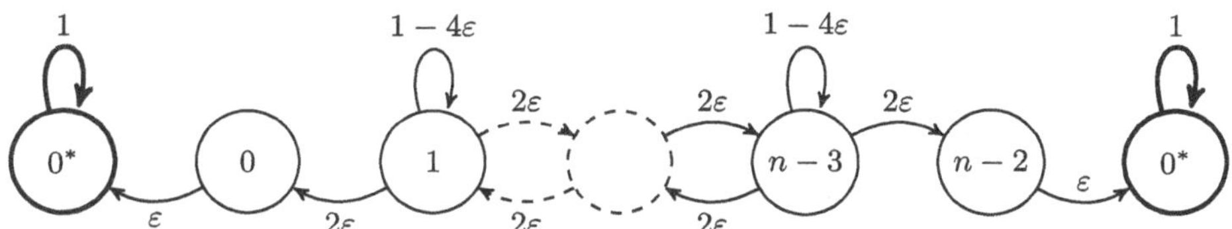

Fig. 3. Representation of the Markov chain which describes the evolution of the even rule from a configuration $z_i = 10^i10^{n-2-i}$. The state of the Markov chain represents the value of i and 0^* is the homogeneous configuration all-zero. This state has been duplicated for the sake of readability. The quantity ϵ is equal to $1/n$.

(c) Upper bound. As a first step, starting from an arbitrary even configuration, we bound the time needed to reach an *archipelago*, that is, a configuration where all the 1's are isolated. Let us denote by τ_i the random variable that it takes for the i-th region to shrink to a single 1. It is easy to remark that the expectation of τ_i is linear in the ring size n and that, since $\mathbb{E}\{\max(\tau_i)\} \leq \sum_i \mathbb{E}\{\tau_i)\}$, and since the number of regions is linear, the time needed to reach an archipelago is upper-bounded by a quadratic function (in n).

Let us now consider an evolution (x^t) from an archipelago $x = x^0$ formed of $k \in 2\mathbb{N}$ isolated 1's. We can map x^t into a configuration y^t according to the following operation: we build y^t by reading x^t from left to right and consider that the 1's in x^t encode a change of state in y^t, while the 0's encode that the same state is kept. In other words, the state of k-th cell of y^t is the parity of the number of 1's contained in the k first cells of y; formally: $y_k^t = |\{j, x_j^t = 1\}| \bmod 2$.

It can be checked that the dynamics of (y^t) is as follows: the frontiers of the 1-regions (and the 0-regions) move left or right with probability $1/n$ and the isolated 0's and 1's disappear with probability $1/n$ (this correspond to updating a neighbourhood 0110 in x). This means that it is equivalent to the dynamics of ECA 178 [6]. As a consequence, the second step has an average classification time which scales quadratically with n and the whole process also scales quadratically. □

We thus have a classifying system composed of two sub-systems: one will almost surely answer if the configuration is even, the other one if the configuration is odd. This means that the classification operation should be stopped as soon a consensus is established in one of the two systems. Note that one may also use several copies of the even and odd classifiers and stop the search as soon as a consensus is established in one of the classifiers.

5 Numerical Experiments

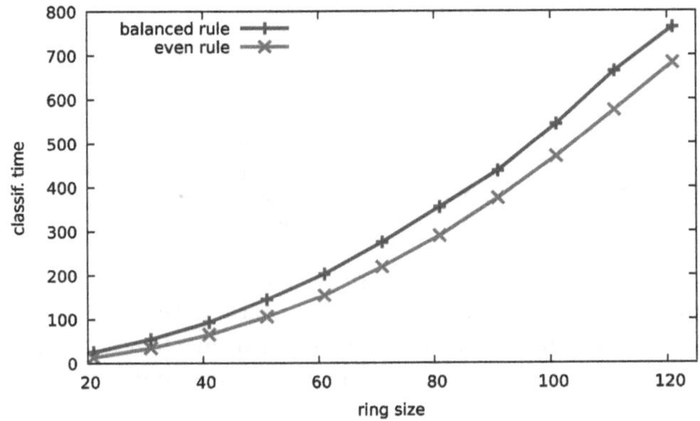

Fig. 4. Classification time as function of the ring size. Statistical measures for 100 000 samples.

In order to have a more precise estimation of how the classification time varies with the ring size, we carry out some numerical experiments. Here, we are no longer interested in the worst expected classification time but in the *mean* expected classification time, which means that we measure an average of averages.

We repeat the experiment which consists in drawing 100 000 times an initial condition and measuring classification time. For the classification with the balanced model, the initial configurations are drawn uniformly in the set $\mathcal{E}_n$. For the two-system experiment with the *even and odd rules*, we simply draw a configuration x uniformly as before, but apply it to the *even rule only* with the condition that if this configuration is odd, we take $\bar{x}$, the conjugate of x where each cell has its state flipped, as an initial configuration. For reasons of symmetry, since only one of the two systems can converge, this is equivalent to running the two systems on x and taking the classification time of the first system which converges.

Figure 4 displays the mean classification time as function of the ring size. As expected, the classification time is lower for the even rule than for the balanced rule, but the difference is not overwhelming. It was also verified that the measures are in a good agreement with a quadratic scaling: fitting a second-degree polynomial to the data yields a curve whose position is visually almost indistinguishable from the actual measures.

6 Perspectives

This study demonstrated the possibility to solve the cellular automata parity problem with a simple rule where updates occur by pairs at random times and positions, and with a local rule which is expressed in two lines. We showed how to analyse formally the classification time of the models with Markov chains and analytical techniques inspired by the study of Elementary Cellular Automata with fully asynchronous updating [6].

The only deterministic rule known so far has a neighbourhood size of 9 (a radius-4 rule) and requires a perfect synchronisation of the transitions. The Elementary Cellular Automaton 150 used with an alternation of the cells with even and odd positions is also a good deterministic solution, but still requires a global synchronisation of the transitions. In contrast, the proposed stochastic rule makes the updating procedure totally local; however, it has a slower operation mode, as its average time of classification scales quadratically in the ring size. In return, its implementation is potentially simpler as only a local synchronisation of the transitions by pairs is required.

The asynchronous nature of the transitions may facilitate the use of a truly decentralised computing device as it eliminates the need for a clock that sends a signal to trigger the computation in the cells. For example, such systems could be implemented with Brownian cellular automata, where tokens move freely on a line [7]. In such systems, the only requirement would be to guarantee that the two cells make their transitions together in order to preserve the global parity of the configurations. We leave for future work a more precise analysis of these processes but one can assume that such systems could be made robust to various kind of perturbations, such as miscalculating the next state or misreading the state of the neighbours. It is also worth considering more general cases with interactions embedded on a graph, with or without spatial locality constraints.

More generally, this research goes along the lines that aim to develop robust computing schemes, where noise is considered as an ally rather than an obstacle to overcome. Various authors have demonstrated that stochastic cellular systems can acquire suitable properties for computing in a purely decentralised way. For example, self-correcting discrete lines [8], stochastic solutions to the density classification problem [9–11] or to the synchronisation problem [12] have been proposed. It is probably too early to say if a new trend is emerging but, for sure, this field of research opens some promising paths out of the classical computing paradigm.

Acknowledgments. The author wishes to express his sincere gratitude to Barbara Wolnik (univ. of Gdansk, Poland) and Irène Marcovici (univ. of Rouen, France) for their precious advice and remarks. The comments of the anonymous reviewers were a great help to improve the manuscript.

Disclosure of Interests. The author have no competing interests to declare that are relevant to the content of this article.

References

1. Sipper, M.: Computing with cellular automata: three cases for nonuniformity. Phys. Rev. E **57**, 3589–3592 (1998). https://doi.org/10.1103/PhysRevE.57.3589
2. Betel, H., de Oliveira, P.P.B., Flocchini, P.: Solving the parity problem in one-dimensional cellular automata. Nat. Comput. **12**(3), 323–337 (2013). https://doi.org/10.1007/s11047-013-9374-9
3. Ruivo, E.L.P., de Oliveira, P.P.B.: A perfect solution to the parity problem with elementary cellular automaton 150 under asynchronous update. Inform. Sci. **493**, 138–151 (2019). https://doi.org/10.1016/j.ins.2019.04.045
4. Ruivo, E.L.P., Balbi, P.P., Perrot, K.: An asynchronous solution to the synchronisation problem for binary one-dimensional cellular automata. Physica D **413**, 132554 (2020). https://doi.org/10.1016/j.physd.2020.132554
5. Balbi, P.P., Ruivo, E., Faria, F.: Synchronous solution of the parity problem on cyclic configurations, with elementary cellular automaton rule 150, over a family of directed, non-circulant, regular graphs. Inform. Sci. **615**, 578–603 (2022). https://doi.org/10.1016/j.ins.2022.10.045
6. Fatès, N.: Asynchronous cellular automata. In: Encyclopedia of Complexity and Systems Science, pp. 1–21. Springer, Berlin (2018). https://doi.org/10.1007/978-3-642-27737-5_671-2
7. Peper, F., Lee, J., Isokawa, T.: Brownian cellular automata. J. Cell. Autom. **5**(3), 185–206 (2010)
8. Regnault, D., Rémila, É.: Lost in self-stabilization: a local process that aligns connected cells. Theoret. Comput. Sci. **736**, 41–61 (2018). https://doi.org/10.1016/j.tcs.2018.02.015
9. Fukś, H.: Nondeterministic density classification with diffusive probabilistic cellular automata. Phys. Rev. E **66**(6), 066106 (2002). https://doi.org/10.1103/PhysRevE.66.066106
10. Schüle, M., Ott, T., Stoop, R.: Computing with probabilistic cellular automata. In: Alippi, C., Polycarpou, M., Panayiotou, C., Ellinas, G. (eds.) ICANN 2009. LNCS, vol. 5769, pp. 525–533. Springer, Heidelberg (2009). https://doi.org/10.1007/978-3-642-04277-5_53

11. Fatès, N.: Stochastic cellular automata solutions to the density classification problem - when randomness helps computing. Theory Comput. Syst. **53**(2), 223–242 (2013). https://doi.org/10.1007/s00224-012-9386-3
12. Fatès, N.: Remarks on the cellular automaton global synchronisation problem: deterministic versus stochastic models. Nat. Comput. **18**(3), 429–444 (2019). https://doi.org/10.1007/s11047-018-9683-0

A Note on Skew-Asynchronous Cellular Automata

Souvik Roy[1(✉)], Virendra Kumar Gautam[2], and Sukanta Das[2]

[1] Ahmedabad University, Ahmedabad, Gujarat, India
souvik.roy@ahduni.edu.in, svkr89@gmail.com

[2] Indian Institute of Engineering Science and Technology, Shibpur, Howrah, India
sukanta@it.iiests.ac.in, gautamvirendra2018@gmail.com

Abstract. Atomicity property (in other words, fully asynchronism) is a well-studied source of the noise or perturbation in cellular systems where two consecutive cells are not allowed to be updated simultaneously. In this work, we question this restriction and introduce the notion of skewed environment where atomicity property is not respected. The proposed *skew-asynchronous* cellular automata update two consecutive cells chosen uniformly at random in each step. The present work focuses on elementary cellular automata, which are classified based on their dynamical behaviour under the proposed skewed environment. The dynamical behaviour of these cellular automata are compared with the fully-asynchronous cellular automata, which points out varieties of rich phenomenon under skewed environment. Some elementary cellular automata shift from convergence nature to divergence and some from non-convergence to convergence nature, if update style shifts from fully asynchronism to skewed asynchronism. We identify the cases where the divisibility of the lattice size by 2 or 4 introduces massive repercussion in the system following presence or absence of the atomicity property. Lastly, we theorize the reason behind convergence towards all 0 and all 1 point attractors under the proposed skewed environment which partially validates our experimental observations.

Keywords: Asynchronous cellular automata · Atomicity property · Fully asynchronism · Skew-asynchronism

1 Introduction

To break the assumption of global clock, cellular automata (CAs) community has explored the notion of asynchronous cellular automata in the last two decades, see [7]. Asynchronism is seen as an uncontrolled phenomenon where the cells are independent and are updated independently during the evolution of the system. To introduce this notion of independence (of cells), researchers have introduced different updating schemes [1–3,5,10], where the most studied schemes are fully asynchronous updating scheme [9,14] and α-asynchronous updating scheme [2]. In fully asynchronous updating scheme [9,14], a random cell is selected at each

Published by Springer Nature Switzerland AG 2024
M. Gadouleau and A. Castillo-Ramirez (Eds.): AUTOMATA 2024, LNCS 14782, pp. 146–158, 2024.
https://doi.org/10.1007/978-3-031-65887-7_10

time step to update following uniform distribution. On the other hand, each cell has a given probability α to update and a probability $1 - \alpha$ not to update in α-asynchronous updating scheme [2].

In the literature, some researchers have considered fully asynchronous updating scheme as 'just' a sequential updating scheme [1]. On the contrary, Fatès [7] has argued that fully asynchronous cellular automata (ACAs) is the most 'natural' updating scheme following the continuous nature of 'real' time. In the same direction, a strong counter argument provides the justification that fully asynchronous updating scheme is a special case of *atomicity property* which is capable to model concurrent and distributed systems [4,11].

Following the atomicity property [11], during the update of a cell's state, we say that the cell is enabled for update. While enabled, a cell first reads the states of its self and neighbours following the neighbourhood dependency, and then acts following the state transition function to update its state. This entire operation, i.e. reading of self and neighbour's states and update of the cell's own state, is considered as *atomic*. Therefore, during the enablement of a cell, its neighbours can not update their states. In other words, no two neighbouring cells can be enabled simultaneously. We call this cell update property as *atomicity property*. However, more than one cell at the same time step can be enabled following the atomicity property. For instance, at most half of the cells can be enabled following three-neighbourhood dependency in one-dimensional system.

However, this assumption of atomicity property is not always applicable if we see cellular automata as a model of societal phenomenon. For example, in society, some neighbouring populations follow the same societal norms which violate the independence introduced by atomicity property. Moreover, for modelling natural systems, atomicity property is not a 'good' choice as the perturbation (or noise) is applied to all cells of a small part of the system. With this motivation, this study observes the effect of the cellular system after breaking the atomicity property. To start in this direction, we introduce the notion of *skew*-asynchronous updating scheme, where two neighbouring cells are allowed to be enabled simultaneously. Specifically, for a one-dimensional system, at each time step we randomly and uniformly select one cell and update the state of that selected cell and the state of it's right neighbouring cell. That is, two neighbouring cells are bound to update together, however, the notion of independence is still there in the overall system.

Particularly, in this paper, we observe the effect of breaking the atomicity property in elementary cellular automata (ECAs). Recently in [12], we have completed the characterization of the dynamics, i.e. convergence, recurrence, and non-convergence non-recurrence, of ECAs following fully asynchronous updating scheme. In the light of this characterization, here, we classify 88 minimal ECAs following qualitative and quantitative approaches under proposed skewed environment in comparison with fully asynchronous environment. This displays the overall picture after breaking atomicity property. As we will see, this study is sufficiently rich to provide many kinds of worthy examples. Some ECAs show their absolute irritation in the absence of atomicity property, where some convergent ECAs under fully asynchronous scheme show opposite divergence dynamics in the absence of atomicity property, and vice versa. Moreover, some ECAs show dependency on CA size for convergence following atomicity property [15], however, the same is not applicable for skewed environment. Obviously, some ECAs ignore the absence of atomicity property. Following this, in Sect. 4, we theorize the conditions for convergence towards all 0 and all 1 point attractors under proposed skewed environment.

2 Cellular Automata and Asynchronism

In this work, we consider elementary cellular automata (ECAs), i.e. 1-dimensional 3-neighbourhood (left, self, right) and 2-state ($\{0,1\}$) cellular automata. Here, we consider periodic boundary condition, i.e. cells are arranged as a ring. The set of indices that represent each cell is denoted by $\mathcal{L} = \mathbb{Z}/n\mathbb{Z}$, here, the number of cell is n. The collection of all states at a given time is called a configuration. We denote $\varepsilon_n = \{0,1\}^{\mathcal{L}}$ as the set of configurations. Following the local transition function $f : \{0,1\}^3 \to \{0,1\}$, we define elementary cellular automata which indicates how a cell updates its state according to its own state and the state of its left and right neighbours. In Table 1, we express local transition function in a look-up table format where Rule Min Term (RMT) represents each argument by $r = 4 \times x + 2 \times y + z$, see Table 1 (row 2). Finally, the decimal equivalent of the eight outputs is called "rule", i.e. $f(1,1,1) \cdot 2^7 + f(1,1,0) \cdot 2^6 + \cdots + f(0,0,0) \cdot 2^0$. We call an RMT active if it changes the state of a cell, i.e. $f(x,y,z) \neq y$, otherwise it is passive. Note that, a configuration can also be written as a sequence of RMTs. We have $2^8 = 256$ ECAs, out of which 88 are minimal representative ECAs and the remaining are their equivalent. Following Table shows example ECA 134 where RMT 6 (resp. 7) is active (resp. passive).

(x,y,z) (RMT)	111 (7)	110 (6)	101 (5)	100 (4)	011 (3)	010 (2)	001 (1)	000 (0)	Rule
$f(x,y,z)$	1	0	0	0	0	1	1	0	134

Here, we update the system following fully asynchronous and proposed skew-asynchronous updating schemes. In fully asynchronous updating scheme, one cell is selected randomly and uniformly for update at each time step. Similarly, in the proposed *skew*-asynchronous scheme, one cell (say i) is selected randomly and uniformly, and the local rule is applied for update to cell i and $i+1$ (right neighbouring cell of the selected cell) at each time step. Let $(U_t)_{t\in\mathbb{N}} \in \mathcal{L}^{\mathbb{N}}$ denotes the random sequence of selected cells for update. Evolution of the ECA under these asynchronous updating scheme from an initial configuration x is represented by the stochastic process $(x^t)_{t\in\mathbb{N}}$, and defined recursively by: $x^0 = x$ and $x^{t+1} = F(x^t, U_t)$ with

$$\text{(For fully asynchronous): } x_i^{t+1} = \begin{cases} f(x_{i-1}^t, x_i^t, x_{i+1}^t) & \text{if } i = U_t \\ x_i^t & \text{otherwise.} \end{cases}$$

$$\text{(For skew-asynchronous): } x_i^{t+1} = \begin{cases} f(x_{i-1}^t, x_i^t, x_{i+1}^t) & \text{if } i = U_t \text{ or } i = U_t + 1 \\ x_i^t & \text{otherwise.} \end{cases}$$

Next, a configuration $x \in \varepsilon_n$ is called a *point attractor* if we have $F(x, u) = x$ for all $u \in \mathcal{L}$, that is, when all the RMTs of x are passive. Note that, this property of point attractor is independent of the updating environment. We have also introduced the recurrent property of (fully) ACA by introducing the notion of *recurrent* and *transient* configuration, see [8,13]. Here, a configuration $x \in \varepsilon_n$ is recurrent if for every configuration y that is reachable (following a sequence of successor relations) from x, x is also reachable from y; a non-recurrent configuration is transient (i.e. after some finite time, it is not possible to return back again). Following three are the possible dynamics: (i) For convergent system, starting from any initial configuration, the system converges to point attractor; (ii) For recurrent system, the system shows kind of reversible 'eternal return' phenomenon where all configurations are recurrent; and (iii) For non-convergent non-recurrent system, it shows the dynamics of convergence towards *multi-length* attractor, where few configurations are recurrent and rest are transient.

Following this, in this first experiment, we follow the well-established [10] qualitative and quantitative experimental approaches: (a) Firstly, we need to observe the evolution of the system through space-time diagrams which can be able to provide an important qualitative visual comparison. We consider $n \in [90, 100]$ and evolve the system for 1000 time steps; and (b) Secondly, we need to calculate the density of a configuration x which can be written as $d_x = x_1/n$ (x_1 is the number of 1s in configuration x and n is the lattice size). We start with $n = 100$ considering initial density $d_{ini} = 0.5$; and evolve the system again for 1000 steps; and calculate the density of the configuration in every step. The change in density during evolution of the system provides the formal quantitative comparison of two asynchronous updating schemes.

3 Dynamics of Skew-Asynchronous Cellular Automata

This section classifies the dynamics of ECA under skew-asynchronous scheme in comparison with fully asynchronous dynamics. In Table 1, $\texttt{Fully}_P$ denotes the dynamics (property) of these 88 minimal ECAs under fully asynchronous updating scheme where convergence, recurrence and non-convergence non-recurrence dynamics are respectively denoted as `C`, `R` and `NC-NR`. We have identified 50 convergent ECAs under fully asynchronous environment [14] where starting from any initial configuration cellular system converges to point attractor. Moreover, some ECAs [15] show convergence dynamics depending on the lattice size ($n \in 2\mathbb{N}$ or $n \in 3\mathbb{N}$) under atomicity property. In the (opposite) divergence dynamics, we have identified 18 recurrent ECAs [8] following atomicity property which can be able to capture reversible 'eternal return' phenomenon. We have marked the remaining divergent fully asynchronous ECAs as non-convergent non-recurrent where some configurations are recurrent and some are transient (in a different view, they depict convergence towards multi-length attractor) [12].

Next, we compare the dynamics of these 88 minimal ECAs following skewed environment. Following are the most remarkable observations of this study: (a) ECAs **26**, **58**, **90** and **122** show convergence dynamics (mostly towards all

Table 1. 88 minimal ECAs with their dynamics under fully and skew-asynchronous environment. Here, C, R, NC-NR respectively notes convergence, recurrence and non-convergence non-recurrence dynamics.

ECA	Fully_P	Skew_C	ECA	Fully_P	Skew_C	ECA	Fully_P	Skew_C
0	C	✓	1	NC-NR	✓	2	C	✓
3	NC-NR	✓	4	C	✓	5	C	✓
6 ($n \in 2\mathbb{N}$)	C	✓	**6** ($n \in 2\mathbb{N}+1$)	NC-NR	×	7 ($n \in 2\mathbb{N}$)	C	✓
7 ($n \in 2\mathbb{N}+1$)	NC-NR	✓	8	C	✓	9	NC-NR	✓
10	C	✓	11	NC-NR	✓	12	C	✓
13	C	✓	14 ($n \in 2\mathbb{N}$)	C	✓	14 ($n \in 2\mathbb{N}+1$)	NC-NR	✓
15 ($n \in 2\mathbb{N}$)	C	✓	15 ($n \in 2\mathbb{N}+1$)	NC-NR	✓	18	C	✓
19	NC-NR	✓	22 ($n \in 2\mathbb{N}$)	C	✓	**22** ($n \in 2\mathbb{N}+1$)	NC-NR	×
23 ($n \in 2\mathbb{N}$)	C	✓	23 ($n \in 2\mathbb{N}+1$)	NC-NR	✓	24	C	✓
25	NC-NR	✓	**26**	C	×	27	NC-NR	✓
28	NC-NR	✓	29	NC-NR	✓	30 ($n \in 2\mathbb{N}$)	C	✓
30 ($n \in 2\mathbb{N}+1$)	NC-NR	✓	32	C	✓	33	R	✓
34	C	✓	35	R	✓	36	C	✓
37 ($n \in 3\mathbb{N}$)	C	✓	37 ($n \notin 3\mathbb{N}$)	NC-NR	✓	**38**	R	×
40	C	✓	41	R	✓	42	C	✓
43	R	✓	44	C	✓	45 ($n \in 3\mathbb{N}$)	C	✓
45 ($n \notin 3\mathbb{N}$)	NC-NR	✓	46	R	✓	50	C	✓
51	R	✓	**54**	R	×	56	C	✓
57	R	✓	**58**	C	×	60	R	✓
62	R	✓	72	C	✓	73	NC-NR	✓
74	C	✓	76	C	✓	77	C	✓
78	C	✓	**90**	C	×	94	C	✓
104	C	✓	105 ($n \notin 4\mathbb{N}$)	R	✓	**105** ($n \in 4\mathbb{N}$)	R	×
106	C	✓	108	R	✓	**122**	C	×
128	C	✓	129	NC-NR	✓	130	C	✓
132	C	✓	**134**	R	×	136	C	✓
137	NC-NR	✓	138	C	✓	140	C	✓
142	R	✓	146	C	✓	**150**	R	×
152	C	✓	154	C	✓	156	R	✓
160	C	✓	162	C	✓	164	C	✓
168	C	✓	170	C	✓	172	C	✓
178	C	✓	184	C	✓	200	C	✓
204	C,R	✓	232	C	✓			

0 point attractor) under fully asynchronous updating scheme. However, these ECAs depict divergence dynamics in the absence of atomicity property; (b) In an opposite direction, ECAs **38**, **54**, **134**, and **150** depict recurrence (reversible 'eternal return' phenomenon) dynamics following atomicity property. Surprisingly, these ECAs show convergence (towards all 0 point attractor) under skewed environment; (c) ECAs **6** and **22** show most interesting dependency on lattice size following atomicity property. The system converges to point attractor for

$n \in 2\mathbb{N}$, and, show multi length attractor of length $2n$ (i.e. NC-NR) for $n \notin 2\mathbb{N}$ (see [12]). However, under skewed environment, the cellular system shows convergence for any $n \in \mathbb{N}$; and (d) Lastly, ECA **105** shows strange behaviour which shows convergence dynamics under skewed environment for lattice size divisible by 4 ($n \in 4\mathbb{N}$). However, for $n \notin 4\mathbb{N}$, ECA 105 shows divergence under skewed environment. Note that, this rule depicts recurrence behaviour under fully asynchronous updating for any lattice size $n \in \mathbb{N}$.

To sum up, in Table 1, $\texttt{Skew}_C$ denotes the class of these 88 ECAs under skewed environment where '✓' depicts (overall) similar dynamics under both of the updating schemes, i.e. no effect of breaking atomicity property, and '×' shows drastic difference in the dynamics of fully and skew-asynchronous systems. For evidence, Fig. 1 (top) depicts the dynamics of ECA 26 where the system shows convergence towards all 0 for fully asynchronous environment, and depicts divergence for skewed environment ($\texttt{Skew}_C = \times$). Similarly, Fig. 1 (bottom) shows the dynamics of ECA 38 which shows divergence (specifically, recurrence) dynamics following atomicity property. On a contrary, ECA 38 depicts convergence towards all 0 following skewed environment, i.e. $\texttt{Skew}_C = \times$. In this context, note that, Fatès [2] has identified peculiar *phase transition* behaviour for ECAs 26, 38, 58, 134 for changing value of α following α-asynchronous scheme. Here also, these ECAs (26, 38, 58, 134) show phase change (convergence to divergence) in the presence or absence of atomicity property. However, work is still needed for identify atomicity property as (one of the) reason behind phase transition.

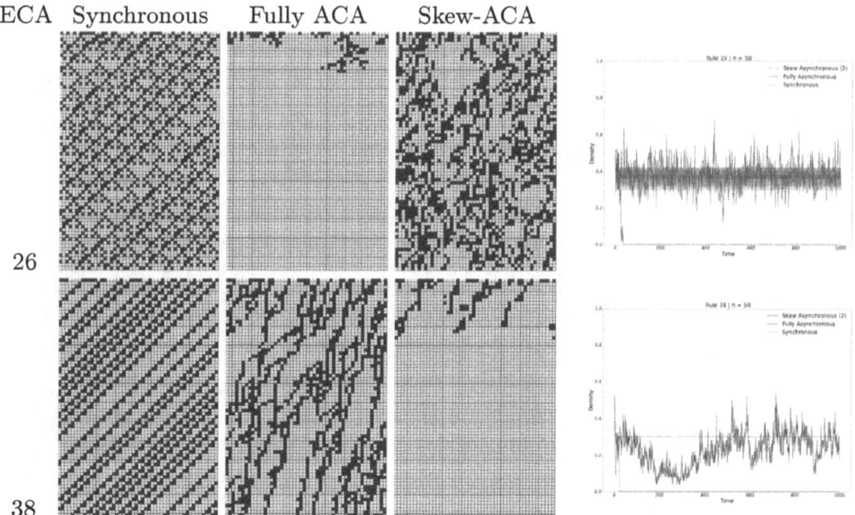

Fig. 1. Dynamics of ECAs 26 and 38 for - synchronous, fully asynchronous and skew-asynchronous systems. This figure also depicts the density-time plot. Here, $n = 50$ where the time goes form top to bottom. Each line represent the configuration of automata after 1, n, $n/2$ updates respectively for changing updating schemes. Blue and light blue squares represent cells in state 1 and 0. (Color figure online)

As a limitation, Table 1 only captures the extreme differences of these two asynchronous updating schemes, not microscopic details. However, the dynamics of many ECAs are not exactly same in microscopic view following these two updating schemes. For example, see ECA 6, Fig. 2 shows their non-convergence non-recurrence dynamics ($n \notin 2\mathbb{N}$) for fully asynchronous update, however, ECA 6 show convergence to all 0 point attractor for skewed environment. Importantly, if we consider $n \in 2\mathbb{N}$, ECA 6 shows convergence for both of the updating schemes. However, there are differences: for fully asynchronous update, the only point attractor is $(001)^{n/3}$; for skewed environment, the system mostly converges to all 0 point attractor, see Fig. 2. Therefore, both updates show convergence ($n \in 2\mathbb{N}$), but there are differences following the microscopic view. Figure 2 also shows ECA 105 which converges to $(0011)^{n/4}$ for $n \in 4\mathbb{N}$ under skewed environment, however, depicts recurrence dynamics for $n \in 4\mathbb{N}$ under fully asynchronous update. To sum up, a proper theoretical claim about many microscopic facts are not possible with this experimental approach. However, the experimental results guide us towards the richness of this study. In the next section, we theoretically explore part of the ECA rule space under skew-asynchronous updating scheme.

4 Convergence Towards All 0 and All 1 Point Attractors

It is quite obvious that an asynchronous CA is a Markov chain [15]. In fact, we have also observed that convergent ACAs are absorbing Markov chain [15]. Following this, we can write,

Lemma 1. *Convergent skew-ACAs are absorbing Markov chain.*

In this direction, we use the fact: in a absorbing Markov chain, the probability that the chain eventually enters to an absorbing state (and stays there forever) is 1 [15]. Next, we write the conditions for convergence under skewed environment.

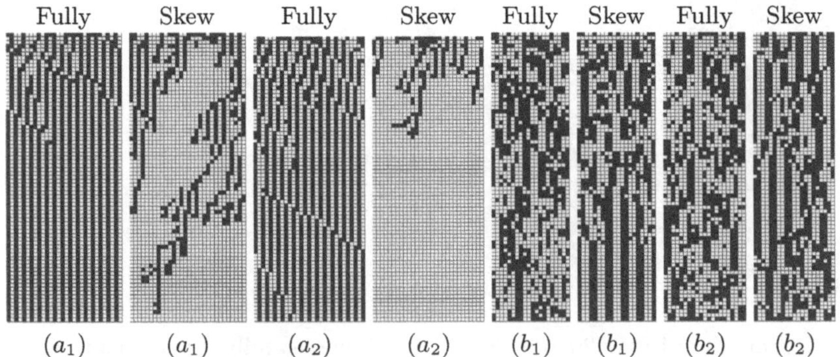

Fig. 2. Dynamics of ECAs 6 (a_1: $n \in 2\mathbb{N}$, a_2: $n \notin 2\mathbb{N}$); and 105 (b_1: $n \in 4\mathbb{N}$, b_2: $n \notin 4\mathbb{N}$) under fully asynchronous and skew-asynchronous updating schemes for different lattice size.

Here, in the following theorem, we denote two homogeneous configurations all 0 and all 1 as **0**, **1**, respectively. Moreover, we introduce the notion of 1-region (resp. 0-region) which corresponds to a maximal set of contiguous cells with state 1 (resp. 0) in a given configuration.

Theorem 1. *ECA R converges to **0** (resp. **1**) point attractor under skew - asynchronous updating scheme if one of the following condition is satisfied:*

1. *RMT* 0 *(resp. RMT* 7*) of R is passive, RMT* 2 *(resp. RMT* 5*) of R is active, and atleast one RMT from the pair of RMTs* $\{1, 4\}$ *(resp.* $\{3, 6\}$*) of R is passive.*
2. *RMT* 0 *(resp. RMT* 7*) of R is passive, RMTs* 3 *and* 6 *(resp. RMTs* 1 *and* 4*) of R are active.*

Proof. **Case (1). Let us first consider that for a rule** R**, RMT** 0 **is passive, RMT** 2 **is active, and RMT** 1 **or** 4 **is passive:** Since, RMT 0 of R is passive, therefore **0** is clearly a point attractor for the CA. Next, we show that **0** is reachable from any configuration if it is the only point attractor. Otherwise, the CA reaches to other point attractor(s) for the configurations for which it does not reaches to **0**.

Since skew-ACA forms an absorbing Markov chain (see Lemma 1), we need to show here that there exists an update pattern for which the CA converges to a point attractor. Here, we consider $n \geqslant 3$.

Let Us First Assume that RMT 7 is Active: From any configuration x different from **0**, we need to show disappearance of state 1 to reach **0** configuration. Let us denote l_1 (resp. l_0) as the length of an arbitrary 1-region (resp. 0-region).

If $l_1 > 3$, then we can directly apply active RMT 7 for couple of two cells. Say, i is the left most cell of 1-region (note that, for $x = \mathbf{1}$, any cell can be able to play the role of cell i). Following this, $i+1, i+2$ cells move to state 0. Then again, we apply active RMT 7 in $i+4, i+5$ cells. Sequentially following this, cells $i+1, i+2, i+4, i+5, i+7, i+8, \cdots$ move to state 0. On the other hand, cells $i, i+3, i+6, i+9, \cdots$ remain in state 1. Following this, the original 1-region of length l_1 is divided into many (say m) number of 1-regions of length one. Here, RMTs 1, 2, 4 are the member of RMT sequence for these (first m) 1-regions of length one. For the $m+1^{th}$ 1-region (rightmost) following are the possibilities:

A: If $l_1 = 3m+1$, $m \in \mathbb{N}$, the rightmost 1-region of size one.
B: If $l_1 = 3m+2$, $m \in \mathbb{N}$, the rightmost 1-region of size two.
C: If $l_1 = 3m+3$, $m \in \mathbb{N}$, the rightmost 1-region of size three. However, we can update pattern 11 in this length three 1-region. For active RMT 7 and passive RMTs 3 and 6, it creates two 1-regions of length one. For active RMT 7 and active RMT 3 or 6, it creates single 1-region of length one. Note that, the above argument is also applicable for independent 1-regions of $l_1 = 3$.

Now, for the first m 1-regions with RMT sequence 1, 2, 4, active RMT 2 and passive RMT 1 or 4 applies, it moves the pattern 01/10 to 00. Hence, state 1 disappears.

For the rightmost ($m+1^{th}$) 1-region of length one (situation A and C), either the RMT sequence is 1, 2, 4 (right side 0-region of length $l_0 > 1$) or 2, 5 (right side 0-region of length $l_0 = 1$). For RMT sequence 1, 2, 4, state 1 disappears directly following active RMT 2 and passive RMT 1 or 4. For RMT sequence 2, 5, if RMT 5 is passive, we update pattern 10/01, which vanishes state 1, we can achieve the target. Otherwise, if RMT 5 is active, we get 1-region of length two (or more) by flipping the pattern 10 (resp. 01) to 01 (resp. 10). If again, the new 1-region is with right side 0-region of length $l_0 = 1$, we further follow the same, i.e. we increase (or decrease, if possible) the length of 1-region, until and unless we get a right side 0-region of length atleast two (which returns us back to the previous case). Note that, we definitely get a right side 0-region of length atleast two following the early updates. During this process, if we again create 1-region of length more than two, we return back to the initial problem. Note that, the above argument is also applicable for independent 1-regions of $l_1 = 1$. The remaining situation, if the 1-region of length two, the situation we discuss next.

For the rightmost ($m+1^{th}$) 1-region of length two (situation B), either RMT sequence is 1, 3, 6, 4 or 3, 6, 5. For both of the situations, if RMT 3 or 6 or both are active, we update pattern 11, either single or both 1 disappear. If RMTs 1, 3, 6, 4 all are passive, it is itself a point attractor. Similarly, if RMTs 3, 6, 5 all are passive, it is again itself a point attractor. If the above situations are not true, then either RMT 1 or 4 is active. In that case, we increase the size of the 1-region by updating pattern 01/10 to 11. Following this, we can be able to create 1-region of size $l_1 = 3m + 1$, $m \in \mathbb{N}$, which returns us back to the previous case. For RMT sequence 3, 6, 5, the same argument of increasing length of 1-region is applicable for active RMT 5. Note that, the above argument is also applicable for independent 1-regions of $l_1 = 2$.

Therefore, the above arguments include all possible situations for disappearance of 1-region of length by from $l_1 \in \{1, \cdots, n\}$ considering active RMT 7. If there are more such 1-regions, one can use the above rationale for their disappearance which allows the CA to reach all **0**.

Next, We Assume that RMT 7 is Passive: Therefore, **1** configuration is clearly a point attractor. Now, for any configuration x different from **0** and **1**, if 1-region is of length $l_1 = 1$, it contains either RMT sequence 1, 2, 4 or 2, 5. For RMT sequence 1, 2, 4, active RMT 2 and passive 1 or 4 are applied, state 1 disappears. For RMT sequence 2, 5: for passive RMT 5, we update pattern 10/01, state 1 disappears; for active RMT 5, it flips the pattern 10/01, and creates 1-region of length $l_1 = 2$ or more. This situation, we discuss next.

Next, if x contains 1-region of length $l_1 = 2$ or more, following are the situations: if one of the RMTs 3 or 6 is active, we update pattern 11 (starting from left or right side of 1-region), it makes sure that state 1 disappears in each update, which returns us back to the previous case with RMTs 1, 2, 4. If both RMTs 3 and 6 are passive, x can not able to reach **0** configuration. If RMT 5 and one of the RMTs 1 or 4 are active, we update pattern 10 or 01, state 0 disappears, x can be able to reach **1** configuration. On the other hand, if RMT

5 is passive and one of the RMTs 1 or 4 is active, it reaches to point attractor where the RMT sequence is $5, 3, 7, 6$. Otherwise, the configuration itself a point attractor.

Therefore, the above arguments include all possible situations for disappearance of 1-region of length by from $l_1 \in \{1, \cdots, n-1\}$ considering passive RMT 7. If there are more such 1-regions, one can use the above rationale for their disappearance which allows the CA to reach all **0**.

While RMT 7 is passive, RMT 5 is active, and RMT 3 or 6 is passive, this property is the symmetric by the conjugation operation, i.e. exchange of 0's and 1's.

Case (2). Next, let us consider for a rule R, RMT 0 is passive, and RMTs 3 and 6 are active: Since, RMT 0 of R is passive, therefore **0** is clearly a point attractor. Here, we follow the similar construction.

Let us first assume RMT 7 is active: If length of 1-region is even, we can be able to divide it into multiple 1-region of size two using active RMTs 3, 6, 7. If $l_1 = 2$, active RMTs 3 and 6 applies, both state 1 disappear. If $l_1 > 2$ (even), cell $i, i+1, i+4, i+5, \cdots$ remain in state 1, cell $i+2, i+3, i+6, i+7, \cdots$ move to state 0 using active RMTs 6 and 7. If $l_1 > 1$ (odd), the region is divided into (say) $m+1$ number of 1-regions, where the first m 1-region is of length two (return us back to the previous case), active RMTs 3 and 6 are applied, and the rightmost $(m + 1^{th})$ 1-region is of length one (will discuss later). The above argument is also applicable for **1** configuration where any cell can be able to play the role of cell i.

Let Us Now Assume RMT 7 is Passive: If $l_1 > 1$, we can apply active RMT 3 or 6 and passive RMT 7 by updating pattern 11 (from left or right hand side of 1-region), single state 1 disappears in each step. Following this, we remain with 1-region of length two, active RMTs 3 and 6 are applied, we can achieve the target. Here also, the remaining issue is with 1-region of length one (will discuss next). Here, **1** configuration is a point attractor.

Next (independent of active/passive RMT 7), we discuss the remaining issue with 1-region of length one. For $l_1 = 1$, the possible RMT sequences are 1, 2, 4 and 2, 5. For RMT sequence 1, 2, 4: if RMT 2 is active and RMT 1 or 4 is passive, we update pattern 10/01, state 1 disappears. For RMT 2 passive and RMTs 1 and 4 passive, it is a point attractor. For RMT 2 passive and RMT 1 or 4 active, we update pattern 10/01 to get the pattern 11, creates 1-region of length $l_1 = 2$, returns back to the previous case. For RMT 2 active and RMT 1 or 4 active, we update pattern 10/01, the length of 1-region remains unchanged, but it moves towards left or right direction. Now, if the new (after movement) 1-region have a neighbouring 0-region of length $l_0 > 2$, we update pattern 00 using passive RMT 0 and active RMT 1 or 4, creates 1-region of length two, returns back to the previous case. Otherwise, if the new 1-region have a neighbouring 0-region of length $l_0 = 2$, we move the 1-region to create neighbouring 0-region of length $l_0 = 1$, RMT 5 applies (discuss next).

For RMT sequence 2, 5: if 2 is active and 5 is passive, state 1 disappears. For 2 and 5 passive, it is a point attractor itself. For RMT 2 active and RMT

5 active, we update pattern 10/01, it creates 1-region of length two or more, returns back to the previous case. For 2 passive and 5 active, we update pattern 10/01, it creates 1-region of length three or more, returns back to the previous case. To conclude, the above arguments include all possible situations.

While RMT 7 is passive, RMTs 1 and 4 are active, this property is the symmetric by the conjugation operation, i.e. exchange of 0's and 1's.

Now, using Theorem 1, following 34, out of 88, minimal ECAs converge to point attractor **0** and/or **1** for $n \in \mathbb{N}$: 0, 2, **6**, 8, 10, 18, **22**, 24, 32, 34, **38**, 40, 42, 50, **54**, 56, 74, 104, 106, 128, 130, **134**, 136, 138, 146, **150**, 152, 154, 160, 162, 168, 170, 178, 184. Note that, ECAs 38, 54, 134 and 150 (in bold) show recurrence under fully asynchronous updating scheme, however, these ECAs depict convergence to point attractor **0** following Theorem 1 which validates our finite lattice size experimental findings. The same is true for ECAs 6 and 22 (in bold) considering odd lattice size. As an observation, ECAs 146, 150, 168, 170, 178, and 184 show convergence towards both of the point attractor **0** and **1**. Following this property of convergence towards both of the point attractors, these ECAs (146, 150, 168, 170, 178, 184) may establish themselves as a potential candidate for density classification problem [6], which is still open for us.

5 Conclusion

To sum up, we have explored the effect of breaking atomicity property in elementary cellular automata. Towards the first step in this direction, we have introduced the notion of skew-asynchronous updating scheme where two neighbouring cells are bound to update together. In the absence of atomicity property, ECAs have shown following rich variety of results: (i) A phase change (convergence $\rightarrow$ divergence) for ECAs 26, 58, 90, and 122; (ii) Another opposite phase change (divergence, i.e. recurrence $\rightarrow$ convergence) for ECAs 38, 54, 134, and 150; (iii) On the other hand, some remarkable behaviour emerged; phase change (divergence $\rightarrow$ convergence) depending on the lattice size ($n \in 2\mathbb{N}$) for ECAs 6 and 22; and phase change (divergence, i.e. recurrence $\rightarrow$ convergence) depending on the lattice size ($n \in 4\mathbb{N}$) for ECA 105. Finally, we have identified the theoretical reasons behind convergence towards **0** and **1** point attractors which partially validates our finite lattice size experimental findings.

However, we are still open about many questions which guides us towards following extensions: In this first paper, we have only theorized convergences towards **0** and **1** point attractors. We are still open about convergence towards other point attractors considering the notion of primary RMT sets [15]. Moreover, we have only classified the system into convergence and divergence under skewed environment. The immediate question is for the dynamics of divergence systems; what can be said about recurrence and non-recurrence properties of the divergence systems? Lastly, Fatès [2] has identified peculiar phase transition behaviour for ECAs 26, 38, 58, 134 for changing value of α. Here also, these ECAs (26, 38, 58, 134) show phase change (convergence to divergence) in the presence or absence of atomicity property. However, we are still open to identify atomicity property as (one of the) reason behind phase transition. Most importantly, in this direction, the hidden agenda is to understand probabilistic system (α-asynchronism) following the dynamics of (kind of) deterministic environment (skewed environment).

Acknowledgements. This work is supported by CRG project (File No.: CRG/ 2023/006799) of SERB, Govt. of India. The authors acknowledge the anonymous reviewers for their comments and suggestions, which have helped to improve the quality and readability of the paper.

References

1. Bandini, S., Bonomi, A., Vizzari, G.: An analysis of different types and effects of asynchronicity in cellular automata update schemes. Natural Comput. **11**(06), 277–287 (2012)
2. Bouré, O., Fatès, N., Chevrier, V.: Probing robustness of cellular automata through variations of asynchronous updating. Nat. Comput. **11**(4), 553–564 (2012)
3. Caron-Lormier, G., Humphry, R.W., Bohan, D.A., Hawes, C., Thorbek, P.: Asynchronous and synchronous updating in individual-based models. Ecol. Model. **212**(3), 522–527 (2008)
4. Cori, R., Metivier, Y., Zielonka, W.: Asynchronous mappings and asynchronous cellular automata. Inf. Comput. **106**(2), 159–202 (1993)
5. Dennunzio, A., Formenti, E., Manzoni, L., Mauri, G.: M-asynchronous cellular automata: from fairness to quasi-fairness. Nat. Comput. **12**(4), 561–572 (2013)
6. Fatès, N.: Stochastic cellular automata solutions to the density classification problem - when randomness helps computing. Theory Comput. Syst. **53**(2), 223–242 (2013)
7. Fatès, N.: Guided tour of asynchronous cellular automata. J. Cell. Autom. **9**(5–6), 387–416 (2014)
8. Fatès, N., Sethi, B., Das, S.: On the reversibility of ECAs with fully asynchronous updating: the recurrence point of view. In: Adamatzky, A. (ed.) Reversibility and Universality. Emergence, Complexity and Computation, vol. 30, pp. 313–332. Springer, Cham (2018). https://doi.org/10.1007/978-3-319-73216-9_15
9. Fatès, N., Thierry, E., Morvan, M., Schabanel, N.: Fully asynchronous behavior of double-quiescent elementary cellular automata. Theoret. Comput. Sci. **362**(1), 1–16 (2006)
10. Roy, S.: A study on delay-sensitive cellular automata. Phys. A **515**, 600–616 (2019)
11. Roy, S.: Distributed computing on cellular automata with applications to societal problems. Ph.D. thesis, Indian Institute of Engineering Science and Technology, Shibpur (2021)
12. Roy, S., Fatès, N., Das, S.: Reversibility of elementary cellular automata with fully asynchronous updating: an analysis of the rules with partial recurrence. Working paper or preprint, February 2024
13. Sethi, B., Fatès, N., Das, S.: Reversibility of elementary cellular automata under fully asynchronous update. In: Gopal, T.V., Agrawal, M., Li, A., Cooper, S.B. (eds.) TAMC 2014. LNCS, vol. 8402, pp. 39–49. Springer, Cham (2014). https://doi.org/10.1007/978-3-319-06089-7_4

14. Sethi, B., Roy, S., Das, S.: Asynchronous cellular automata and pattern classification. Complexity **21**(S1), 370–386 (2016)
15. Sethi, B., Roy, S., Das, S.: Convergence of asynchronous cellular automata: does size matter? J. Cell. Autom. **13**(5/6), 527–542 (2018)

Author Index

Published by Springer Nature Switzerland AG 2024
M. Gadouleau and A. Castillo-Ramirez (Eds.): AUTOMATA 2024, LNCS 14782, p. 159, 2024.
https://doi.org/10.1007/978-3-031-65887-7

GPSR Compliance

The European Union's (EU) General Product Safety Regulation (GPSR) is a set of rules that requires consumer products to be safe and our obligations to ensure this.

If you have any concerns about our products, you can contact us on ProductSafety@springernature.com

In case Publisher is established outside the EU, the EU authorized representative is:

Springer Nature Customer Service Center GmbH
Europaplatz 3
69115 Heidelberg, Germany

Zeitfracht Medien GmbH
Ferdinand-Jühlke-Straße 7
99095 Erfurt, Deutschland
produktsicherheit@kolibri360.de